People-Based Safety™
The Source

E. Scott Geller

Edited by Dave Johnson

Published by

COASTAL®

Dedicated to my university students and colleagues who collected and analyzed the data to make this book research-based; and to my partners at Safety Performance Solutions who help organizations worldwide execute the principles of People-Based Safety™.

People-Based Safety™
The Source

First Reprinting: December 2005

Editor: Dave Johnson   *Illustrator: George V. Wills*

Published by

Coastal Training Technologies Corporation
500 Studio Drive, Virginia Beach, Virginia 23452
757-498-9014 • www.coastal.com

Library of Congress Control Number 2005926417

ISBN 0-9664604-0-5

Printed in the United States of America

Contents

CHAPTER THREE

The **Coaching** of People-Based Safety™

CHAPTER FOUR

The **Thinking** of People-Based Safety™

CHAPTER FIVE

The **Seeing** of People-Based Safety™

CHAPTER SIX

Gaining and Sustaining **Engagement** in People-Based Safety™

Foreword

Three years ago I heard Dr. Geller present a keynote speech at a safety conference in New Jersey. I was amazed at his gift for taking research-based principles and theories about behavior-based safety and presenting them in a way that had his audience smiling and obviously "getting" the message.

This prompted me to bring Dr. Geller to my company for a two-day leadership program. Again I watched this psychology professor – "the Doc" – have absolutely no problem connecting with managers and construction workers fresh in from the job site. He's got the "human touch," that's all I can say. And he's one outstanding teacher.

You'll see what I mean as you read through the pages of *People-Based Safety™: The Source*, a collection of his best articles from the magazine *Industrial Safety & Hygiene News*. These columns, written over 15 years and edited by ISHN's chief editor, Dave Johnson, form the basis for Dr. Geller's unique People-Based Safety™ skill-building and life-changing process. The articles are based on research, principles and practices from applied psychology. They will give you "profound knowledge," as Dr. Geller likes to say, far beyond behavior-based safety. People-Based Safety shows you how to build a culture based on self-management, self-discipline, and getting everyone at all levels in an organization to take responsibility for making safe choices.

Dr. Geller writes in a down-to-earth style that motivates everyone to wake up to this new way of developing a safety culture. I think you will find *The Source* practical, positive, caring and empowering. You can process his user-friendly strategies, take ownership, and most important, make a difference.

I know Dr. Geller has made a difference in my life. Embrace his ideas and teachings and watch what a positive difference they will make in your quality of life, from your home to your workplace.

Joanne Dean
Safety Director
The Gale Construction Company
Florham Park, New Jersey
February 2005

Preface

More than a decade ago, in 1994, I first proposed the need to address person-based factors to improve workplace safety and prevent unintentional injury. For years I've used the term "people-based safety" to describe a more people-oriented approach to safety issues than traditional engineering controls and rules and policy compliance.

This book, based on columns I've written for *Industrial Safety & Hygiene News*, gives you the background, the source material, for understanding People-Based Safety™. The first chapter gives you the basic underpinnings, the fundamentals, of People-Based Safety. The final chapter offers strategies for sustaining People-Based Safety. In between are chapters on Acting, Coaching, Thinking, and Seeing (ACTS) – the specifics of how you implement People-Based Safety.

People-Based Safety embraces the human side of our coworkers. Yes, this includes observing behaviors and giving feedback – the principles of behavior-based safety. But People-Based Safety is much broader in scope than defining behaviors, handing in observation cards and giving feedback.

You see, at the heart of People-Based Safety is the need for us to view each other as people – rather than objects or a means to an end. And in safety, people can indeed turn into objects – statistics on recordkeeping forms, signatures on policies, or when a behavior-based safety process turns into a numbers game of "counting the observations" or "calculating a percent-safe score."

People-Based Safety requires a very sincere, honest appreciation of other people. It requires an understanding and acceptance of the internal feelings, needs and perceptions of other people. Each person's uniqueness and individuality must be recognized and appreciated.

That's just the starting point. To improve workplace safety, People-Based Safety builds and strengthens feelings of self-effectiveness, personal control, optimism, and belonging. For people to work safely over the long haul, often without direct supervision, we must nurture personal pride, dignity, and self-respect. Yes, we can do this for each other!

How? First by viewing our organization as a family of people working together. This is a key aspect of People-Based Safety. Think about it. We see our own family members as people with their own unique set of feelings and beliefs, and we never hesitate to actively care for their health and safety.

But we must do more than respect people for the individuals they are. We must go into action if we want to improve safety. Actively caring behavior is essential to the success of People-Based Safety. Actively caring behavior in an organization increases directly with the number of employees, including managers, who view their coworkers as family. So you see, People-Based Safety enables us to successfully approximate a family atmosphere in the workplace.

Actively caring for the safety of our coworkers means taking a sincere interest in their feelings, intentions and aspirations. Just like a family. It means listening closely, nurturing talents, and offering positive encouragement and recognition.

Actively caring means stepping in quickly when help is needed. It's a natural reaction in families. It involves teaching, offering corrective feedback and instruction. It calls for being sensitive to the language we use, the words we choose.

In families, we also know when to let go. This is another key to understanding actively caring and People-Based Safety. In fact, today many safety professionals know from experience the best way to increase safety involvement is to allow the workforce to have substantial control and authority over their safety procedures.

We're not telling people what to do to remain safe (that's the old command-and-control model). Instead, we care enough to give people knowledge and tools to increase personal choice, ownership, and empowerment. This is how you sustain safe behavior.

Of course this is easier said than done. Honesty is one of the core characteristics of People-Based Safety. We must admit we don't actively care for each other's safety as much as we should and could. All sorts of barriers can interfere: the atmosphere of our work culture, top-down rules and threats, the attitudes of our leaders, the goals we set, the slogans we display, the words we use when we talk about safety, and the at-risk behaviors that are encouraged or ignored.

Don't blame others for not actively caring. Use the principles of People-Based Safety described in this book to identify the cultural, behavioral, and person-based constraints that inhibit actively caring. Then use this book's tools and teachings to set actively caring examples yourself. The more familiar you become with People-Based Safety, the more opportunities you'll find to embrace the human side of your coworkers – and protect their well-being in the process.

E. Scott Geller
Alumni Distinguished Professor
Virginia Tech
Blacksburg, Virginia
March 2005

Acknowledgments

People-Based Safety™: The Source reflects the best of the 10 safety-related books I've authored in the last decade, and thus has benefited from the cumulative advice, support, and inspiration of literally hundreds of colleagues, teachers, students, and safety leaders. My prior books thanked many of these individuals. In this Acknowledgment I recognize those whom I worked with directly to accomplish this scholarship.

First and foremost, I'm grateful for the talent, dedication, and insight of the Editor, Dave Johnson, who introduces each of the six chapters. As a friend and professional colleague for over 15 years, Dave teaches me how to translate academic theory and research into real-world language for public service.

Each part of this book is based on an article published in my "Psychology of Safety" column in *Industrial Safety & Hygiene News* (ISHN), which Dave Johnson edits. To date, I've authored 168 articles for ISHN, the best 72 of which are included here. Each was refined especially for this book and made more interesting and instructive by illustrations drawn by George Wills, an extremely talented artist who has helped me add humor to my books and keynote addresses for almost two decades.

Because the first drafts of my scholarship are handwritten, I am always indebted to someone's word-processing skills. For this book, I had the very best. Elise Drake coordinated the challenge of preparing the text and illustrations for the publisher. She was assisted daily by Kristin Williamson and Matt Cox. I am profoundly grateful for the special commitment and care this team gave to *People-Based Safety™: The Source.*

Finally, I sincerely appreciate the dedication of the talented staff at Coastal Training Technologies Corporation who brought this book to life – from the initial vision of Paul Michels, who sought a "doctrine" to underscore and drive the human dynamics of Coastal products, to the various editing, printing, distributing, and marketing efforts needed for this book to make a difference. In this regard, the daily leadership of Nancy Kondas and the content support of Anne Lewis were invaluable.

I thank you all very much, as well as the hundreds of others who have contributed to my 40 years of preparation to author *People-Based Safety™: The Source.* The synergy from all your sustenance provides a legacy – principles and procedures – readers can use to apply human dynamics to enrich their work culture, and thereby improve safety, job satisfaction, work quality/production and interpersonal relationships.

E. Scott Geller
April 2005

CHAPTER ONE

Orientation to People-Based Safety™

Introduction

Imagine asking Dr. Geller: "What do I need to do to pave the way for implementing People-Based Safety in my workplace?"

The 12 articles in this chapter serve as Dr. Geller's answer. Before you go any further in implementing specific tools for Acting, Coaching, Thinking and Seeing – the skills to keep you and your coworkers injury-free – read these 12 articles: they form a "to-do" list from Dr. Geller.

First, it's important to understand that the People-Based Safety approach is all about caring – actively caring *(Part 1)*. We simply can't pass up opportunities to demonstrate how we care for the well-being of our coworkers. It starts with caring.

This means getting comfortable with the "touchy-feely" soft side of safety *(Part 2)*. Feelings are crucial. As Dr. Geller explains: "We sense when others truly care about us." You can't build on Dr. Geller's vision of a Total Safety Culture if your workers don't possess this feeling.

Accepting the importance of the soft side of safety represents a paradigm shift for some safety professionals reared on the engineering side of the fence. Before moving ahead with People-Based Safety, you need to embrace a number of revolutionary shifts in traditional safety thinking *(Part 3)*.

Dr. Geller's list of "to-do" prerequisites for succeeding with People-Based Safety includes a few basic action items. You simply must take responsibility for safety at every opportunity – stop passing the buck *(Part 4)*. You need to be mentally prepared to intervene for safety's sake – step in and speak up *(Part 5)*. And when you do get involved – watch your language *(Part 6)*. As Dr. Geller says, "Some words we habitually use in the safety and health field send the wrong message."

This notion of stepping in, speaking up and taking responsibility for safety issues is not some thankless, self-sacrificing challenge that only do-gooders take on. Get yourself comfortable with Dr. Geller's contention *(Part 7)* that participating in safety rewards a basic human need to make a difference – to serve others and feel competent in what we do. You won't go far with People-

Based Safety approaches without believing it's natural for your employees to care about each other.

What else do you need – beliefs, attitudes, behaviors and values – to succeed with People-Based Safety? Chapter 1 gives you five more essentials:

• Assure managers, supervisors and your employees that empirical research backs everything taught in People-Based Safety *(Part 8)*. This is not a warm and fuzzy, pop psychology approach to protecting people. It's based on science, not what sounds good.

• Never stop teaching *(Part 9)*. Always look to make the most of your training opportunities – and Dr. Geller shows you how.

• See your work site as a living system of relationships *(Part 10)*. A Total Safety Culture is woven through and through with caring, interdependent working relationships. Dr. Geller shows how to strengthen the fabric of these relationships, not tear them apart.

• Building truly productive and caring relationships takes empathy *(Part 11)*. Emotional intelligence is the ability to grasp the needs and feelings of those around you, whether you're in a one-on-one conversation or leading a team. This skill is central to the success of People-Based Safety.

• And finally, to succeed with People-Based Safety requires you to take a leadership role *(Part 12)*. That's why you're reading this book. As Dr. Geller explains, always look for ways to show you care, expect the best, be alert to how your culture really operates, keep your communication personal and "real," of course set a safe example, and celebrate small wins and big payoffs whenever they come along. That's how you keep the energy of People-Based Safety flowing throughout your workplace.

Dave Johnson, Editor
Industrial Safety & Hygiene News

PART 1

It's All About Actively Caring

If only we could all view our organization as a family of people working together to achieve common goals. We see our own family members as people, and we never hesitate to actively care for their safety and health. In fact, we inflate the virtues of those in our family and often communicate these virtues to others. Such "positive gossip" increases appreciation and admiration within the family, making it natural to actively care for each other.

Actively caring behavior in an organization increases directly with the number of employees (including managers) who view their coworkers as "family." We show empathy for family members, we don't betray family members, and any distortions of the qualities of family members are more likely to be positive than negative. People-Based Safety enables us to successively approximate a family atmosphere in the workplace.

People-Based Safety

For many years, I've claimed a comprehensive approach to address the human dynamics of industrial safety requires "people-based safety." This perspective combines the objective, research-supported tools of behavior-based safety (BBS) with person-based safety or the internal, feeling states of individuals.

The person-based approach might be considered the soft side of psychology. Let's consider a connection between actively-caring behavior and person-based safety as reflected in the book *Leadership and Self-Deception,* distributed by the Arbinger Institute.[1] This article reviews the key points in this book as they relate to People-Based Safety.

From Self-Betrayal to Self-Deception

We often find ourselves in situations where we consider helping another person but don't follow through, according to the Arbinger Institute. We observe an environmental hazard in a person's work area but don't remove it. We see someone working without the proper safeguards or personal protective equipment (PPE) and walk on by. Or, while buckled up in a vehicle, we notice another occupant is not using the available safety belt, but we don't say anything.

This experience of not actively caring when you know you should leads to self-betrayal and then to self-deception, according to the Arbinger Institute. Since it's uncomfortable to accept and maintain self-betrayal, we engage in a variety of self-deceiving thought processes to justify our lack of caring.

To live with our self-betrayal, we inflate the faults of the person we didn't help while inflating our own virtues. For example, we might presume the worker not using proper PPE is incompetent, complacent, unmotivated, uncaring, or not a team player. At the same time, we pump up our own positive characteristics, including the qualities that make us effective at our important work. We conclude we have better things to do than to help an incompetent, mindless worker decrease risks of personal injury.

Faults over Facts

This kind of distorted self-deception facilitates fault-finding over fact-finding – a common problem in the safety world. The easiest way to justify one's self-betrayal or lack of actively caring is to blame someone else. It's not my fault for not helping, it's their fault for not being responsible or self-accountable. The defensive personal script might be something like, "Safety is a personal issue. If those workers don't care enough to protect themselves, why should I?"

Notice the self-serving cycle of distortion in fault-finding. The more blame we connect to others, the less possible fault we find in ourselves. To reduce the tension that comes from betraying our better selves, we find the other person(s) blameworthy. This leads to more self-deception, feeding an already distorted reality.

Actively Caring for Family

- We don't pick on the mistakes of family members.
- We brag on the accomplishments of family members.
- We don't rank one family member over another.
- We pick up after family members.
- We intervene for the safety of family members.
- We accept the corrective feedback of family members.
- We actively care because they're family.

Breaking the Cycle

So what can we do about this universal problem?

First, we need to recognize we don't actively care for other people's safety as much as we should and could. Next, we need to own up to personal misrepresentations of reality we hold in order to justify this self-betrayal. Third, we need to realize the power of seeing others as people with their own feelings, intentions, and aspirations rather than viewing these individuals as merely objects providing a service. When we embrace the human side of our coworkers, we are more likely to actively care for their well-being and less likely to practice self-deception to justify our self-betrayal.

By apologizing for not actively caring and finding other opportunities to actively care and follow through, we break the cycle of self-serving self-deception. Focus your mental scripts on what you do right rather than what you do wrong. This prevents feelings of self-betrayal and a need for self-deception.

Don't blame others for not actively caring. See these individuals as people with a variety of interpersonal and cultural constraints inhibiting their helping behavior. Then, set the actively caring example yourself. Show you have overcome personal and environmental factors that hold back actively caring behavior and facilitate self-betrayal and self-deception.

Bottom line: Take a people-based approach to industrial safety and health. Realize the power of empathy when listening, recognizing, helping, and leading people. Anything less will initiate a cycle of self-deception that distorts perceptions of people, confines the benefits from interpersonal interaction, and makes it impossible to bring out the best in people and achieve an injury-free workplace.

PART 2

Feelings Are Crucial

Many safety professionals, especially those with a background in engineering, view psychology as a subjective "touchy-feely" discipline. When I hear this I'm quick to defend the science of psychology. I assert that psychological principles are founded on objective empirical research, and not on common sense.

So along with the science of engineering and medicine, we have the science of human behavior. Just as we have engineering and medical technology to benefit our quality of life, we also have behavioral technology to improve human performance.

That said, there is a "soft" side to psychology.

When Commitment Runs Low

The other day, while meeting with five top executives of a Fortune 100 company, I realized the need to consider the soft side of psychology. This four-hour meeting was about achieving an injury-free work culture. I was expected to provide insight on how to make it happen. The 15,000 employees at the various work sites of this organization had been taught the systematic observation and feedback techniques of behavior-based safety (BBS), as well as basic interpersonal communication and recognition tools.

The underlying problem was low commitment and participation. Many employees were merely going through the motions (such as checking the safe versus at-risk columns of environmental and behavioral checklists without actually conducting careful and thoughtful observations).

As a result, the culture was not benefiting as much as it could have from various safety-related procedures. Yes, some environmental hazards were removed, and some at-risk behaviors were corrected. But many opportunities for safety-related improvement were overlooked. Some employee involvement did not appear to be genuine or heartfelt.

Throughout the meeting, we talked about the need to get more supervisors educated about the value of injury prevention methods and to develop accountability systems. Workers need to be held accountable for their involvement in various safety procedures, and supervisors need to be held accountable to do what it takes to maintain employee involvement.

The supervisors' poor communication skills seemed to be a barrier to increasing and sustaining participation in safety initiatives. So we discussed providing communication training for all supervisors, from active listening techniques to the most effective ways of delivering supportive and corrective feedback. We also discussed various leadership strategies supervisors need to learn in order to be more effective managers of human behavior.

Reflecting on the process and outcomes of this meeting, which was typical of many others I've had with corporate management, I'm glad we addressed intervention approaches informed by the science of psychology. But I'm disappointed we failed to discuss a critical ingredient – genuine actively caring.

This is the heart of an effective safety process – the soft side of psychology.

Do They Really Care?

Consider this fundamental principle of human nature: We all react to how others feel about us.

In other words, we sense when others truly care about us. It's not in the words or even in the technique, but in the intentions. And these are displayed in passion, verbal intonation, body language, and various aspects of the relevant context. When we believe our supervisor is well-intentioned, we forgive awkward or clumsy applications of accountability techniques.

On the other hand, when we sense management doesn't really care about us, applications of the best performance-improvement process will fail.

For example, some safety-bonus systems or safety-incentive programs send the message that management is most concerned about keeping the numbers low (such as the total recordable injury rate). With a focus on injury statistics rather than people, the impact of the best injury-prevention techniques will be disappointing. People participate only halfheartedly when they

Behavior-based rewards motivate action.

believe those in charge care more about the numbers than them. They might go through the motions, but with minimal ownership and commitment.

Now, I'm talking only about perceptions. But perceptions are reality to the beholder. Supervisors might really care but give the impression they don't. They might, in fact, operate in a culture or work system that seemingly puts numbers and operations before people. And such a perspective might have historical precedence in the work culture. It can be very difficult to make caring prominent in a competitive, results-oriented work culture. But without a people-focused, actively caring attitude, an organization's output will always be less than optimal.

Power of Perception

The way we view others influences the feelings and actions of everyone involved. For example, we can see others as objects or a means to an end. Or we can see others as other people with personal needs, feelings, and expectations.

Current circumstances and prior experiences influence which viewpoint we take. But take heart, it's certainly possible to alter our perspectives.

In the university setting, for example, it's easy to view students and teachers as objects providing a means to an end. From the student's perspective, the professor provides knowledge and, most importantly, a passing grade. From the professor's viewpoint, students are bodies in a classroom who enable one's course to be taught and provide opportunities to display profound knowledge.

Large classes and busy schedules are among the circumstances that facilitate and sustain this "people-as-objects" perspective on a campus. But teachers and students do have opportunities to treat each other as people. Some students and professors work together on research and scholarship projects, and in the process get to know each other as individuals rather than impersonal objects in a self-serving process. In fact, these are the relationships of a profession that make a career most fulfilling.

Without the opportunity to work closely with talented and motivated students as research and scholarship colleagues, my 35+ years as a university professor would have been only a busy, self-satisfying routine. I would have left that environment years ago. Instead, I regret – actually I fear – the time when I'll be asked to relinquish my teaching and research opportunities at Virginia Tech. While my research, teaching, and scholarship have focused on the hard science of psychology, my inspiration and passion to keep going comes from my people-based experiences and relationships – the soft side of psychology.

A Critical Role

Feelings play a critical role in attempts to manage safety. Proven techniques to improve the human aspects of safety cannot have optimal impact unless those of us implementing the procedures genuinely care. As you know, I call this "actively caring." For this to happen, we need to view each other as people rather than objects that fulfill a self-serving need.

A key concept here is empathy. Whether the topic is empathic listening, empathic leadership, or empathic performance appraisals and corrective action (as addressed later in this book), the focus is on the other person's feelings, needs, or perceptions. Starting with this viewpoint makes every other management strategy more effective. Remember the Platinum Rule: Treat others as they want to be treated.

PART 3

Revolutionary Change

A number of articles and speeches in the safety field have centered on the concept of paradigms.[2] For example, Dan Petersen's speech at the 1993 meeting of the American Society of Safety Engineers was titled, "Safety's Paradigm Shift."

What is a "paradigm shift"? Some safety professionals define it as a revolutionary change in ideas, beliefs, and approaches. Here, I define ten basic changes in beliefs, attitudes, or perceptions required to develop the ultimate Total Safety Culture.

1) From OSHA regulations to corporate responsibility

Much of the safety activities and programs in industry are perceived as driven by OSHA rather than by the companies that benefit from the safety process.

In other words, many industry personnel perceive they are doing "safety stuff" because the government requires it rather than because it was their idea and initiative.

Government regulations leave little room for personal responsibility.

But remember that people will be more motivated and willing to go beyond the call of duty when they perceive they are achieving their own self-initiated goals, rather than when they are merely fulfilling requirements set by an outside agency.

2) From failure-oriented to achievement-oriented

When people work to fulfill someone else's requirements rather than to achieve their own goals, they are apt to develop an attitude of "working to avoid failure" rather than "working to achieve success." In safety this failure-oriented attitude is facilitated by a scoring system based on failures (such as OSHA recordables).

People feel more in control when working to achieve than when working to avoid failure. They display more consistent attention, less procrastination, and a healthier attitude when working to achieve quality and production goals than when working to avoid a potential loss from injury.

Giving safety an achievement perspective requires a different scoring system, as applied in the next paradigm shift.

3) From outcome-focused to behavior-focused

Companies are ranked according to their OSHA recordables and lost-time injuries, and within companies, work groups or individual workers earn safety

Outcome numbers remove critical focus from process behaviors.

awards according to outcomes – those with the lowest numbers win.

Providing incentives for lower numbers (such as injuries) can often reduce the numbers (such as the reported outcomes) while not improving safety.

When the pressure is placed on reduction of outcomes without changing the process (such as ongoing behaviors), employees often cover up their injuries. And how many times have you heard of injured employees being driven to work each day to sign in and then return to the hospital or their home to recuperate? This behavior keeps the outcome numbers low but does more harm than good to the corporate culture.

A scoring system based on what people do for safety (a behavior-based process) not only attacks the contributing factors of most work injuries but can also be achievement-oriented, thus placing safety in the same motivational framework as productivity and quality.

4) From top-down control to bottom-up improvement

A behavior-based, achievement approach to safety requires continual involvement from the operations personnel (hourly workers). After all, these are the employees who know where the safety hazards are located and when the at-risk behaviors occur.

Also, these are the individuals who have the most influence in supporting safe behaviors and correcting at-risk behaviors (and conditions).

In fact, the ongoing processes involved in developing a Total Safety Culture (TSC) need to be supported from the top but driven from the bottom. This is more than employee participation; it is employee ownership, commitment, and empowerment.

5) From rugged individualism to teamwork

An employee-driven safety process requires teamwork founded on interpersonal trust, synergy, and win/win goals. However, from childhood most of us have been taught an individualistic, win/lose perspective, supported by such popular slogans as "You have to blow your own horn," "Nice guys finish last," "No one can fill your shoes like you," and "The squeaky wheel gets the grease."

Furthermore, grades in school, the legal system, and many athletic contests orient us to think individualism and win/lose.

Thus, a true team approach to safety involving interpersonal observation and feedback of safe versus at-risk work practices is not easy to achieve. It runs counter to the rugged individualistic attitudes developed during childhood and supported through adulthood by our culture.

6) From a placement to a systems approach

A TSC can only be achieved with a systems approach, including balanced attention to all aspects of the corporate culture. Three basic domains, for example, need attention when designing and evaluating safety processes and when analyzing contributing factors of close calls and injuries:

1) Environment factors (such as equipment, tools, machines, housekeeping, heat/cold, engineering);
2) Person factors (employees' knowledge, skills, abilities, intelligence, motives, personality);
3) Behavior factors (employees complying, recognizing, communicating, "actively caring").

Two of these categories involve human factors. Each generally receives less attention than the environment, largely because it is more difficult to obtain visible consequences of efforts to change the human factors.

Some human factors programs focus on behavior-based safety management, whereas others focus on attitudes (as in a person-based approach). A total safety culture requires integrating both behavior-based and person-based approaches to understand and influence the human element of a corporate culture.

7) From fault-finding to fact-finding

Blaming a particular individual or group of individuals for an "accident" is not consistent with a systems approach to safety.

Instead, an injury or close call provides an opportunity to consider facts from all aspects of the system that could have contributed to the incident. Not only are the immediate environment, person, and behavior factors

Behavior-Based
\+ Person-Based
= People-Based

explored as potential contributors, but numerous historical factors are also considered.

How common, for example, was the at-risk behavior? How many observed the at-risk behavior without intervening? And what aspects of operations and the management system supported the at-risk behavior?

8) From reactive to proactive

Investigating events preceding an incident (a "near miss" or injury) reveals the need to think and act proactively. Unfortunately, a proactive stance is extremely difficult to maintain, especially in a corporate culture that is increasingly complex and demanding, resulting in a higher and higher price tag on "free time."

With barely enough time to react appropriately to the crises each day, how can we find time to be proactive?

9) From quick fix to continuous improvement

Obviously there is no quick-fix answer to the challenging question posed above. Only with a systems perspective and an optimistic mind-set of continuous improvement can "proactive" be substituted for "reactive."

This can be facilitated greatly by integrating behavior-based and person-based psychology, and that is the theme of this book – People-Based Safety.

10) From priority to value

As long as safety is a priority, it is legitimate to shift its priority ranking, depending on other priorities at the time. It usually takes external forces (policy directives, special training, incentives, and rewards) to boost safety's priority ranking.

When individuals hold safety as a value, however, there is never a compromise for safety. The "safe way" is linked with each of the priorities of the day, whether at work or at home.

Do we have a long way to go? Perhaps, but we can get there and prevent many injuries along the way by adjusting our paradigms or viewpoints toward safety.

Each of the ten paradigm shifts discussed here should be considered a mission to reach in order to achieve a Total Safety Culture. That is, the safety process should be regarded as a company responsibility, achievement-oriented with a focus on behaviors, and driven from the bottom through teamwork.

A systems approach is necessary, which leads to a fact-finding perspective, a proactive stance, and an appreciation of continuous improvement. With these perspectives as the ultimate safety mission, it is indeed possible to shift from safety as a priority to safety as a value.

Cultural Experiences Reflect Win/Lose Individualism or Win/Win Collectivism

Individualistic

- The squeaky wheel gets the grease.
- You have to blow your own horn.
- He travels fastest who travels alone.
- Nice guys finish last.
- No one can fill your shoes like you.
- Where there is a will, there's a way.
- I am the captain of my soul, captain of my fate.

Collectivistic

- Still waters run deep.
- The nail that stands above the board invites a hammering down.
- A wise man does not speak, for it is the shallow water that makes the noise.
- One doesn't make the wind but is blown by it.
- What is possible depends upon the circumstances.
- The greatness of a person may be measured by one's humility, not by one's assertiveness.

PART 4

Stop Passing the Buck

Returning to her office after a field safety inspection, Joanne noticed packaging littered all about her building's main entrance. Without hesitating, Joanne collected the litter and disposed of it in a trash receptacle. Entering the office, a coworker asked, "Why did you pick up that litter? We have custodial staff for that job. You could have called them." Joanne responded, "I couldn't just walk by and let that mess deface our attractive building."

Joanne's experience is not only a story of taking personal responsibility; it illustrates a common technique of denying responsibility. No one watching Joanne pick up trash ventured outside to help her. They took time to observe and criticize, but not to participate.

If they could understand, they'd lend a hand.

Certainly these onlookers did not view themselves as irresponsible or even lacking personal responsibility. They had a handy excuse for not helping: "It's not my job." How many times have you heard that? This is probably the most common reason for not going beyond the call of duty to help another person. This rationale for "passing the buck" is actually supported by the typical questions we ask when noticing a problem.

Questions that Deflect

Questions beginning with who, what, and when avoid personal responsibility by putting accountability somewhere else.

Who made that work station so messy?

What safety regulation was not followed?

When will the company install an adequate ventilation system?

I'm not saying these are bad questions to ask, not at all. They represent the kind of questions needed to identify and solve problems related to occupational safety. But they do imply the problem is beyond the individual and a solution requires support and action from other people.

Surely we can ask "why?" But some "why" questions are nonproductive and facilitate denial of personal responsibility. Why was I given this assignment? Why me? These "why" questions activate and support victim thinking and contribute to the avoidance of personal responsibility.

What Can I Do?

The simple question "What can I do?" reflects the essence of personal responsibility. That's the implicit question Joanne asked when noticing a littered entrance to her office building. She didn't ask, "Who did that?" or "Why did they do it?" or "Whose job is it to fix that?"

Instead, Joanne asked "What can I do to help?" and then she did what she could do. She took personal responsibility. Instead of asking questions that give us an excuse to "pass the buck" to someone else sometime later, we should ask, "What can I do right now to help?"

We Can't Do It All

Joanne's personal action was sufficient to resolve the litter problem. Similarly, many of our own actively-caring behaviors can provide quick-fix solutions to relatively minor problems. But often we find ourselves in the midst of a safety-related issue that has no quick-fix solution. A long-term investment of financial and interpersonal resources is needed. As a result, it's easy to deny personal responsibility with the claim, "There's nothing I can do without more support."

The big picture may seem overwhelming, and a solution to a certain safety problem may seem remote even with substantial support. But doing nothing at all helps nothing, and could be risky. So break it down. Find something small within your own domain of influence that relates to the problem and take personal responsibility to perform that action.

Start by defining the problem in terms of actions or behaviors, then identify talents or work assignments related to each action, and then select something from this list you can accomplish. Personal responsibility starts with the creation of this list of problem-related activities. Consider persuading someone else to take on a solution-related assignment commensurate with his or her talent and position in the organization. Then find others to contribute within their domain of personal control.

PART 5
Step In and Speak Up

Imagine you're watching the following story unfold. After you hear what happened, I'd like you to consider what you would have done (if anything) had you been there.

You're at one of those restaurants known for heckling diners, supposedly all in good fun. At a table nearby sit a mom, dad, their two children – ages five and seven – and their 17-year-old niece. From the start, Anna, the 17-year-old, is targeted for ridicule. Her waiter, nicknamed Buttercup, first teases her about the small "star" tattoo on her shoulder. Then he brings out a paper hat with the label "Puberty Stinks" and puts it on her head.

When Anna ignores this badgering, Buttercup gets more aggressive. He

The hassling begins.

takes out a black magic marker and writes "SLUT" across Anna's bare back. Onlookers laugh aloud, but Anna looks quite embarrassed. She doesn't say a word, though, and continues to eat her meal. The waiter still wants to get a rise from Anna. He returns from the kitchen with a meringue pie, and you guessed it, pushes it directly into Anna's face.

Buttercup finally gets the rise he wanted – literally. The 110-pound

Anna gets a meringue pie in the face.

teenager springs from her chair and tackles the six-foot, 200-pound waiter. After a brief scuffle, Buttercup holds Anna upside down by her ankles and proceeds to carry her outside and drop her safely in a dumpster.

Anna gets a trip to the dumpster.

Anna returns to her table in tears; she's immediately consoled by her aunt, who accompanies her to the restroom. When the waiter delivers the check, Anna's uncle pays it – and adds a ten percent gratuity.

Normal Reactions?

This story is absolutely true; it happened in the summer of 2002 at Myrtle Beach, South Carolina. When I heard it, I was initially stunned by the lack of intervention. I imagined myself standing on a chair after the waiter took a magic marker to Anna's back – that's when he crossed the line, right? – and telling the crowd: "Management will gladly cover everyone's food and drink to avoid the million-dollar lawsuit."

How could anyone allow this incident to escalate to its outlandish outcome without intervening? I was astounded to learn that Anna's uncle not only paid the check, but also added on a significant tip. When later challenged by Anna's parents, the defense was, "Everything happened so fast."

I bet your reaction is similar to mine. You can visualize yourself helping Anna. At the very least, you would not have given the waiter a financial reward.

Don't be so sure.

Several factors inhibited intervention in Anna's case. Similar factors also hinder workplace involvement for safety and health. Situations occur every day at work where we could say or do something about undesirable or risky behaviors.

Ask yourself...

- Have you observed at-risk behavior and said to yourself, "What a dumb thing to do; if he gets hurt he deserves it"?
- Have you avoided getting involved in a situation because you felt untrained or ill-equipped to deal with it?
- Have you ever held back from actively caring for safety because you figured someone else would or should help?
- Have you held back because you felt your work environment condoned risky behavior?

After a person gets hurt, our hindsight kicks in. "Why didn't someone warn her?" I'm sure you can recall instances where an injury would have been avoided if someone had stepped in or spoken up. So why don't we get involved? Let's consider four barriers that impeded intervention in the restaurant, and see whether they are relevant to industrial settings.

1) "That's the Way It Is."

The restaurant is known for hassling its customers. The climate invites confrontation. Obviously, we're talking about culture – a critical determinant of behavior.

I've visited many plants where the behavior of people in leadership positions is not consistent with safety rules and regulations. This sets the stage for compromising safety in the name of efficiency or productivity. In such a work culture, you can expect many opportunities for safety intervention to be overlooked.

2) "Someone Else Will Help."

Social psychologists have found that the more people witnessing an event calling for intervention, the lower the probability any one person will help.

A popular explanation for this "bystander apathy effect" is diffusion of responsibility – people assume another onlooker will help.[3]

It's logical to assume the most appropriate people to intervene on Anna's behalf were those at her table. Perhaps onlookers thought Buttercup had a special relationship with Anna or her family, and this explained the outrageous behavior.

Have you ever held back from actively caring for safety because you figured someone else would or should help? Maybe you thought you'd be meddling in someone else's business. In many work cultures it's natural for individuals to feel this reluctance. Not only might you be intruding, but it's reasonable to think that someone else – a team member or a friend – might be in a better position to help.

3) "What Should I Do?"

What should have been said to Buttercup when he wrote "SLUT" on Anna's back? What feedback should Anna's uncle have given to Buttercup and his manager, perhaps after refusing to pay the check? What should Anna have said to stifle the belittling?

Researchers have shown that individuals are more likely to help others in emergency situations when they know what to do. Observers without relevant training are quick to defer the responsibility to someone else.[4]

People have many excuses for not actively caring.

Assertiveness training, for example, helps people stand up for their rights and come to the realization their feelings and opinions matter and should be expressed. Such training involves direct instruction and role-playing of specific verbal expressions to regain control in certain situations.[5]

Practicing what to say to resolve or alleviate a conflict beforehand enables people to intervene effectively in the "heat" of the moment. Likewise, practicing what to say before asking a peer to work safely will increase the likelihood you'll actually intervene and be effective. Instead of saying, "Why don't you follow the safe operating procedure?" ask, "What barriers are holding you back from doing the job safely?"

4) "She Asked for It."

Did it ever cross your mind that Anna's reactions, or lack of actions, influenced the series of unpleasant exchanges? In the same vein, have you ever thought the victim of an unpleasant workplace conflict or an injury did something to deserve it? It's common for people to view victims as causing their own fate. Social psychologists call this phenomena the "just world hypothesis" – people assume that we get what we deserve and deserve what we get.[6]

Consider how this belief can be a barrier to helping others. Most observers of the confrontation between Buttercup and Anna derived their own explanations for the incident, and given the just-world bias, many probably blamed Anna for her misfortune.

Here's hoping the next time you see someone taking a risk at work you'll overcome these four obstacles and step in for safety's sake.

PART 6

Watch Your Language

Did you ever stop to think that certain expressions used in the safety and health field actually hurt safety efforts? Words have a powerful influence on our attitudes and behaviors,[7] and I think some words we habitually use in the safety and health field send the wrong message. Here are a few of the more commonly used words that should be eliminated from our everyday language if we want to achieve a Total Safety Culture.

Accident Implies Chance

The first definition of "accident" in my *New Merriam-Webster Dictionary* (copyright 1989) is "an event occurring by chance or unintentionally." Are workplace accidents truly chance occurrences? Don't we try to develop the belief and expectation that accidents can be prevented by controlling factors such as environmental conditions, behaviors and attitudes? Accident is the wrong word to use when referring to unintentional injuries. Continuing to use this term will reduce the number of people who believe accidents can be prevented.

Language can be a turn-off.

Restraints Don't Invite Use

For more than a decade I've been urging transportation and safety professionals to stop using the terms "occupant restraints" and "child restraints" for vehicle safety belts and child safety seats, respectively. These terms imply discomfort and lack of personal control, and they fail to convey the real function of these devices.

"Seat belt" is better than "occupant restraint," but this popular term is not really adequate because it does not describe the function or appearance of the device. Vehicle safety belts were once only lap belts; now they are combination lap-and-shoulder belts.

We need to get into the habit of saying "safety belt" and "child safety device." Then we are conveying the critical function of these devices. However, the most appropriate label for "safety belt" is "life belt."

Is Safety a Priority or a Value?

The term priority implies importance and a sense of urgency. Safety professionals are often quick to say "safety should be a priority." This seems appropriate, since my dictionary defines "priority" as "taking precedence logically or in importance." However, our everyday experience with "priorities" teaches us that priorities come and go. A priority today might not be a priority tomorrow. Depending upon the demands of the moment, one priority often gets shifted for another.

Do we really want to associate safety with such a term?

I believe a Total Safety Culture requires a shift from safety as a priority to safety as a value. The relevant definition of "value" in my dictionary is "something (as a principle or ideal) intrinsically valuable or desirable." Safety should be a "value" that employees bring to every job, regardless of the ongoing priorities or task requirements. Our safety mission statement should refer to safety as a "value" rather than a "priority."

Don't Say "Behavior Modification"

The 1994 conference brochure for the annual meeting of the American Society of Safety Engineers included a session description with the words, "behavioral *(sic)* modification or behavior management is an idea whose time has come." And I still hear this term used today by safety pros.

Since behavior modification has been used for more than 25 years to improve behaviors in institutions, corporations, and communities, this statement is not accurate. More importantly, however, this is the wrong terminology to use if we want buy-in and involvement from the people who are to be "modified."

This lesson was learned the hard way more than 30 years ago by the behavioral scientists and therapists who developed the principles and techniques of "behavior modification." Whether applying behavior-change technologies to help teachers, students, employees, or prisoners, the term "behavior modification" was a real turn-off because it conveys images of manipulation, top-down control, loss of personal control, and the movie *A Clockwork Orange*.

For example, in 1974 I developed a behavior-change system and associated training process for the Virginia prison system, but our innovative and very effective plan was never fully implemented, partly because the inmates and guards associated "behavior modification" with brainwashing techniques and lobotomies.

Actually, the term "behavior" has negative associations for many people (as in, "Let's talk about your behavior last night"). But I can't see any way around using this term. We need to teach and demonstrate the benefits of focusing on behaviors, especially desirable behaviors, to achieve safety excellence. But linking "modification" with behavior is not necessary, and only adds to negative feelings about behavior itself.

"Behavior analysis" is the term used by researchers and scholars in the field. This implies that behavior is analyzed first, and if change is called for, an intervention process is developed with input from the client(s). Given that "analysis" can also sound a bit threatening or academic, I've been

Language affects behavior.

recommending the label "behavior-based approach" for several years. This contrasts nicely with the "person-based approach" that focuses on attitudes, feelings, and expectancies rather than behaviors. A Total Safety Culture requires consideration of both behavior-based and person-based psychology. We call it ***People-Based Safety.***

This is obviously a limited list of word substitutions we should consider, but I hope the basic message is clear. We need to understand that our language can activate feelings and even behaviors we don't want.

To illustrate further, ponder the following questions regarding word-attitude associations:

Should we say "peer pressure" or "peer support"?

Should we refer to safety professionals as "loss control managers" or "safety achievement facilitators"?

Should we discuss the results of a safety audit as "meeting OSHA standards" or "fulfilling a corporate mission"?

Do you have a "safety compliance" task force or a "safety achievement" task force?

Did you work "30 days without an injury" or did you work "30 safe days"?

Considering the ramifications of using these various phrases can be a useful personal or group exercise. Adding alternatives to this list would be even more beneficial. But understanding the critical relationship between words, attitudes, and deeds is only half the battle. We need to change our verbal habits, and this is easier said than done.

PART 7
It's Natural to Care

Do you assume employees will not want to participate in your safety process because it's inconvenient or time-consuming? Consider this alternative: Your employees really want to participate, to play a role in keeping coworkers safe.

I think it's time to challenge old assumptions about safety participation. It's not a thankless job requiring self-sacrifice or a special degree of altruism. Instead, let's assume that helping others reaps personal gains for everyone involved. This behavior is not sacrificial, nor even unselfish. It rewards a basic human need to make a difference – to serve others. In other words, serving others is self-rewarding, not self-sacrificing, because it meets three basic needs.

Competence

Several researchers of human motivation have proposed that people naturally enjoy being able to solve problems and successfully complete worthwhile tasks.[8] In their view, we are motivated to learn, to explore possibilities, to understand what is going on, and to participate in achieving worthwhile goals. The label for this fundamental human motive is "competence."

Motivational psychologists assume the desire for competence is self-initiating and self-rewarding. Behavior that increases feelings of effectiveness is self-directed and does not need extrinsic or extra reinforcement to keep it going. In this case, feeling competent to do worthwhile work motivates continued effort. As a result, behavioral skills that increase competence are readily learned and practiced. Think about the avenues this opens for safety leadership and participation.

Self-Efficacy

This is a critical concept in People-Based Safety. Having self-efficacy means the participant believes he or she can organize and perform the procedures needed to achieve a desired goal. When people learn specific procedural steps for carrying out a particular safety process, they gain self-efficacy. They feel competent.

Response-Efficacy

But it's not enough to feel competent at a task – we need to believe our participation contributes to making a beneficial difference. Thus, effective training not only teaches step-by-step procedures; it includes a rationale for why the process is useful.

In safety, we must convince participants that applying the lessons learned will help people remain injury-free. The need to feel competent is satisfied not only by self-efficacy (believing one has the skills to implement a particular intervention), but also response-efficacy (believing the intervention will have a desirable impact).

Power of Feedback

So how do we know we are competent at something? How do we know our competence makes a valuable difference?

You know the answer – feedback.

Feedback about our ongoing behavior tells us how we are doing and enables us to do better. Sometimes this feedback comes naturally, such as when we see our behavior produce a desired result. But often behavioral feedback requires careful and systematic observation by another individual, a trainer or coach, who later communicates his or her findings to the

Feedback can be reactive, remote, and destructive.

performer. In each case, feedback enables us to develop self-efficacy and fulfill our need for competence.

In Chapter 3 of this book, "The Coaching of People-Based Safety", I'll discuss various ways to deliver and receive individual and group feedback. Here I only want to drive home the point that feedback delivered well, whether supportive, corrective or both, feeds the basic human desire to be competent. It's not a payoff for doing the right thing. Rather, it's objective information a person uses to feel competent or to learn how to become more competent. I believe there's no other consequence with greater potential to improve performance.

A New Perspective

Instead of calling on guilt or sacrifice to get people involved in procedures to eliminate hazards or decrease at-risk behavior, let's assume that people are naturally motivated to make beneficial differences. People hate feeling incompetent or helpless. They want to learn, to discover, to become more proficient at worthwhile tasks. People want opportunities to ask questions, to study pertinent material, to work with people who know more than they do, and to receive feedback that can increase their competence.

Safety participation puts people in control of environmental and human factors that can cause serious injury or death. It avoids one of the most aversive human states – the feeling of incompetence or helplessness. Participation in an effective safety process provides opportunities to satisfy a basic human need – the need for competence. And effective and frequent delivery of behavior-based feedback provides a mechanism for improving the quality of safety participation, as well as cultivating feelings of competence throughout a work culture.

Research is an evolving process.

PART 8

Rely on Rigorous Research

Many presentations on the psychology of safety base assertions solely on common sense. Statements are made that sound good but are actually incorrect or unfounded.

Unfortunately, it's not always easy to determine which psychology-related statements are valid. My writing has always been based on scientific investigation rather than speculation or hearsay. I continue to stress that the psychology of safety is not a matter of common sense, but the result of rigorous behavioral research.

Some invalid statements are given so often by motivational speakers or pop psychologists they are accepted as fact. Let's examine seven of these fallacies.

"Reprimand privately, recognize publicly."

Sound familiar? Actually, whether you're correcting behavior or giving recognition, it's always better to communicate one-to-one in private. Never recognize a person in front of a group without that person's permission. Some people are embarrassed by public commendation; others fear verbal harassment from peers. They imagine someone saying, "Why did you deserve that 'safe-employee-of-the-month' award? I've done as much around here for safety as you have. Have you been kissing up to the boss?"

"We learn from mistakes more than successes."

Think about what's being said here. What do you learn when you make a mistake? You learn what not to do. That's something worth learning, but consider how much more you learn when you do something correctly and receive feedback that you're correct. You learn what you need to continue in order to be successful.

"77% of our mental thoughts are negative."

We do need to be recognized more for our safe behavior, primarily because we learn more from correct than incorrect performance. But to claim a certain proportion of negative thoughts pervade the minds of human beings is absurd. Ask yourself the question, "How could they know?" This is a ridiculous statement, yet I've heard it used by a number of pop psychologists.

"Do something 21 times and it becomes a habit."

This is the theme of several self-help books. Behavior needs to be repeated many times to develop fluency and then a habit. That's why it's important to support the safe work practices of our friends and teammates. But to presume there's a set number of repetitions needed for habit formation is downright silly, and frankly, insults the intelligence of most listeners. And later in this book you'll learn that habits are often undesirable, especially when the behavior is for safety.

For years I've wondered where the "21" came from. Then a local farmer reminded me it takes 21 days for an egg to hatch into a chicken.

Some behaviors are so complex or inconvenient they never become habitual. Consider the chain of behaviors needed to lock out a power source, complete a behavioral audit, or follow a stretch and exercise routine. These important safety-related behaviors are never likely to become automatic. Their occurrence will probably always require some deliberate motivating influence, whether external or self-imposed.

Inconvenient safe behaviors don't become habitual.

"We can only motivate ourselves, not others."

If this were true, we couldn't motivate others to choose the safe way of doing something when the at-risk alternative is more comfortable, efficient, convenient or perhaps habitual. Later in this book I discuss the role of external motivational intervention to increase safe behavior and decrease at-risk behavior. Here I only want to discredit the myth that only self-motivation works.

"Incentives and rewards are detrimental to self-motivation."

Yes, you can insult one's intelligence or self-motivation by using the wrong type of intervention to improve a particular behavior as I discuss later in Chapter 4 on Thinking. And this can have a temporary detrimental effect on individual performance.

But research indicates this negative impact is relatively infrequent, and if it does occur it is short-lived.[9] Incentives and rewards are far more likely to benefit desired performance and even self-motivation for long-term behavior change if they are used correctly. The key is to use a behavior-based approach to incentive/reward programs, as I detailed later in this book.

"For every 300 unsafe acts there are 29 minor injuries and one major injury."

I couldn't end this brief list of unfounded claims without adding the most popular myth in the field of industrial safety. This ratio between at-risk behavior and injury was first proposed in the 1930s by H. W. Heinrich. It has been repeated so often, some safety pros refer to it as "Heinrich's Law." It started as a mere estimate, and after years of use in safety speeches and publications, without any empirical verification, its status was elevated to "basic principle" or "natural law."

This statement does show the connection between behavior and injury, and implies that a proactive approach to injury prevention requires attention to behaviors and near misses. However, the number of at-risk behaviors per injury is much larger than 300, as verified empirically by Frank Bird in 1966, who also found property damage to be a reliable predictor or leading indicator of personal injury.[10] My point here is not about a proactive versus reactive approach to safety. More important, think about how the long-term repetition of an unfounded proclamation that sounds good can become a common myth with presumed validity. Too often in safety we accept what "sounds good," without asking for the research evidence. This is particularly true if the claims are packaged with slick marketing.

Don't take statements at face value. Ask for objective scientific research to support the claims. The information in this book is founded on empirical research, not common sense.[11] Throughout this book, I cite literature that can be consulted for further clarification and verification.

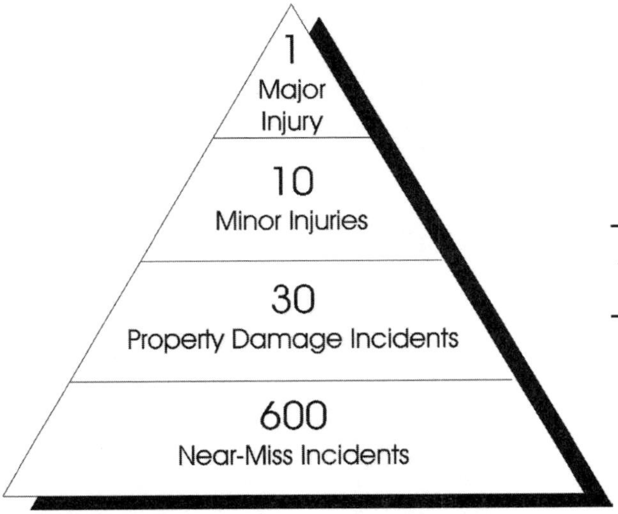

F. E. Bird estimated more near hits than did H. W. Heinrich.

PART 9

Never Stop Teaching

How can we make the most of our training opportunities? I'd like to explain seven research-based principles to consider when you have the opportunity to teach, whether one on one or in a group setting.

1) Explain why

There is a distinction between education and training. Education targets thinking or thought processes and usually includes the theory or rationale behind a particular lesson. In contrast, training targets behavior, and includes steps to assure the learner knows what to do to satisfy certain performance criteria.

With this first principle, I'm saying effective training should include education. The entire learning process is facilitated when people realize up front the potential benefits to be gained from their learning. Tell people what positive consequences they could gain and/or negative consequences they could avoid from a training program, and they will be more motivated to learn.

2) Specify objectives

It's critical to clarify what the learner will be able to do as a result of the training session. The focus here is on behavior, not

Training without education can be ineffective.

understanding or thinking. Explain the relevance of the behavior for obtaining the benefits outlined in Principle 1.

State learning objectives from the perspective of the learner. For example, "You will be able to complete a behavioral checklist" rather than "I will show you how to complete a behavioral checklist." And state objectives in behavioral terms. For example, "You will be able to conduct the four essential steps of a behavior-based coaching session" rather than "You will understand how to implement a behavioral coaching process."

3) Provide memory aids

Learning can be enhanced with a memory aid. My colleagues and I use acronyms to facilitate safety training, and you'll see a number of these in this source book for People-Based Safety. For example, we use "DO IT" to teach the four steps of a behavior-based safety process (define critical behaviors, observe these behaviors, intervene to influence these behaviors, and then test for intervention impact). We also use the letters of COACH to review the consecutive steps of a people-based coaching process – Care, Observe, Analyze, Communicate, and Help.

4) Inspire action and reaction

Learners must see a meaningful connection between their mental or behavioral activity and the lesson. The best activities stimulate the learner to relate the information to their own life events and to create personal links between such experiences and specific training principles or procedures.

There are many ways to provoke mindful or active learning. You can relate real-world events to the information you're presenting; you can pose questions to stimulate meaningful overt or covert reaction from the audience; or you can facilitate a group discussion or exercise that exemplifies certain points of a lesson.

5) Provide feedback

When learners contribute overtly in a training session, effective teachers provide constructive feedback. You should provide specific information to show whether a verbal response or a skit is relevant or off the mark. Confirming feedback tells an individual or group certain principles or procedures of a lesson are understood; corrective feedback points out a discrepancy between an overt reaction and a particular learning objective.

When giving corrective feedback, don't make the learner feel like a failure. Maintain the mindset that observing an off-target reaction says more about teaching than learning. It gives you information you can use on the spot to explain miscommunication or misunderstanding.

6) Reward on-target reactions

Confirming feedback tells learners they understand certain essentials of a lesson. This bolsters a sense of personal accomplishment. Of course, the more important a learner perceives a lesson to be, the more rewarding is the confirming feedback. Recall Principle 1 – Begin instruction by explaining the value or rationale of a lesson.

Use more than confirming feedback to reward your learners. Emphasize the significance of the information you are teaching, and express delight

Small successive steps to success are often best.

whenever someone in the group shows evidence of learning. Sometimes extrinsic rewards like points, trinkets, or recognition credits can keep people motivated and facilitate learning. But it's critical to focus on natural rewards or positive consequences inherent to the learning process.

7) Always evaluate

The term "evaluation" is a turn-off to most participants in a training session, including the teacher. Evaluation implies a "test," and most people dislike tests. Teachers don't like developing and scoring them, and learners don't like taking them. As a result, many adult education/training sessions, from professional development sessions at conferences to special on-site industrial programs, do not include an end-of-session evaluation.

But let's be frank. Wouldn't knowledge that a test will be administered at the end of a training session make you more mindful from the start? If learners don't understand a concept they think they could be held accountable for knowing, they are likely to ask relevant questions. They hold the teacher accountable for explaining material they could be tested on later. And for many people, such mindful learning increases even when they are not required to put their name on the test. Such an anonymous evaluation is invaluable for the teacher.

PART 10

Build Interdependence

In his popular books on total quality management, *Out of the Crisis* and *The New Economics*, W. Edwards Deming tells us to focus our efforts on optimizing the system.[12]

Peter Senge stresses that "systems thinking" is the Fifth Discipline, and key to continuous improvement.[13]

And Stephen Covey's discussions of interdependency, win/win contingencies, and synergy in his best seller, *The Seven Habits of Highly Effective People*, are founded on systems thinking.[14]

So what is systems thinking anyway, and how can this concept be applied to industrial safety and health? Let's address this question from the perspective of behaviors, attitudes, and commitment to safety improvement.

Every time I travel to and from the Roanoke, Virginia, airport on Interstate

Systems thinking enables a view of the big picture.

81, I'm reminded of the interdependency inherent in a transportation system, and of the great number of people whose driving behavior demonstrates an individualistic, win/lose attitude rather than the win/win cooperative attitude needed to optimize the system. Consider drivers who dart back and forth between lanes, often without signaling, just to shave a few seconds off their trip time. They're thinking only of themselves. It doesn't occur to them their inconsiderate, at-risk behavior could cause a crash and shut down the entire transportation system.

How about those slow drivers clogging up the left lane, perhaps because they'll eventually make a left-hand turn several miles ahead. They also display a win/lose perspective, perhaps unconsciously or unintentionally, which makes our transportation system less efficient.

None of these drivers probably realize their effect on the overall system, a system that works best when everyone follows the same rules, norms, and courtesies of the road. Nor do they see the interdependency, the connection, between driving behavior and the attitudes and emotions of themselves and other drivers. Discourteous and risky driving easily triggers negative emotions in other drivers, prompting them to reciprocate with dangerous actions. It's a disruptive chain reaction.

When we consider this broad interdependency between people's driving behaviors, attitudes, and emotions, we are engaging in systems thinking. This systems perspective on driving becomes more clear to me as I peer from the window of the plane as it leaves Roanoke. I see the bigger picture below and appreciate the complex interplay between the behaviors and attitudes of the drivers operating each vehicle.

Like my view from the plane, we need a big-picture perspective of our work situation to see the many win/win interdependencies that go into a Total Safety Culture. This is systems thinking for safety. Here are seven principles that emanate from such a perspective:

1) There is no single root cause

Systems thinkers do not try to find one root cause of an incident or injury. At-risk behavior contributes to 95 percent or more of most injuries, whether intentional or unintentional. But this does not mean an individual's at-risk behavior is the root cause of the injury. A number of factors contribute to all injuries.

2) Consider environment, behavior, and person factors

These factors are interactive, dynamic, and reciprocal. For example, changes in an environmental factor affect behaviors and attitudes. And behavior change usually results in some change in the environment. When people choose to change their behavior, they adjust their attitudes and beliefs (personal factors) to be consistent with their actions. This change in attitude can influence more behavior change and then more attitude change – a spiraling, reciprocal interdependency between our outward actions and inward feelings. And an initial change in behavior or attitude can be sparked by an environmental factor.

An organization's management system is one environmental factor that has dramatic impact on the human factors. A top-down authoritarian approach might dictate certain behaviors, but it also creates a negative attitude that might bring about contrary behaviors.

3) Measure these factors

Environment and behavioral factors can be systematically assessed with periodic audits of workplace conditions and work practices. And perception and attitude surveys can be useful barometers of person-based factors. Traditional reactive measures of safety, such as OSHA recordkeeping, have absolutely no diagnostic value to help understand or change system variables that cause outcomes. Keep in mind that outcome measures can be influenced by numerous factors, such as punishment and reward programs that can lead to under-reporting of injuries or close calls.

4) Investigate facts, not faults

Because it's critical to investigate minor injuries and "near misses," systems thinkers attempt to remove any aspect of their environment that could inhibit the reporting of safety-related incidents. They also add factors to facilitate the reporting and analysis of close calls,[15] first-aid cases, and minor

Some work cultures promote win/lose independency over win/win interdependency.

injuries – incidents that are not typically recorded but could help prevent more serious injuries.

If factors in the system promote a fault-finding perspective toward injury investigation, then information critical to preventing injuries could be stifled. It's been my experience that the fault-finding perspective usually begins with undue focus on outcomes rather than processes.

5) Feedback directs and motivates

Rarely if ever does safe behavior have a built-in feedback system to support and direct it. When we take the extra time and inconvenience to protect ourselves or others from a potential injury, we usually do not receive a natural consequence to motivate us to continue. With systems thinking, though, we see the bigger picture and realize that someday someone in the work system will gain directly from our effort.

Systems thinkers don't need immediate quick fixes to keep them safe. They understand that cause and effect are not necessarily immediate nor linear. Taking the time to be safe today can help develop a personal routine that could pay personal dividends in the future. Or it could teach others by example and protect them now or later from injury.

Systems thinkers realize the special need to add extra feedback to motivate and activate safe behavior. They understand that the natural feedback from convenience, comfort, or a faster outcome usually competes with the completely safe way to do something.

Systems thinkers look for ways to support safe behavior and correct at-risk behavior. They use feedback as a consequence to motivate an individual to continue or stop a particular behavior, and they use feedback as an activator to direct improvement in particular work practices. Details on how to give safety feedback are covered in Chapter 3 on the Coaching of PBS.

6) Consistency develops commitment

When we choose to do something, we experience internal pressure to maintain a personal belief system or attitude consistent with that behavior. And when we have a certain belief system or attitude toward something, we tend to behave in ways that are consistent with such beliefs or attitudes. Commitment and total involvement result from this spiraling effect of action feeding attitude, then attitude feeding more action, which strengthens the attitude and leads to more behavior.

Researchers have found three ways to make an initial commitment to do something lead to total involvement. First, people live up to what they write down, so ask for a signed statement of a commitment.[16] Second, the more public the commitment, the greater the relevant attitude and behavior change, presumably because social pressures are added to the personal pressure to be consistent in word and deed.

Third, and perhaps most important, for a public and written commitment to initiate that spiraling effect of behavior supporting attitude and vice versa, the commitment must be viewed as a personal choice. When people believe their commitment was their idea, the consistency principle is activated. But when people believe their commitment was unduly pressured by outside forces, they don't feel a need to live up to what they were coerced to write down.[17]

7) Embrace reciprocity

Simply put, the reciprocity principle[18] is reflected in the slogan, "Do for me and I'll do for you." In other words, if you're nice to someone, they'll feel obligated to return the favor. And consistent with a systems perspective, the favor might be returned to someone other than the original source.

A systems thinker sees this principle as powerful rationale for going beyond the call of duty for another person's safety. Such actively caring behavior will provoke reciprocity, and motivate the recipient of active caring to return the favor to someone else in the system.

Systems thinkers also realize that how they react to people after doing

Relationships are based on reciprocity.

them a favor can either stifle or mobilize a spiral of reciprocity. When a person thanks them for actively caring, system thinkers do not demean the favor by saying things like, "No problem," or "It was really nothing." Anything that makes active caring seem insignificant or trivial will reduce the impetus for reciprocity.

To maintain a comfortable verbal exchange that is not belittling nor stifling, systems thinkers react to a "Thank you for actively caring" with something like, "Thank you for appreciating my effort; I know you'd do the same for me." This shows genuine admiration for the thank-you, supports the reciprocity principle, and increases the likelihood more thanks will be given.

As you can see from these principles, a systems approach to achieving a Total Safety Culture forces us to move away from traditional safety management concepts like trying to find one root cause of a "near miss" or injury, or focusing on outcome-based measures of safety performance. Systems thinking also changes our perspective from linear to circular or spiraling when looking at the connection between activators, behaviors, and consequences. We can see how small changes in behavior can result in attitude change, followed by more behavior change and more desired attitude change, leading eventually to personal commitment and total involvement in the process.

Ultimately, we have interdependent work teams regularly caring for the safety of each other with a win/win attitude and a proactive vision. And it all started with systems thinking for safety.

PART 11

Cultivate Emotional Intelligence

Dr. Stephen Covey has said more than once that one of his most important early lessons in life was that it is not necessary for people to respond reflexively to environmental events.[19] Instead, we have freedom and power – to choose not to respond or to decide on a plan from a variety of alternatives. And this choice does not depend on the most immediate and certain consequence.

This challenges the teaching of many behavioral safety consultants. Their ABC model (for antecedent-behavior-consequence) is often taught as if behavior is "triggered by antecedent stimuli" and motivated most effectively by "soon, certain, and positive consequences."

Let's consider the liabilities of this rather narrow model of human behavior and the advantages of realizing there is a valuable "space" between environmental stimuli and people's responses.

The bell activates running for ice cream and may trigger salivation.

Reflex Behavior

A stop sign triggers drivers to apply their brakes, right? A behavioral audit causes workers to increase their safe work practices, right?

The fact is that only involuntary behavior can be triggered by a stimulus like a stop sign. This occurs through natural or unlearned reflexive action, as when cold air causes you to shiver. Through a certain kind of learning called classical conditioning, previously neutral stimuli can also cause a reflexive response, as when viewing the cold weather outside triggers shivering.

But most daily behavior, including safe behaviors, is voluntary. It is not triggered by external stimuli. Antecedent conditions or events – activators – can provide direction for behavior, as when a safety sign tells people what PPE is required. Individuals decide whether to follow the directive, based largely on the consequences expected after performing the behavior. But the most influential consequences are not necessarily "soon, certain, and positive."

Powerful Motivators

Negative and delayed consequences can be very powerful motivators, especially when certainty is a quality. Think about it. Believing one more cigarette will assuredly cause sudden death ten years from now, a cigarette smoker would probably choose to stop smoking "cold turkey."

If workers truly believed their risky work practice would lead to personal injury, they would likely avoid such behavior.

But there are exceptions. Some people actually continue to smoke cigarettes after suffering from emphysema and needing an oxygen tank to breathe. My point is that behavior cannot always be predicted by knowing the qualities of its consequences. People often choose to perform a certain behavior for personal consequences that are not obvious. Aaron Feuerstein, the 70-year-old owner, president, and CEO of a textile mill, was apparently not motivated by soon, certain, and positive consequences after a massive fire in 1995 destroyed his Malden Mill textile plant in Lawrence, Massachusetts. The workforce of 3,400 was jobless right before Christmas.

Feuerstein did not close the business, pocket the $300 million in insurance, and walk away a very wealthy man. Instead, he sacrificed millions by paying his jobless employees for three consecutive months, including a $275 Christmas bonus per family. He risked many more millions by choosing to rebuild the plant in the same location, instead of relocating somewhere with lower wages.

When asked why he acted selflessly and against his own best interests in the CBS show *60 Minutes*, Feuerstein replied, "Because it was the right thing to do."

Emotional Intelligence

What we're talking about, what Aaron Feuerstein exhibited, is emotional intelligence.[20] When it comes to wearing personal protective equipment, it's the ability to forego immediate rewarding consequences (such as comfort and convenience) for the possibility of a larger but delayed and uncertain benefit – avoiding personal injury. That's really the bottom line. Successful safety management requires that people develop the emotional intelligence to do the right thing, even when the soon and certain consequences are relatively negative. Actively caring for safety often means resisting the influence of the basic ABC principle of behavior-based safety. This clearly reflects Dr. Covey's critical lesson regarding that "space" of freedom and power between stimulus and response.

Now, how are you going to use that space to do the right thing for safety?

PART 12

Lead with Safety Conversations

One Sunday evening I received a very rewarding phone call from a long-time friend and colleague, Mike Hedlesky. For almost a year Mike has been managing the construction of my log home, so we have frequent phone conversations. But this phone call was different. Before giving me a progress report, Mike thanked me for possibly saving his life. Then he told me about his freak bicycle crash earlier that day.

He was traveling about 25 miles per hour when the rear wheel broke away from the frame. Mike sailed over the handlebars and hit the road head first. It happened so fast he didn't even have time to put his hands forward to break his fall. Mike's face was painfully bruised, but imagine how serious his injuries might have been if he had not been wearing a bicycle helmet. Mike claimed that he put the helmet on that day because of me – thus the reason for the "thank you."

Two weeks earlier I saw Mike biking on a country road without a helmet. He was wearing a cowboy hat instead. There were no other vehicles on

Personal experience provides for powerful personal testimony.

the road, so I came up beside him to say "hello." We stopped for a brief conversation. After exchanging friendly words, I said I was surprised to see he was not wearing a bike helmet. Then I reminded him of a bicycle crash I had two years earlier in which my bike helmet probably saved my life. I also remarked that his girlfriend who was riding a bike about 50 yards behind him was protected with a bike helmet.

Mike told me he thought about that conversation when he and his girlfriend embarked on a bike ride the Sunday of his crash. As a result, he wore a bike helmet that day. And that protective behavior may well have saved his life.

Six aspects of my conversation with Mike gave it the power to make a difference. Perhaps you can put them to use when you try to correct the actions of your friends, coworkers, or family members.

1) Show you care

I did not criticize Mike for not using a bike helmet. Our conversation was friendly and not confrontational. Within the context of our friendship and my caring demeanor, my remarks about safety were accepted. I didn't admonish Mike for not being safe, nor did I tell him to comply with a safety rule. Instead, I only indicated surprise that he was not practicing a particular safe act. This approach created conflict or dissonance between Mike's personal values and his overt behavior.[21]

2) Expect the best

When I noted a discrepancy between what I expected from Mike and his biking behavior, I may have created conflict or dissonance between an internal value and external behavior. In other words, I suggested that Mike was not the kind of person who would ride a bicycle without using the proper protective equipment. If Mike recognized an inconsistency between his safety values and his behavior in this situation, he felt some internal pressure to resolve the discrepancy. Perhaps this inconsistency was made more salient when I pointed out that his girlfriend was wearing a bike helmet.

3) Point out peer practices

Reminding Mike that his biking partner was wearing a protective helmet probably did more than make him aware of the inconsistency between his personal values and behavior. It drove home the fact that the safe behavior is practiced by others, in this case a significant other. And when his partner put on her bike helmet that critical Sunday, Mike followed her example, resolving any inconsistency he might have noted.

When safe behavior is viewed as the norm, we have the basic principle of consensus or social conformity on our side.[22] But when desired behavior is

The social norm is to conform.

not practiced by the majority, as is the case with bike helmet use, it can be particularly useful to point out specific occurrences of the safe practice. Sometimes a single case study is persuasive because it provides for a clear example to follow. It also allows for a supporting mental image to be formed that can be both directional and motivational.

4) Use personal testimony

In that critical conversation, I reminded Mike of my bicycle crash and how a bike helmet might have saved my life. I had told him the gory details two years earlier, soon after the crash. Perhaps my brief mentioning of that earlier incident provided Mike with an image that influenced his ultimate decision to use a bike helmet.

Why is personal testimony so influential? Well, it's personal, and it's real. Listeners can visualize themselves in a similar situation. They can form a mental image of the event and relevant behavior. Later they can retrieve that image for personal direction and motivation. Thus, in a Total Safety Culture, individual testimonials about personal injuries and close calls are promoted and appreciated, and are catalysts for safety improvement plans.

5) Set a safe example

A personal testimony is also influential because it's credible. After all, it describes a real experience. And if the testimony includes an example of the safe behavior being advocated, the source of that testimony becomes credible as an advocate of the desired behavior. My own bicycle story not only illustrated that dangerous bike crashes can happen and bike helmets prevent serious injury, it also made me credible as an advocate of bike helmet use.

On several occasions, Mike has seen me before or after one of my biking sessions, and every time I was wearing a bike helmet. My consistent use of this protective device gives me credibility as an advocate of helmet use when biking. To be consistent with their message and to be a credible source of safety information, safety leaders are obligated to always set the safe example.

6) Promote your successes

Safety leaders spend significant time and energy persuading others to follow certain precautions. Usually the safe behavior they advise is more inconvenient or less efficient than the at-risk alternative. Plus, it's rare the safe behavior results in a clear benefit in terms of injury prevention. Those who continue at-risk behavior in spite of your admonitions usually complete their tasks unscathed.

Once in a while taking a leadership role in People-Based Safety pays off big. Whenever a serious injury is obviously prevented by proactive intervention, the episode needs to be shared through personal testimony. This was the primary rationale for sharing my story here. Interpersonal conversation is key to promoting safety-related behavior and safety leadership on a large scale.

Notes

1. Arbinger Institute (2002). *Leadership and self-deception.* San Francisco: Berret Koehler Publishers, Inc.

2. For more on paradigms see a videotape by Joel A. Barker titled "The power of vision" (New York: Chart House International Learning Corp., 1993), and three articles in *Professional Safety*: Petersen, D. (1991). Safety's paradigm shift, *36*(8), 47-49; Winn, G. L. (1992). In the crucible: Testing for a real paradigm shift, *37*(12), 30-33; Winn, G. L., & Probert, L. L. (1995). Philosopher's stone: It may take another Monograph, *40*(5), 18-22. Also, for more details on these paradigm shifts see Geller, E. S. (2001). The *Psychology of Safety Handbook* (Chapter 3), Boca Raton, FL: CRC Press.

3. Latané, B., & Darley, J. M. (1970). The unresponsive bystander: Why doesn't he help? New York: Appleton-Century Crafts; Schroesder, D. A., Penner, L. A., Dovidio, J. F., & Piliavin, J. A. (1995). *The psychology of helping and altruism: Problems and puzzles.* New York: McGraw-Hill, Inc.

4. Beaman, A. L. Barnes, P. J., Klentz, B., & McQuirk, B. (1978). Increasing helping rates through information dissemination: Teaching pays. *Personality and Social Psychology Bulletin, 4,* 406-411.

5. For more on assertiveness training see the audiotape series entitled "Assertiveness: The right choice" by National Press Publications (1991, P.O. Box 2949, Shawnee Mission, KS).

6. Lerner, M. S. (1980). *The belief in a just world: A fundamental delusion.* New York: Plenum Press.

7. For more on the power of language see Hayakawa, S. I. (1978), *Language in thought and action*, Fourth Edition. New York: Harcourt Brace Jovanovich Publishers.

8. Kaplan, R., & Kaplan, S. (1989). *The experience of nature.* Cambridge: Cambridge University Press; White, R. W. (1959). Motivation reconsidered: The concept of competence. *Psychological Review, 66*, 297-333.

9. See research review by Cameron, J., & Pierce, W. D. (1994), Reinforcement, reward, and intrinsic motivation: A meta-analysis, *Review of Educational Research, 64*(3), 363-423; and commentaries by Carr, C., Mawhinney, T., Dickinson, A., & Pearlstein, R. (1995). Punished by rewards? A behavioral perspective. *Performance Improvement Quarterly, 8*(2), 125-140; and Eisenberger, R., & Cameron, J. (1996). Detrimental effects of reward, *American Psychologist, 54*(11), 1153-1166.

10. See Bird, F. E., Jr., & Germain, G. L. (1997). *The property damage accident: The neglected part of safety.* Loganville, GA: Institute Publishing, Inc.

11. For more on the essential role of research for safety improvement see Geller, E. S. (2004). Critical research principles and procedures for safety management: Industrial illustrations and practical strategies. *Professional Safety, 49*(9), 22-29.

12. Deming, W. E. (1986). *Out of the crisis.* Cambridge, MA: Massachusetts Institute of Technology, Center for Advanced Engineering Study; Deming, W. E. (1993). *The new economics for industry, government, education.* Cambridge, MA: Massachusetts Institute of Technology, Center for Advanced Engineering.

13. Senge, P. M. (1990). *The fifth discipline: The art and practice of the learning organization.* New York: Doubleday.

14. Covey, S. R. (1989). *The seven habits of highly effective people.* New York: Simon and Schuster, Inc.

15. The common term is "near miss," but because of the literal meaning of a near miss, I prefer "near hit" or "close call."

16. See Cialdini, R. B. (2001).). *Influence: Science and practice*, Fourth Edition. New York: Harper Collins College Publishers; Geller, E. S., & Lehman, G. R. (1991). The buckle-up promise card: A versatile intervention for large-scale behavior change. *Journal of Applied Behavior Analysis, 24*, 91-95.

17. Geller, E. S. (2002). *The participation factor: How to increase involvement in occupational safety* (Chapter 7), Des Plaines, IL: American Society of Safety Engineers.

18. Gouldner, A. W. (1960). The norm of reciprocity: A preliminary statement. *American Sociological Review, 25*, 161-178.

19. Covey, S. R. (1989). *The seven habits of highly effective people.* New York: Simon and Schuster Inc.; Covey, S. R. (2004). *The eighth habit: From effectiveness to greatness.* New York: Simon and Schuster, Inc.

20. Goleman, D. (1995). *Emotional intelligence: Why it can matter more than IQ.* New York: Bantam Books; Goleman, D. (1997). *Working with emotional intelligence.* New York: Bantam Books.

21. Technically, Mike experienced "cognitive dissonance" as originally conceptualized by Festinger, L. (1957). *A theory of cognitive dissonance.* Evanston, IL: Row, Peterson.

22. For more on the social influence of consensus or social conformity see Cialdini, R. B. (2001). *Influence: Science and practice*, Fourth Edition. New York: Harper Collins College Publishers; and Geller, E. S. (2001). *The participation factor: How to increase involvement in occupational safety* (Chapter 7), Des Plaines, IL: American Society of Safety Engineers.

CHAPTER TWO

The *Acting* of People-Based Safety™

Introduction

The components of People-Based Safety – ACTS – give you the skills and tools to build a Total Safety Culture. We act safe, we coach each other, we talk to ourselves and think before we act, and we focus and scan to see the hazards.

Chapter 2 presents you with the most important principles supporting the "Acting" component of ACTS and People-Based Safety. It begins with Dr. Geller's admonition: "Whether you're using training, feedback, injury analysis, coaching, or incentives, you should focus on behavior. Why? You can be objective and impersonal about behavior, unlike discussions of attitudes and feelings." (*Part 1*)

Behavior also has the power to define who we are (*Part 2*). Dr. Geller advises helping people act themselves into new, safer ways of thinking through positive consequences. This can lead to new labels, and behavior consistent with that label: "I'm wearing my safety glasses, so I'm a safe worker and I should also use all other personal protective equipment."

Consequences indeed drive us on (*Part 3*). But since we rarely see the benefits of working safe (no one gets hurt), we need motivation through feedback, interpersonal approval, and self-talk. All these are both principles and skills you'll learn in People-Based Safety. Methods for how to increase safe behavior (*Part 4*) and specific tools (*Part 5*) such as slogans, near-hit reporting and group safety sharing are described here in Chapter 2.

Just what does motivate us to work safely? Is there any value to incentives, goals, posters? "Confusing, isn't it?" admits Dr. Geller. A key lesson is not to overjustify safe behavior (*Part 6*). Too often in safety, someone follows procedures only to get a reward or avoid a penalty. There is no internal rationale for the safe behavior – and so no personal control sustains safe behavior in the absence of carrots and sticks. You'll see that much of People-Based Safety focuses on developing an inner sense of control over one's safety.

Rewards are one of the most common ways of trying to control behavior in traditional safety programs – often at the expense of self-motivation. Rewards must be perceived as being earned (*Part 7*) by effort, and they must be genuine displays of appreciation – not bribes. Handled correctly, a simple compliment or a large group celebration can boost feelings (*Part 8*) critical to actively caring about safety – self-esteem, self-efficacy, personal control, optimism, and belongingness. Recognizing and nurturing these "feeling states" is a central tenet of People-Based Safety.

Traditional safety goals that hold employees accountable for workplace-wide injury numbers beyond the control of any one person can do more harm than good – making people less optimistic and interested in safety. That's why it's important to set "smart" goals (*Part 9*) that boost self-motivation for safety.

Discipline, Dr. Geller argues, is another traditional safety tool that often misses the mark (*Part 10*). To change at-risk behaviors, open and frank discussions about contributing factors are needed, and "this is only possible when the threat of punishment is removed," asserts Dr. Geller.

On a larger scale, to change your workplace culture, managers need to encourage employee involvement, and this calls for debunking ten myths of behavior-based safety (*Part 11*). Building a safe business also means spending less time on paperwork and putting out fires, and more time on education, motivation and evaluation (*Part 12*). "Continuous improvement in safety management requires putting more emphasis on these elements," writes Dr. Geller.

Dave Johnson, Editor
Industrial Safety & Hygiene News

PART 1

Begin with Behavior

"Behavior modification"– a top-down, controlling and manipulative term I find obnoxious – does not reflect the behavioral principles of People-Based Safety. But the fact is "behavior modification" is used all too often in the safety and health field. Some people use the term to refer to the popular "behavior-based" approach to industrial safety and health. Others use the label to dismiss the behavior-based approach in favor of strategies that sound better, like improving attitudes, building awareness, changing culture, and optimizing systems.

The broad principles of People-Based Safety do in fact address management systems, as well as the inner dimensions of people, such as attitudes and belief. Using people-based principles appropriately builds feelings of self-effectiveness, personal control, optimism, and belonging. They increase the willingness of workers to actively care for the safety and health of others.

People who know these principles would never use the term "behavior modification."

Let me review three basic principles to demonstrate that behavioral safety is more than a narrow program of interpersonal observation and feedback.

Acting is all about behavior.

1) Observable behavior

Whether you're using training, feedback, injury analysis, coaching, or incentives, you should focus on behavior. Why is it important to focus on behavior?

Well, you can be objective and impersonal about behavior, unlike discussions on attitudes and feelings.

Plus, behavior is affected by equipment design, the management system, the behavior shown by others, and various social dynamics. Openly discussing these environmental and interpersonal influences can lead to practical modifications of the work culture.

Behavioral observation and feedback are powerful techniques to improve behavior and attitudes, but other intervention strategies can also be very effective, from safe behavior promise cards to behavior-based goal-setting and incentive and reward programs.

The principle that incentives motivate behavior change is not wrong. Rather, the way people use incentives to promote safety can be very wrong, and can do more harm than good. The key is to focus on behavior and you'll be on the right track. Whatever the intervention approach, focus on behavior.

2) System causes

Attitudes are difficult to define objectively and change directly. So stop trying. Most of us don't have the education, training, experience, nor time to deal with people's attitudes directly. Instead, target behaviors caused by systems factors. Empower people to analyze behavior from a system perspective, and to implement interventions to improve behavior. Do this and you'll indirectly improve attitudes, commitment, and internal motivation.

Give people effective tools to improve safety, empower them to customize and use these tools, and they will rise to the occasion. And if you include a measurement system based on objective process achievements – rather than subjective attitudes or feelings or remote and infrequent outcomes – you'll get the kind of accountability that motivates long-term involvement and continuous improvement. Holding people accountable for process numbers they can control enables true empowerment. It gives people the dignity they deserve for all they must do to actively care for health and safety.

3) Positive consequences

The ABC contingency is a basic tenet of behavioral safety. "A" stands for "activator," or the antecedent conditions or events that direct "behavior" – "B." And "C" refers to "consequences," or the environmental stimuli or events that motivate behavior. We do what we do either to enjoy a positive consequence or to avoid a negative one. And we stop doing what we're doing when our behavior results in immediate negative consequences or the removal of positive ones.

The most powerful motivating consequences are "soon" and "certain." That's why much at-risk behavior occurs. Compared with safe behavior, at-risk behavior provides soon and certain consequence such as comfort, convenience, ease, and faster job completion.

The certainty and probability of a significant negative consequence, like property damage or personal injury, is low – but only when we take a narrow individualistic perspective. From a large-scale systems perspective, property damage and injuries are happening out there to people in our culture, and we care about that, right? So we need to teach and encourage systems thinking and interdependency throughout a work culture.

Using positive over negative consequences is critically important to "attitude" and many other internal dimensions of people. Think about it. How does a reward, personal recognition, or a group celebration make you feel, compared with a reprimand or criticism?

When positive recognition is delivered correctly, it increases the frequency of the behavior it follows. Plus, it increases the likelihood other safe behaviors will occur and that positive recognition will be used more often to benefit both behavior and attitude.

Contrary to the view of several current pop psychologists, we learn more from our successes than our failures. So recognizing people's safe behavior facilitates more learning and positive motivation than criticizing at-risk behav-

Acting to avoid failure is not fun.

ior. Only with positive consequences can you improve both behavior and attitude at the same time.

These three basic principles of behavioral safety should silence the critics who claim this approach is too narrow, focusing only on behavioral observation and feedback while neglecting inside dimensions of people and outside systems factors. Behavioral safety, as reflected in the three principles described here, is based on 50 years of rigorous research. And with ongoing application of the scientific method, we build and refine our approach and become more effective managers of safety-related behaviors and attitudes.

PART 2

Our Actions Label Us

Let's talk about those personal improvement goals you've set. How are you going to accomplish them? How will you motivate yourself to lose weight or exercise more or be a safer worker?

In many cases, we need to change our self-perceptions to meet these kinds of goals. Maybe we don't think of ourselves as the kind of person who can diet, work out, or work safely. It could be because our actions or behavior up to this point show we don't do these things well.

Think about how much our behaviors define and label us. We observe ourselves doing certain things and use that behavior to define who we are. Then we might attempt to live up to that self-perception through follow-up behavior. And if that behavior involves taking risks, cutting corners, or otherwise acting at-risk, you can see the potential consequences in the workplace.

Self-Perception Theory

The notion that we define who we are from our behaviors is founded in the teaching and research of B. F. Skinner[1] and the follow-up scholarship of Daryl J. Bem, an eminent professor of psychology at Stanford University. Dr. Bem developed a comprehensive theory of self-perception based on the premise that "Individuals come to 'know' their own attitudes, emotions, and other internal states partially by inferring them from observations of their own overt behavior and/or the circumstances in which this behavior occurs."[2]

According to Bem's theory, when we want to know how we feel, we look at our own behavior and the circumstances surrounding it. We eat too much and say, "I must have been hungrier than I thought." We play a poor tennis match and conclude, "I'm not as good at this as I thought I was." Or we go out of our way to help another person and think, "I must care more than I thought I did."

Power of Circumstances

Research has demonstrated how circumstances and behaviors influence our emotions, attitudes, and moods. In classic research by Stanley Schachter and Jerome Singer,[3] experimental subjects were given injections of epinephrine or adrenaline, which made them feel physically aroused. Then these subjects waited individually with one other person who presumably had received the same injection. Moments later the experimenter returned and asked the two individuals to complete a questionnaire about their feelings.

What emotion did these subjects experience? The physiological arousal

Euphoric behavior triggered euphoria.

was the same for every subject, but some reported extreme anger while others said they were very happy. Why? The subject's own behavior and that of the other person in the waiting room, who was actually a research assistant, determined whether the subject felt extreme anger or joy.

During the waiting period, the research assistant, posing as another subject, acted in one of two ways. In the "euphoric" condition, he threw paper airplanes, shot crumpled balls of paper into a wastebasket, and twirled in a hula hoop. He encouraged the subject to join in the fun, and most did.

In the "anger" condition, both individuals were asked to complete a questionnaire while waiting for the experimenter to return. The questions were intimate and quite inappropriate, especially the question, "With how many men has your mother had extramarital affairs – four and under, five to nine, or ten and over?" When the research assistant read this question, he ripped up his survey in a fit of rage.

Angry behavior triggered anger.

Schachter and Singer showed that emotional reactions are shaped by the behavior people observe in themselves and in others. In another series of studies, subjects' emotions were manipulated by giving them false auditory feedback about their heartbeat. When they presumably heard their heart beating faster, they felt more sexually aroused or fearful, depending on other external events.[4]

It's possible to change

self-perception by altering external conditions. Think about what this means for our work in safety. We can act ourselves – or others – into thinking or feeling a certain way, perhaps a safer way.

Setting the Stage

I don't mean to imply that behavior always precedes and influences thinking. In fact, it's commonly believed our personal motivation comes from within us, implying we think ourselves into acting in certain ways.

But suppose you want to motivate another person to do something, say to work safely on the job. How would you do it?

Even if you believe people can only truly motivate themselves from within, you can at least establish an external condition (or environmental context) that facilitates this inner motivation. Yes, you can do things to increase the probability people will do what you want. We're talking about interventions, and they can vary from developing an external accountability system or incentive program to setting up opportunities for personal choice, ownership, or constructive interpersonal conversation.

I think the most efficient way to motivate certain action in others, such as working safely, is to set up circumstances or consequences (feedback processes, teams, rewards, etc.) that help people act themselves into new ways of thinking. Their new behavior can influence a new way of perceiving themselves. This can lead to a new personal label and then to more behavior consistent with that label. "I'm wearing my safety glasses, so I'm a safe worker and I should also use all other personal protective equipment."

A Safety Tool

It doesn't matter which comes first – certain behavior or certain thinking. What matters is that we have a tool – we can improve safety by focusing attention on safe behaviors. When people see themselves working safely, they might change how they view themselves. They might act themselves into thinking of themselves as safety conscious, and thus motivate themselves to sustain the new behavior.

I emphasize "might" because not all behavior change leads to consistent changes in thinking and self-perception. We know intuitively that concepts like "personal control," "empowerment," and "ownership" determine whether our behavior influences supportive thinking, attitude, and self-perception.

Appreciate the potential of your own behavior to define who you think you are. Your actions can initiate a self-motivating spiral of behavior feeding thinking, thinking motivating more behavior, and so on. Then, accomplishing your personal improvement goals will define the better person you have become.

PART 3

Consequences Keep Us Going

One of B. F. Skinner's most important legacies is "selection by consequences,"[5] which means behavior is motivated by events or conditions that follow it. Pleasant consequences increase behavior, and unpleasant consequences decrease behavior. This is a key principle for understanding why people act the way they do.

It also explains the special challenges of promoting safety and health in the workplace. You see, at-risk and unhealthy behaviors are often followed naturally by immediate and pleasant consequences – comfort, convenience, excitement, sensory stimulation. In contrast, safe and healthy behaviors are usually accompanied by inconvenience, discomfort, or boredom.

Plus, the presumed benefits of safe and healthy behaviors are either not experienced – no incident occurs to demonstrate the protection of PPE – or benefits are too delayed or uncertain to have much impact on current behavior. For example, the physical benefits of exercise and nutrition are usually noticeable only after substantial time and effort.

Here are various types of consequences:

Natural Consequences

Motivating consequences are inherent or intrinsic to the ongoing task. In other words, behavior is often followed naturally by supportive or nonsupportive consequences. Athletic behaviors from bowling and golf to basketball and tennis result in immediate consequences that provide invaluable feedback for improving performance.

Natural consequences lead to intrinsic motivation.

Creating a Consequence

But since task-intrinsic consequences are not usually available to support safe and healthy behaviors, it is often necessary to add extra consequences to keep the desired behavior going.

Often the most powerful consequence is personal and genuine recognition or appreciation. Interpersonal coaching feedback after a behavioral observation exemplifies the use of extra consequences to sustain desired behavior. Reminding people their safe behavior sets an important example for others can go a long way to keep safe behavior going.

Extra consequences keep us going.

Inner Motivation

These intrinsic and extra consequences are external to the participant; they can be observed by another person. Behavioral scientists focus on these types of consequences to evaluate and develop motivational processes because they are objective and scientific. But behavioral scientists do not deny the existence of internal determinants of motivation and action. There is no doubt we talk to ourselves before and after our behaviors, and this "self-talk" influences our performance. We often give ourselves internal verbal instructions before acting, and afterward we often evaluate our performance. We might motivate ourselves to continue the behavior – with self-commendation – or to discontinue the behavior – with self-condemnation.

Internal consequences to support the right behavior are terribly important when it comes to safety and health. As mentioned, external and task-intrinsic consequences for safe and healthy behaviors are not readily available, and we can't expect others to keep us making proactive, safe, and healthy choices. So we need to talk to ourselves with sincere conviction, and with genuine self-reinforcement, when we do the right thing.

We need to savor special external consequences for our efforts whenever we receive them, and use this recognition or feedback later to bolster our self-reinforcement. Often it's useful to hear about the special consequences experienced by others for their safe and healthy behaviors. We can relate these success stories to our own situations to keep us going.

The following case study might help you justify certain proactive behaviors, such as actively caring for safety, while also illustrating the motivational role of various types of consequences – intrinsic versus extra, and internal versus external.

The "Airline Lifesaver"

Since November 1984, I have been using a proactive intervention behavior whenever I board an airplane. I hand the flight attendant an "Airline Lifesaver" card that asks the recipient to announce this statement near the end of the flight:

"Now that you have worn a seat belt for the safest part of your trip, the flight crew would like to remind you to buckle up during your ground transportation."

This small act is rewarded with a natural consequence whenever the announcement is made, which has been relatively often. From November 1984 to January 1993, I distributed the Airline Lifesaver on 492 flights, and 36 percent of the time the flight attendant gave a public buckle-up reminder. From March 1994 to February 1995, I gave the Airline Lifesaver to 118 flight attendants and was rewarded with a buckle-up reminder on 54 percent of these flights.

Why did I separate the two time periods when reporting these results? And what could account for the significantly higher announcement percentages during the second time period?

Well, I used different Airline Lifesaver cards during these periods. The cards distributed during the first phase merely requested the buckle-up announcement, whereas the new cards (used during the second phase) offer prizes valued from $5 to $30 if the buckle-up reminder is given. If the announcement is made, I give the attendant a postcard to mail to my office in order to redeem a reward. To date, of the attendants who received this extra consequence, 65 percent stamped and mailed the postcard.[6]

So what types of motivation and rewards are involved here? The value of the extra consequence in motivating flight attendants to give a buckle-up reminder is demonstrated by the high percentage of postcards mailed to my office and by the greater percentage of flight attendants making the safety announcement when prizes were offered.

Recording the results of this safety intervention at the end of each flight and later tallying the percentages gives me feedback (natural consequences) to keep me going. Feedback graphs depicting percentages of buckle-up reminders per 10 consecutive trips have been a primary motivator for over a decade of using the Airline Lifesaver.

Often the most powerful consequence is personal and genuine recognition or appreciation.

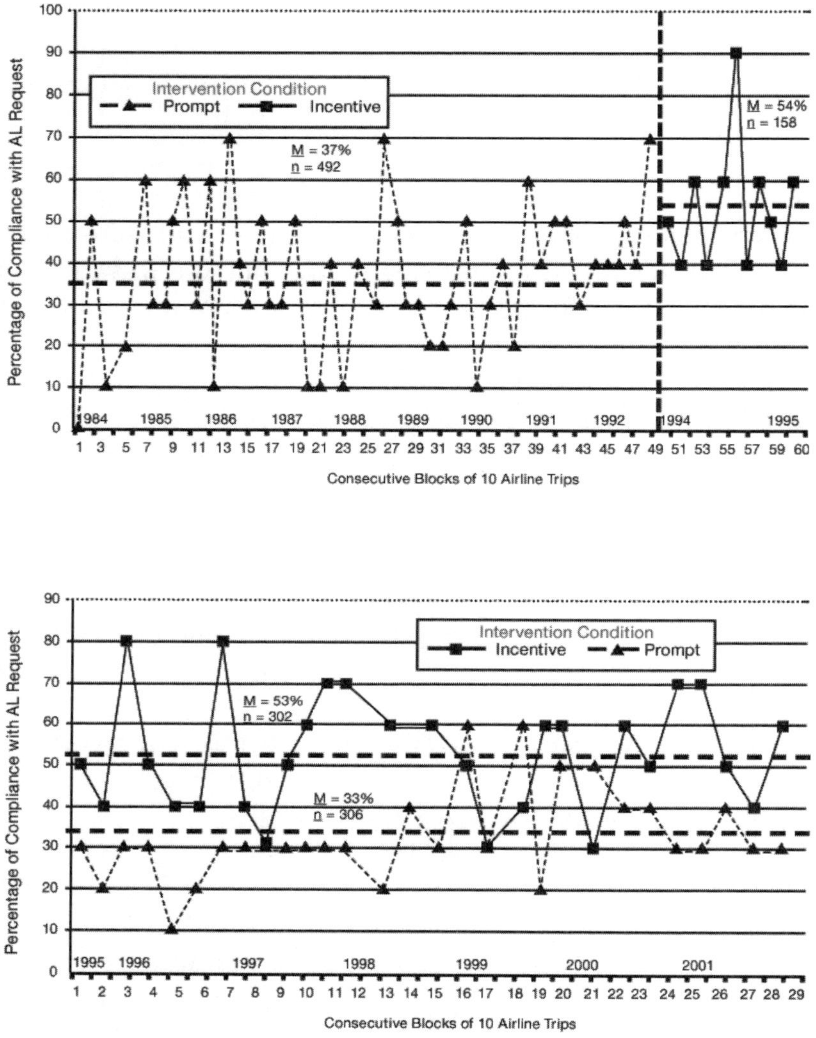

Feedback from our 17-year field study shows an advantage of incentives.

But I must admit I've been tempted to avoid this intervention on some trips, especially when I'm tired and have to rush to make the flight. On these days I ask myself whether the personal expense of the prizes and the extra effort involved in administrating this reward contingency is worth it. It's on these occasions that internal intentions and consequences are important. I need to tell myself it's worth it and anticipate the consequences of adding to the feedback graphs. But most importantly, I need to convince myself that a buckle-up announcement on an airplane could result in more safety-belt use in vehicles and maybe prevent an injury or safe a life.

Many of my friends have laughed at the Airline Lifesaver and claimed I'm wasting my time. A common comment is, "No one listens to the airline announcements, and even if they did hear the buckle-up reminder, do you really think it's enough to get them to buckle up if they don't already use a safety belt?"

I had one personal experience that motivates me to answer "yes," and I remind myself of this story whenever I begin to doubt my proactive safety efforts. I once observed a woman approach the driver of an airport bus and ask her to "please use your safety belt." The driver immediately buckled up. When I thanked the woman for making the buckle-up request, she replied that she normally would not be so assertive but she had just heard a buckle-up reminder on her flight, "and if a flight attendant can request safety belt use, so can I."

The Best Motivation

Of course, the primary purpose of promoting safe and healthy behaviors is to prevent injury or improve a person's quality of life. Unfortunately, we rarely see these benefits, so we need motivation through feedback consequences, interpersonal approval, and self-talk. We tell ourselves we're doing the right thing, and someday an injury will be prevented. We usually can't count the number of injuries prevented by our efforts, so we just need to "keep the faith."

On December 28, 1994, I received a special letter from Steven Boydston, assistant vice president of Alexander & Alexander of Texas, Inc., that helps me "keep the faith" that the Airline Lifesaver and other proactive efforts for safety do make a difference. The essence of this letter is given below, as a success story you can use to keep intervening for industrial safety and health. It worked for me.

> *THANKS!!! On December 11, 1994, I was a passenger on Flight 499 from Houston to San Francisco. At the end of the flight the pilot came on the speaker and said: "Now that the safest part of your journey is over and you are about to make the most dangerous part of your journey, please remember to use your seat belt...." I may have the words a little off, but I think you know the message. This was the second time I had heard the message. The first was at the ASSE Professional Development Conference in Dallas.*
>
> *I am an obsessive seat-belt user but when I got into the taxi, the seat belt was, as usual, buried in the seat. Usually when I find this in a cab I say, "the heck with it," but I can honestly say the pilot's message motivated me and I "dug out" the seat belt.*
>
> *At over 70 mph the taxi hydroplaned and struck the guardrail. Thank God for the new barriers that prevent cars from being thrown back into traffic. Thank you and the pilot for the reminder. My wife and children are also grateful. I suffered a neck and shoulder injury – I think it*

is relatively minor. It could have been much worse. I should mention the driver was OK. He was wearing his seat belt.

Conclusion

Although pop psychology might emphasize we motivate ourselves with goals or intentions, the fact is that behavioral consequences actually motivate our activities. We behave in certain ways to achieve pleasant consequences or to avoid unpleasant consequences. Goals and intentions are motivational when they anticipate consequences achievable from the goal-directed behavior.

Some consequences are inherent or intrinsic to the task at hand, such as the immediate results of swinging a golf club, baseball bat, or tennis racket. These consequences are sufficient to maintain performance as long as the frequency or intensity of the pleasant outcomes overpower any unpleasant outcomes.

Some behaviors are followed intrinsically by more unpleasant than pleasant consequences. The immediate discomfort or inconvenience outweighs any observable benefits, thus extra consequences are needed to sustain appropriate behavior. One of the most powerful, yet inexpensive, consequences is interpersonal approval or disapproval. Ponder for a moment how much you do every day to gain or maintain appreciation from people in your life space, and the power of genuine social attention in managing safety becomes obvious.

Considering the role of intrinsic and extra consequences in motivating our everyday behavior implies "thinking," which is essentially self-talk. We talk to ourselves when solving problems, planning actions, writing manuscripts, and evaluating outcomes. Internal consequences are critical to motivating behaviors, especially when external consequences (intrinsic or extra) are unavailable or delayed. I offer more information on thinking or self-talk in Chapter 4 on "The Thinking of People-Based Safety™."

In safety management, hearing the achievements of other persons' proactive behavior provides ammunition for our own self-talk about motivational consequences. Sharing success stories is the sort of motivating consequence that will keep us all talking up safety.

PART 4

How to Improve Behavior

Whether you succeed in increasing safe behaviors or decreasing risky behaviors at work depends on many factors. What behaviors are you targeting? What are the personal characteristics of the individual you are coaching? Context or the environmental setting also influence behavior. The type of intervention strategy you select is important, too. Some work better than others, depending on the complex interplay between targeted behaviors, environmental circumstances, and personal dynamics.

Here are some basic guidelines for selecting the most appropriate behavioral intervention.

Three Types of Behavior

Most voluntary behavior starts out as "other-directed" in the sense that we follow someone else's instructions. Direction can come from a training program, operation's manual or policy statement.

After learning what to do, essentially by memorizing or internalizing the instructions, our behavior becomes "self-directed." We talk to ourselves before

Other-directed behavior can be dangerous.

acting, cueing memories of what we've learned to guide ourselves. At this point, we're usually open to corrective feedback if it's delivered well.

Some behaviors become automatic after we perform them frequently and consistently over a period of time. Automatic behavior, or a habit, is formed. Some habits are good and some are not, depending on their short and long-term consequences.

Let's discuss what intervention strategies are most appropriate for influencing the following types of behavior change:

- Turning a risky habit (where the employee is unconsciously incompetent) into self-directed behavior;
- Changing risky self-directed behavior (conscious incompetence) to safe self-directed behaviors;
- Taking safe self-directed behavior (where the employee is consciously competent) and turning it into a safe habit.

Three Intervention Strategies

First, we have instructional interventions. They typically serve to activate or direct behavior prior to it happening. (Remember the ABC model: "A" represents activators or antecedent events that precede behavior, indicated by "B", and "C" is the consequence following behavior and produced by it. Activators typically direct behavior, and consequences motivate behavior.)

Instructions can turn automatic habits into self-directed behaviors or improve behavior that is already self-directed. The aim is to get an individual's attention and change unconscious incompetence into conscious competence.

Instructional intervention consists primarily of activators: education sessions, training exercises, and directive feedback. Since your purpose is to instruct, the intervention comes before the target behavior occurs and focuses on helping the individual internalize your instructions. This approach is more effective when instructions are given one to one. Role-playing exercises give instructors opportunities to customize their directions.

Once a person learns the right way to do something, practice is important. This is how behavior becomes part of a natural routine. Continued practice leads to fluency and in many cases to automatic or habitual behavior. But practice does not come easy and can benefit greatly from supportive intervention. Encouragement keeps us going and reassures us we're doing the right thing.

Supportive intervention focuses on applying behavioral consequences. When we give people rewarding feedback or recognition for some particular safe behavior, we show our appreciation and increase the likelihood they will perform the behavior again.

Supportive intervention is used when a person knows what to do. This kind of support assumes the person is already motivated to do the right thing. Incentives or disincentives, promises or threats, are not needed.

When someone knows how to work safely but doesn't do it, motivational intervention is needed. In this case, the person is consciously incompetent about safety-related behavior. Instruction alone is obviously insufficient. And we don't want to support their calculated risk-taking.

Why do we take calculated risks? Usually it's because we perceive the positive consequences to be more powerful than the negative ones. The reasons for taking the risk – comfort, convenience, and efficiency – are immediate and certain. Injury, on the other hand, is improbable and seems uncomfortable, or inefficient. In this situation, we often need both activators and consequences to move people from conscious incompetence to conscious competence.

An incentive/reward program attempts to motivate a certain target behavior by promising people a positive consequence if they perform it. The promise is the incentive, and the consequence is the reward. In safety, the kind of motivational intervention is much less common than a disincentive/penalty program. Employers typically use rules, policies, or laws to threaten employees with a negative consequence if they fail to comply or if they take a calculated risk.

But this approach is often ineffective. Like an injury, the negative consequence or penalty seems remote and improbable. Enforcement programs can have an impact by increasing the severity of the penalty and catching more people taking calculated risk, but large-scale enforcement can seem

Behavior-based rewards and penalties make a difference.

inconsistent and unfair. Plus, threats of punishment appear to challenge individual freedom and choice. The result can be more calculated risk-taking, even sabotage, theft, or workplace violence.

Motivational intervention is clearly the most challenging of the three strategies outlined here. You want to influence behavior without increasing a person's desire to assert personal freedom.

Remember, powerful external consequences might work – but only as long as the intervention is in place. The individual is consciously competent, but his behavior is not self-directed – it comes from excessive outside control. It's possible a long-term motivational intervention, coupled with consistent supportive intervention, can lead to a good habit. This is how other-directed safe behavior can move to unconscious competence without first becoming self-directed.

For example, many people started to use vehicle safety belts because of belt-use laws (a motivational intervention). After this other-directed behavior occurs many times, it becomes part of the routine. Eventually, these people buckle up habitually, without thinking about it.

The Critical Question

How can we change consciously competent/other-directed-behavior to consciously competent/self-directed behavior? I'm talking about facilitating a transition from safety accountability – "I'm working safely because someone is holding me accountable" – to safety responsibility – "I'm working safety because I'm holding myself accountable." Here are five general recommendations, all based on behavioral research.[7]

1) Decrease top-down control

Focus on fact-finding rather than fault-finding. Consider the disadvantages of punishment, and the differences between a human error and a calculated risk. Recognize how interpersonal and environmental context influences at-risk behavior.

2) Increase feelings of empowerment

Hold people accountable for safety performance numbers they can control. Set goals that are specific, motivational, achievable, relevant, and trackable. Recognize progress and milestones toward major accomplishments. And increase the use of supportive interventions.

3) Help people feel important

Increase opportunities for choice. Teach principles, and guide how employees customize procedures. Demonstrate the significance of proactive, behavioral safety, and teach the value of emotional intelligence, including techniques for communicating more effectively with others and with oneself.

4) Cultivate belonging and interpersonal trust

Improve interpersonal communication. Build group consensus for important discussions. Promote systems thinking and interdependence. And teach and demonstrate the principle of reciprocity – the fact that helping others activates an obligation to return the favor.

5) Teach and support safety self-management

Apply the ABC principle of behavioral safety to self-talk and self-management. Chapter 4 on "The Thinking of People-Based Safety" covers this critical approach to developing safety responsibility and an injury-free workplace.

PART 5

Tools to Improve Behavior

People are generally motivated by consequences that are immediate, sizable, certain, and positive. Unfortunately, safe behaviors are not usually supported by soon, certain, sizable, or positive consequences. In fact, they are often followed by soon and certain negative consequences. Wearing personal protective equipment can feel uncomfortable, for instance.

Making life even more challenging for safety professionals is the fact that at-risk behaviors often have positive consequences. Taking shortcuts can achieve production and quality goals more quickly and easily. Sometimes production supervisors inadvertently activate and reward at-risk behaviors in their attempts to achieve more production.

Let's review some techniques that have been quite successful at increasing safe work behaviors. Those that carry some kind of rewarding consequence are more effective, although usually more costly. Also, the most significant improvements involve employees throughout the design, implementation, and refinement phases.

Worker-Designed Slogans

Signs and slogans have only limited behavioral influence, unless they signal the occurrence and availability of motivating consequences. Plus, the same signs, such as "Caution: Hazardous Area," "Please Hold Handrail," and "Buckle

It's often more fun to take risks.

Signs that imply consequences are more influential.

Up" eventually blend into the woodwork and are not noticed.

However, changing signs periodically can increase attention and awareness. If employees design the messages or slogans, perhaps as a result of a company contest, awareness and attention can increase before and after the sign display.

In 1985, employees and visitors driving into the main parking lot at Ford world headquarters in Dearborn, Michigan, passed a series of four signs arranged with sequential messages. The messages were changed periodically as selected from a pool of 55 employee entries in a limerick contest for safety belt promotion.[8] My two favorites were:

First series
Sign 1: *Mary, Mary Quite Contrary*
Sign 2: *Just Wouldn't Buckle, You Know*
Sign 3: *She Had a Fuss with a Greyhound Bus*
Sign 4: *Now She's Planted All in a Row*

Second series
Sign 1: *If Your Wife Says Those Belts*
Sign 2: *Push Her Clothes Helter Skelter*
Sign 3: *Do Her A Favor*
Sign 4: *Reach Over and Belt Her*

Near-Hit Reporting

A proactive stance to occupational safety requires discussion and problem solving regarding near hits – workplace incidents that could have resulted in an injury had the timing or positioning been slightly different.

It's not easy to motivate close-call reporting and discussion, especially if the reporting process is inconvenient and the instigators or victims of an injury or near hit are viewed as "careless," "dumb," "accident prone," or "thoughtless."

Here are two ideas: In the mid-1880s, Air Products and Chemicals in Allentown, Pennsylvania, attempted to encourage near-hit reporting by recognizing near-hit reporters in the company newspaper. The entire Body and Assembly Division of Ford Motor Company promoted attention to near-hit reporting by having reporters reenact their close calls on videotape for later analysis and corrective action.

Group Safety Share

Group meetings at the Hoechst plant in Rock Hill, South Carolina, start by facilitators asking participants to report something they have done for safety since the last meeting. Because this "safety share" is used to open all kinds of meetings, safety is given priority status and integrated into various other functions of the organization, from marketing to quality control. Employees expect to be asked about their safety achievements, and they prepare accordingly, sometimes going out of their way for safety in order to be able to give an impressive report.

This is an awareness booster for safety, and it also contributes to the "teaching culture," instructing employees that safety belongs to the same achievement system as productivity, quality, and profits.

Making a Commitment

Intentions are verbal statements to ourselves or to others that we plan on doing something. These statements activate a personal commitment to behave in a particular way. Years ago, when the nationwide use of safety belts was below 15 percent, many companies more than doubled the use of safety belts in company and private vehicles by distributing "Buckle-Up Promise Cards" and encouraging their employees to sign them.

When intentions are given publicly, the commitment is strengthened through peer influences.[9] For example, Logan Aluminum in Russellville, Kentucky, instituted a "Public Safety Declaration" where employees signed a poster at the plant entrance that specified a safe-behavior commitment for the day, such as "We wear safety glasses in all designated areas."

Public intentions also can take the form of safety reminders ("Didn't you

A Promise Card activates a behavioral commitment.

say you were going to use your ear protectors?") and as reinforcement ("I see you're meeting your personal safety goal, congratulations").

Observation and Feedback

Many companies are realizing the safety benefits of a strategy that involves employees in: 1) Developing a checklist of critical behaviors that can prevent and cause work injuries; 2) Observing coworkers on the job and systematically recording instances of safe and risky behaviors; 3) Summarizing their behavioral records into meaningful numbers, such as the percentage of safe behaviors; and 4) Reporting the results of their behavior analysis through individual feedback sessions and group feedback charts.

When a person approaches a work station to complete a critical behavioral checklist, he or she is likely to prompt some behavior change among those being observed. It's easy to imagine those being watched thinking, "I'm being watched now; I'd better be on my best behavior."

Even with such increased awareness, that person might not realize his at-risk behavior. The person could be unconsciously incompetent regarding some work practices. Plus, safety observers will eventually lose their impact if there is not some consequence to the act of observing.[10] Interpersonal feedback is the consequence in this process that maintains the impact of the observers, and ultimately motivates safer work practices.

Actively Caring Coaching

One-on-one personal interaction is the most influential way to give behavior change feedback. The best safety coaches follow basic principles of: 1) Effective communication, 2) Objective behavioral observation and analysis, and 3) Behavioral-focused rewarding and correcting feedback. Much more on coaching strategies is offered in the next chapter on "The Coaching of People-Based Safety."

One of the most important principles is to balance correcting feedback with sufficient rewarding feedback. In this regard, I find it useful to consider the metaphor of an "emotional bank account." This was introduced by Stephen Covey in his bestseller, *The 7 Habits of Highly Effective People.*[11]

You see, correcting a person's behavior can result in a "withdrawal" from the person's emotional bank account (especially if the individual interprets the correction as a personal embarrassment or indictment). Since you don't want to leave a person emotionally bankrupt, it's important to make periodic "deposits" through rewarding feedback in the person's emotional bank account.

"Thank-You" Cards

Kal Kan of Columbus, Ohio, and two Hoechst Celanese plants (Celco in Narrows, Virginia, and Celriver in Rock Hill, South Carolina) have provided employees with "thank-you" cards to distribute to coworkers when observing them actively caring or going beyond the call of duty for another person's safety. In some cases, observers describe the behaviors they saw on the card, reinforcing their understanding of actively caring behavior.

In one program, the "thank-you" cards could be exchanged for a beverage in the company cafeteria. In another program, the cards contained a removable recognition sticker that could be attached to a variety of objects, the most popular being a hard hat.

Two programs offered a unique reward that extended the actively caring concept beyond the workplace. Specifically, each "thank-you" card was worth 25¢ toward a corporate contribution to a local charity or to needy families in the community when deposited in a special collection container.

We acknowledge actively caring behavior with thank-you cards.

Employees who designed one of these programs called their rewards "START cards" for Safety Thank-you's Are Reaching Teams. This reflects employee understanding, buy-in, and commitment for fundamental principles of a Total Safety Culture, including a positive achievement perspective toward safety, supported by empowered employees on actively-caring work teams.

PART 6

Don't Overjustify Safety

"Incentives don't work." "Goals motivate behavior." "Behavior-based safety produces only temporary results." "People cannot be motivated by others; they can only motivate themselves." "Slogans, posters, games and safety incentives should be eliminated."

Confusing, isn't it? Just what does motivate us to work safely? Is there any value to incentives, goals, posters? I've heard numerous consultants and safety professionals seem to deny the basic principle of behavioral safety. That is, behavior is directed by preceding events (termed antecedent conditions or activators) and motivated by consequences. This activator-behavior-consequence (ABC) sequence is a basic principle of human motivation, founded on years of rigorous behavioral science research. The principle is indisputable.

I believe people who make statements like those above are reacting against the notion of external control, which they attribute to behavioral safety. They might also realize the need for internal control if long-term behavior change is to be achieved.

Yes, internal control is important. But the ABC principle of external control should not be denied. Let's consider it in terms of internal activators and consequences.

Indeed, for employees to work safely over the long haul without external controls like rewards and penalties, they need to develop internal control or motivation. They must give themselves internal activators to direct safe behavior, and internal rewards of pride, dignity, and self-respect after going out of their way for safety.

Really, optimal safety management requires us to intervene in ways that promote balance between external and internal control.

Reviewing the Basics

To help shape this balance, let's first take a moment to review the basics of the ABC principle.

Often, certain events or conditions tell us what to do – or when to do it – if we want to obtain a pleasant consequence (a reward) or avoid a negative consequence (a penalty). These events are activators. Sign, posters, and rules, for example, provide direction or instruction for specific behavior. Incentives are activators that promote rewarding consequences if a target behavior occurs.

In contrast, disincentives threaten negative consequences if a certain behavior is performed.

Positive reinforcers or rewards support behavior and increase the likeli-

Soon, certain, and negative consequences are powerful motivators.

hood it will occur again. Punishers or penalties decrease occurrences of the behavior they follow. In other words, we do things to receive positive consequences, and we stop doing things to avoid or escape negative consequences.

The power of incentives or disincentives depends on the size, immediacy, and certainty of the consequences they announce. Generally, consequences are more influential motivators of behavior when they are large (a valuable reward or severe penalty), immediate (presented soon after the behavior), and certain (likely to occur after the target behavior).

Balancing Act

Let's look at how the ABC model applies to external and internal motivation. Activators and consequences can come from outside or inside. We receive external directions, rewards or punishers from others. But we also give ourselves internal directions, rewards or penalties.

For example, a goal is an activator that can be a powerful motivator if it specifies achievable consequences. This goal can be given to us by others, or we can set a goal for ourselves. A goal from others is an external activator. But if we believe in the goal and feel a sense of commitment to achieve it, the goal becomes internalized and can become an internal activator.

Receiving a reward for reaching a goal is an external consequence, of course. But this might not be the only consequence. The reward might only be seen as a token of appreciation for a job well done. Internal consequences like pride, feelings of accomplishment, greater belongingness to a work team, and increased self-confidence and self-esteem are actually more important to sustain long-term involvement in a safety effort.

Now here's a key point: Realizing the importance of internal activators and consequences influences the way we should exert external control. Let me explain. When a person does something only to get a reward or avoid a punishment, there is no internal rationale for the behavior. And the bigger the external consequence, the less need for internal motivation. If there's a big cash reward for not having accidents – or if you lose your job for getting injured – you feel no obligation to develop an internal justification for your behavior. Your actions are adequately controlled by obvious external consequences.

Now suppose external consequences are not powerful enough to fully control safe behavior all the time. Perhaps we're talking about pats on the back, coffee mugs, or other tokens. If people follow safety requirements in this situation – a big "if" sometimes – it is because they develop internal controls to justify their behavior. In other words, when people perform without sufficient external motivators, they legitimize their actions with internal activators and consequences.

Instructive Research

Pioneering research by professor Jonathan Freedman in 1965[12] demonstrated the need to limit external consequences if we want people to develop internal motivation. Dr. Freedman used a mild or severe threat to prevent seven- to nine-year-old boys from playing with an expensive battery-controlled robot.

In the mild threat condition, the boys were merely told, "It is wrong to play with the robot."

Boys in the severe threat condition were told, "It is wrong to play with the robot. If you play with the robot, I'll be very angry and will have to do something about it."

Then the experimenter left the room. Four other toys were available for the boys to play with. From a one-way mirror, researchers observed that only one of 22 boys in each condition touched the robot.

About six weeks later, a young woman returned to the boys' school and took them out of class one at a time to perform in a different experiment. She made no reference to the earlier study, but instructed each boy to take a drawing test. While she scored the test, she told each boy he could play with any toy in the room. The same five toys from the previous study, including the robot, were available. Of the boys from the severe threat condition, 17 (or 77 percent) played with the robot, compared with only 7 (33 percent) from the mild threat condition.

Presumably, more boys experiencing the mild threat developed an internal rationale for avoiding the robot. As a result, they still would not play with this toy when the external pressure was absent.

Other researchers have followed up this study to demonstrate that people are more apt to develop internal motivation when external rewards or threats are relatively small and insufficient to completely justify a target behavior.[13] This phenomenon has been referred to as the "less-leads-to-more effect." It's most likely to occur when people feel personally responsible for their choice of action and the resulting consequences.

You can see that rewards or penalties that "overjustify" the target behavior can motivate people to perform safely for the wrong reasons. Under these circumstances, people are not likely to develop the kind of internal justification – or personal control – that sustains safe behavior in the absence of carrots and sticks.

Extrinsic rewards can decrease intrinsic motivation and internal justification.

PART 7

Rewards Must Be Earned

"Rewards are not actually solutions at all; they are gimmicks, quick fixes that mask problems and ignore reasons."

"Giving people rewards...is an inherently objectionable way of reaching our goals by virtue of its status as a means of controlling others."

"What rewards and punishers do is induce compliance."

These quotes are from the book, *Punished by Rewards*, by Alfie Kohn.[14] They reflect a popular school of thought that says people cannot be motivated by others, but can only motivate themselves. The emphasis is on self-motivation. So, as the above quotes show, external rewards are seen as doing a disservice. They are perceived as a means of controlling people.

This is an issue for safety professionals to consider. What Kohn – and others such as W. Edwards Deming[15] and Steven R. Covey[16] – are saying is this: Common safety tools such as incentives, recognition, praise and penalties do

Insincere recognition can feel like behavior modification.

more harm than good in the long run because employees view these tactics as a means of controlling their behavior. Feeling controlled, an employee's own inner motivation suffers.

I want to address several points here. In general, there is much research in behavioral science to discredit these assertions.[17] But it is true that self-motivation can decrease if a motivational program is seen as an attempt to control behavior. This underscores the importance of making sure praise, recognition and other rewards are genuine.

Also, individuals or groups receiving special recognition must believe they truly earned the reward through their own efforts. When rewards are associated with one's own efforts, self-motivation increases because the person has a sense of being in control. But this is often not the case when rewards are based on a reduction in OSHA recordable injury rates. Employees often cannot see a connection between their own behavior and a reduction in injury rates.

In my view, the "intrinsic motivation" discussed by Kohn is not about something inside people; rather it has to do with the task being performed. Let me explain: Some tasks have built-in or intrinsic consequences. Most types of athletic performance, for example, have this natural feedback. We know immediately how well we have swung the golf club or thrown the football.

Some tasks do not provide this intrinsic feedback. Many, if not most, safety behaviors fall in this category. In fact, the immediate, built-in consequence of many safety practices are discouraging. Safety gear can be uncomfortable; safety procedures can be inconvenient or slow. This is where rewards such as praise, recognition, and incentives are often needed to shape and maintain safe behaviors.

The intent must not be to control people, but to help them control their own behavior for the safety of themselves and others. This is why terms such as "behavior modification," "discipline," and "enforcement" are inappropriate. They carry the connotations of outside control.

The bottom line is that behavior is motivated by consequences that are obvious and immediate. Self-motivation is shaped by how these consequences are interpreted. If we believe consequences (rewards or penalties) are earned through our own effort, our self-motivation is likely to increase. But if the consequence is seen as being undeserved, or as an insincere attempt to control, then we might be less self-motivated.

PART 8

Rewards Boost Good Feelings

Should you stop using rewards? The question has come up in light of Alfie Kohn's 1995 book, *Punished by Rewards: The Trouble with Gold Stars, Incentive Plans, A's, Praise, and Other Bribes.*[18] And at the second annual Behavioral Safety Now conference held in Houston last October, several attendees listened to Dr. Aubrey Daniels, author of the book, *Bringing Out the Best in People: The Astonishing Power of Positive Reinforcement,*[19] and wondered whether Dr. Daniels was advising people to stop using rewards, recognition, and group celebrations.

Safety professionals need to understand how positive reinforcers – the kind Dr. Daniels talks about – differ from other positive consequences. More important, safety pros need to convince others of the astonishing power of rewards, celebrations, and recognition, as well as positive reinforcement.

Reinforcers vs. Rewards

Technically, a behavioral consequences is a "positive reinforcer" only if it increases the frequency, intensity, or duration of the targeted behavior. In reality, it's usually impossible to know if this happens. For example, the financial bonus a person receives for demonstrating better safety performance last month does not necessarily influence any behavior. And the behavior most often reinforced by recognition ceremonies like a steak dinner celebrating a safety milestone is attendance at the dinner.

When Dr. Daniels warned the Houston audience not to presume their recognition, feedback, and celebration programs were "positive reinforcers," he meant this. Just because you give a person a positive consequence, you do not necessarily influence the behavior you'd like to improve. And if you don't improve targeted behaviors, you don't truly have a positive reinforcer.

This is why I use the term "reward" instead of "positive reinforcer." A reward is a positive consequence given to an individual or a group with the intention of improving or maintaining desired behavior. The reward can be one-on-one recognition, a group celebration dinner, a positive feedback presentation, credits toward the purchase of a catalogue gift item, a financial bonus, or a small trinket containing a safety logo.

A reward given long after the desired behavior has occurred is unlikely to have a direct effect on that behavior. Some rewards are not even associated with specific behaviors. The behavior most likely reinforced by awarding companies with a safety improvement placard is someone walking to the stage to receive the prize and public recognition.

The strict behavioral approach to safety does not recognize much, if any, value in rewards. If a behavior analyst observes no change in a target behavior when a particular consequence follows it, then that consequence is considered useless in that situation and no longer applied.

But here's my point: Even if a reward does not improve behavior directly, it has other special benefits. This is why I urge you not to decrease your use of recognition, feedback, and celebration processes.

What Rewards Do for Us

If given genuinely, interpersonal recognition, group celebration, and positive feedback improve internal, unobservable aspects of people. They make you feel better. This is a worthwhile outcome by itself. Plus, it's likely that safety-related behaviors will be indirectly improved.

Let me explain by asking: How do you feel after being rewarded for exemplary performance?

Do you get a boost in self-esteem? Feel better about yourself?

Do you feel more competent at the task singled out for the reward?

Do you sense a greater degree of personal control over the targeted activity?

Are you more optimistic you'll be successful in the future?

Do you feel more connected with other team members who attend the celebration event?

Genuine recognition boosts self-esteem, confidence, and a sense of personal control.

According to substantial psychological research, when any of these internal feeling states are increased, a person's willingness to look out for the welfare of others is also increased. So whether or not a reward increases the behavior it follows, it is apt to improve one or more feeling states that make people more likely to actively care about the safety of others.

This justifies using rewards, even when behavior is not directly influenced. Delivered appropriately, rewards always bring out the best in people because they improve those feeling states – self-esteem, self-efficacy, personal control, optimism, and belongingness – that make it more likely for an individual to help another person. Look for opportunities to reward quality performance, and deliver the reward well.

Look for the silver lining to build self-esteem.

PART 9

Set SMART Goals

Included among Dr. W. Edwards Deming's 14 points for quality transformation are "eliminate management by objectives, eliminate management by numbers, numerical goals...eliminate slogans, exhortations, and targets for the work force asking for zero defects".[20] Does this mean we should stop setting safety objectives and goals?

Should we stop trying to activate safe behaviors with signs, slogans, and goal statements?

Does this mean we should stop counting OSHA recordables and lost time cases, and stop holding people accountable for their work injuries?

Answers to all of these questions are "yes," if you take Deming's point literally. But I think Deming meant we should eliminate "goal setting, slogans, and work targets" as they are currently implemented. Dr. Deming was not decrying the principles of goal setting, management by objectives, and activators; rather, he was criticizing the current corporate use of these principles. Substantial research evidence supports the use of objective goals and activators to improve behaviors, if behavior change principles are applied correctly.

"Best efforts are not enough – you have to know what to do." – W. E. Deming

Incorrect Goals

Holding people accountable for numbers (outcomes) they do not believe they can control is a sure way to produce negative stress or distress. Some people won't be stressed because they won't take these goals seriously. Experience has convinced them they cannot control the

The best goals are SMART.

Specific
Motivational
Achievable
Relevant
Trackable

ence has convinced them they cannot control the numbers, so they simply ignore the goal-setting exhortations.

What does the goal of zero injuries mean, anyway? Is the goal reached when no work injuries are recorded for a day, a month, six months, a year? Does a work injury indicate failure? And does the average worker believe he or she can influence goal attainment beyond avoiding personal injury?

Setting SMART Goals

I remember the techniques for setting effective goals with the word SMART: "S" for specific, "M" for motivational, "A" for achievable, "R" for relevant, and "T" for trackable. Smart goal setting defines what will happen when the goal is reached and tracks progress toward achieving the goal. Feedback from completing intermediate steps toward the ultimate goal motivates continued progress. Of course, it's critical the people asked to work toward the goal "buy in" or believe in the goal and believe they have the skills and resources to achieve it.

I recently talked with a group of hourly workers about setting safe goals, and each member of this safety steering committee was completely turned off to goal setting for safety. Their past experience with corporate safety goals had created a barrier to listening about SMART goals. It was necessary for these individuals to understand the difference between the right and wrong way to set safety goals, and to practice (with feedback) SMART goal setting for safety.

I've seen several corporate mission statements with the stated safety goal of zero injuries. This is obviously an example of incorrect goal setting. Although injuries are conveniently tracked as OSHA recordables, employees' daily experiences with injuries (usually from others) contribute to a belief they cannot control injuries directly (especially the injuries of others). One injury in the workplace (usually as the result of another person's carelessness) results in failure to reach a goal of zero injuries and leads to a perception of failure.

People pass blame beyond themselves.

"What does the goal of zero injuries mean, anyway?"

No one likes to feel like a failure; so people typically avoid situations where failure is frequent or eminent, or at least attempt to discount their own possible contribution to the failure by blaming factors beyond their own control. This can lead to the belief that goal setting in the realm of safety is useless. Thus, "zero injuries" should not be specified as a safety goal, but instead should be the aim or purpose of a safety mission that depends on various safety processes motivated in part by SMART goals.

Focus on the Process

Safety goals should focus on process activities that can contribute to injury prevention. Workers need to discuss what they can do to reduce injuries, from reporting and analyzing near hits to conducting safety audits of environmental conditions and work practices.

The safety steering committee I worked with recently wanted to increase daily interpersonal communications regarding safety. They set a goal for their group to achieve 500 safety communications within the following month. To do this they had to develop a way to measure and track safety communications. They designed a wallet-sized "SMART Card" for recording communications with persons about safety, and one member of the group volunteered to tally and graph the daily card totals.

Another work group I consulted with recently set a goal of 300 behavioral observations of lifting. The employees had agreed to observe each other's lifting behaviors according to a critical behavioral checklist they had developed. If each worker completed an average of one lifting observation per day, the group would reach their goal within the month.

Each of these work groups reached their safety goals within the expected time period, and as a result they celebrated their "small win" at a group meeting, one with pizza and another with jelly-filled doughnuts.

These two examples illustrate the application of SMART goals, and depict safety as process-focused and achievement-oriented, rather than the standard and less effective outcome-focused and failure-oriented approach promoted with injury-based goals.

More importantly, these examples illustrate an employee-driven approach to safety rather than the more typical and less effective top-down paradigm.

The workers were motivated to initiate the safety process because it was their idea – they owned the process. And they stayed motivated to work on their safety process because, though SMART goal setting, they knew where they were going, they knew when they got there, and they followed their progress along the way.

PART 10

The Stick Misses the Mark

I always make mistakes and take calculated risks on the tennis court. When my focus or concentration wavers, I unintentionally mis-hit the ball or fail to get in position for a solid return. Sometimes I'll rush the net when I shouldn't, or hit the ball long when trying to land a baseline corner.

What I should do is quickly refocus my attention or reconsider the risks I take. Instead, I often yell at myself. Occasionally I'll slam the ball against the fence or toss my racket. Does this self-critical "punishment" ever help? Of course not. It only makes matters worse. The same is true for your golf game, and for meeting the continuous challenge of preventing injuries in the workplace.

Still, we rely too much on punishment to correct behavior. I want to show you the futility of this approach. Errors, or cognitive failures and mistakes (that result from our mental processes involving awareness and judgment), are unintentional. They are often caused by environmental factors. And when errors are intentional (as in calculated risks), the person didn't intend to cause an injury. Rather there were factors that influenced the decision to take the risk. The reasons for errors and calculated risks need to be discovered and addressed.

The influence of "command and control" is limited.

Before meting out punishment, answer the following seven questions. In most cases, you'll find another type of corrective action is more appropriate.

1) Was a specific rule or regulation violated?

If you answer "no," punishment is obviously unfair. Does this mean you need to write more rules or document more regulations? I don't think so. You can't write a rule for every possible unsafe behavior. And since human errors are unintentional, rules won't decrease them. We need to allow for the possibility that noncompliance with a rule or regulation can be unintended. This leads to the next question.

2) Was the behavior intentional?

All human error is unintentional. We mean well but have cognitive failures or "brain cramps." Psychologists call these errors slips or lapses and they are typically due to limitations of attention, memory, or information processing.[21]

Have you ever walked into a room and forgot why you were there? Locked yourself out of your car with the keys still inside? Left your house only to return to get something you forgot?

In the workplace, research has shown these types of errors increase with experience on the job. Skilled people put their actions on "automatic pilot," and perhaps add other behaviors to the situation. How many of us fiddle with a cassette tape or juggle a cellular phone while driving? You can see how an error can easily occur. This "unconscious incompetence" needs to be corrected, but certainly not through punishment.

There is also "conscious incompetence." Sometimes poor judgment is used to intentionally take a risk. This conscious behavior can be classified as either a mistake or a calculated risk. Have you ever miscalculated a parking space and scraped an adjacent vehicle? Pressed the brake pedal too quickly on a slippery road or pumped the brakes in an antilock system? Parking and braking are frequent and intentional driving behaviors, but under the particular circumstances they are mistakes.

Now suppose you don't buckle your safety belt. You know this behavior is unsafe, but you decide to take a calculated risk. In this case, unlike a mistake, you're aware that your behavior is inappropriate. The deliberate or willful aspect of calculated risks might seem to warrant punishment, but punishment won't convince people their judgment was defective. And that's what is needed to change conscious incompetence to conscious competence.

3) Was a rule knowingly violated?

Researchers have proposed that the more knowledge or skill we have at doing something, the less likely we are to demonstrate poor judgment.[22] So the driving mistakes listed above occur more often from inexperience or poor training. On the other hand, the tendency to take a calculated risk increases with experience on the job. This is human nature, and it won't be changed with punishment.

Some errors occur because the rule or proper safe behavior was not known. And it's possible for an experienced worker to forget or inadvertently overlook

Experience and familiarity can lead to risk-taking behavior.

a rule. Training and behavior-based observation and feedback can reduce these types of errors, but punishment certainly won't help in this case.

4) How much were other employees endangered?

Failing to lockout a power source during repair work is the behavior most often targeted for punishment. This is in line with what I've heard many safety professionals say: They only punish employees when a particular behavior risks a severe injury or fatality, or places many individuals in danger. Some pros are quick to add that these risks must involve willful intentions and prior knowledge.

Now if an employee willingly and knowingly avoided a lockout procedure to put himself and others at risk, then the severest punishment is relevant. Actually, this person should be fired immediately. But this rationale for risky behavior is very rare.

Many dangerous behaviors are mistakes resulting from poor judgment, not an unconscious or conscious desire to circumvent policies and hurt someone. And when a calculated risk is taken, it's not with the idea that someone will get hurt. Often specific characteristics of the work environment or culture enable or even encourage a calculated risk.

5) What supports the behavior?

This is the most important question of all. People don't make errors or take calculated risks in a vacuum. Poor judgment occurs for a reason. And it's important to learn an employee's rationale for taking a risk. This leads to truly useful corrective action.

Did the employee lack knowledge or skills? Was a demanding supervisor or peer pressure involved? Did equipment design invite error with poorly labeled controls? Was the "safe way" inconvenient, uncomfortable, or cumbersome?

Let's look at the organizational culture: Is safety taken seriously only after an injury? Is safety performance judged only in terms of injuries reported per month, instead of the number of preventive activities?

These are only some of the questions that need to be asked. Punishment will only make answers – and a practical corrective action plan – harder to come by. Punishment creates a negative attitude toward corrective action, and stifles the type of open conversation needed to develop an effective plan for improving behavior.

6) How frequent is the behavior?

How many at-risk behaviors typically occur before leading to an injury? H. W. Heinrich estimated 300 near-misses per one major injury,[23] and Frank Bird observed this ratio to be 600 to one.[24] Both Heinrich and Bird presumed numerous at-risk behaviors occur before even a near-hit is experienced, let alone an injury.

So what good is it to punish one of many risky behaviors? If the behavior is an error, punishment will only stifle reporting and potential remedies. If the probability of getting caught while taking a calculated risk is low – and it's minuscule if you wait until an injury occurs – any threat of being punished will have little behavioral impact. Remember, punishment reduces involvement in safety improvement efforts more than it reduces risks.

7) How often have others escaped punishment?

To punish an employee for a behavior that others have performed without receiving similar punishment is one sure way to lose credibility and turn a person against your safety efforts.

To summarize: If the threat of personal injury is not sufficient to motivate consistent safe behavior, it doesn't help to add one more threat (punishment) to the situation. We need open and frank discussions with the people working at risk to analyze and change management practices, equipment, or organizational systems that contribute to much of the at-risk behavior we see in the workplace. This is only possible when the threat of punishment is removed.

When is punishment for at-risk behavior warranted?

Culture Encouraged

Intentional	Yes	No
Yes	*Calculated Risk* *No Punishment*	*Calculated Risk* *Punishment May Be Warranted*
No	*Preventable Slip, Lapse or Mistake* *No Punishment*	*Unpreventable Slip, Lapse or Mistake* *No Punishment*

PART 11

Ten Myths of Behavioral Safety

I have read and heard numerous incorrect statements associated with behavioral safety. The more popular this approach becomes, the more it is misrepresented.

Unfortunately, this can lead to behavioral safety being misunderstood and misused, which hinders its overall potential.

Let's set the record straight by dispelling these ten common myths of behavioral safety:

1) It's only common sense.

You know this is wrong. The principles and procedures of behavioral safety have been developed and verified through many years of rigorous research. If a particular behavioral safety project doesn't work, the problem is not with the principles. It's how the principles are translated for a particular work culture.

2) It's just a fad.

Misuse of behavioral safety can lead to failure or less than desired outcomes. If this happens, support for behavioral safety will wane. This is why it's so important to clear up the misperceptions that cause misuses of behavioral safety. If we don't communicate what behavioral safety is really all about, the odds are greater that it will be considered a fad.

3) It's a magic bullet.

In fact, there is "magic" involved. Behavioral safety stimulates and facilitates interdependent teamwork, which leads to innovation and creative synergy. To watch this transformation at work is a magical process. But this magic does not come easily or quickly. It happens with proper top-down support and bottom-up involvement. Expecting too much too soon from behavioral safety can result in disappointment and a label of "'failure."

4) Employees get the blame.

To talk about "behavior" sounds threatening to many people, as in "Let's talk about your behavior last night." That's why the names of the individuals observed in a behavioral coaching process are never recorded. Behaviors of work groups are examined to identify environmental or system factors that influence behavior. Then we change those factors to improve behaviors.

5) It's only observation and feedback.

Behavioral safety coaching depends on interpersonal observation and feedback in order to succeed. But the principles of behavioral safety are applicable to many other aspects of safety performance, including incident analysis, process evaluation, corrective action, education and training, and the design of incentive/reward programs.

6) Management is off the hook.

If you implement behavioral safety with this idea in mind, you're destined for failure. Even an observation and feedback process among work teams will fail without proper management support.

And the many other applications of behavioral safety require managers to be actively involved.

What management measures gets done, and what management recognizes and rewards gets done well.

7) Environmental fixes aren't needed.

At first glance, behavior-based safety can appear to substitute a behavior-based or human factors approach for environmental or engineering solutions. But anyone who has implemented this approach effectively knows this couldn't be further from the truth. When at-risk behavior is identified, the focus turns to finding environmental fixes that can reduce or prevent it.

Behavior is influenced by both environment and person factors.

8) It's "touchy-feely" psychology.

When you think of the human dynamics of safety, concepts like "attitude," "intelligence," "emotion," "motivation," and "self-esteem" come to mind. We see and hear these words used in the media to refer to psychology. Such "touchy-feely" human factors are only studied objectively and scientifically when they are defined according to observable behavior. So behavioral safety represents the objective and reliable aspect of psychology. It's as close to engineering as any human factors approach can be.

9) Attitude change must come first.

Some psychologists who work with the touchy-feely aspects of human dynamics justify their efforts by claiming the focus of their study, whether it's attitude, self-esteem, or intrinsic motivation, must change before behavior can change. Such a notion is contrary to both research and common sense.

For example, when would you feel the emotion of being "scared"? before or after running from a large, wild animal? Research and common sense tell us the behavior precedes the internal touchy-feely state. First, you see the animal; next, you run; and then you experience the fear, emotion.

Likewise, when we contribute voluntarily to a successful process, we adjust our "attitude" to be consistent with our effort. We act ourselves into the right attitude.

Action precedes emotion.

10) There's no bottom-line payoff.

If most injuries are caused in part by at-risk behavior, then, reducing at-risk behavior must eventually lead to injury prevention and financial benefits.

"But how long will it take," asks the plant manager, "and what's the return on investment?"

The reply should be: "That depends on many factors, including your current injury rate; your particular work system; your readiness to implement a behavioral safety process; and a bunch of touchy-feely characteristics of your work culture like degree of trust, optimism, belonging, interdependency, and systems thinking."

Money saved by reducing injuries and workers' compensation claims is not the only bottom-line issue here. What about workers' morale, their self-esteem and sense of accomplishment? What about workers' perceived empowerment for safety? What about the belief that these internal human factors contribute to preventing their friends and coworkers from getting hurt?

These are bottom-line feeling states that lead to continuous and long-term improvement in safety and in both the quality and quantity of production. Yes, these are touchy-feely aspects of human experience, but they do exist inside all of us and they do influence our everyday behavior. They are addressed in People-Based Safety.

Organizational Change

How do we improve these feeling states most effectively in an organization? You know one answer to this important question is behavioral safety. When people are put in control of a process that visibly contributes to preventing themselves and others from getting hurt, they feel responsible. They go beyond the call of duty to make the process work. Working together this way boosts morale, trust, belonging, optimism, and actively caring. Obviously, the individuals experiencing these feelings benefit, as does the organization.

Culture change led by individual and group behavior does not come quickly. It takes time and a continuous commitment from everyone. Management needs to give the kind of consistent support that encourages employee involvement. Understanding the fallacies in the ten common myths reviewed here is a start.

PART 12

Continuous Improvement

Safety managers often spend most of their time catering to crises, such as investigating injuries, and keeping up with paperwork, such as policies and compliance reports. But safety also involves education, motivation, evaluation, and attention to attitudes. In fact, continuous improvement in safety management requires putting more emphasis on these elements and less on crisis management and administration.

Let's review several lessons in behavioral science that apply to effective education, motivation, and evaluation. Special attention will be given to the subject of attitudes. These ideas provide a foundation for innovative and quality-oriented safety management. They are the basis for strategies that increase safe work practices and decrease at-risk behaviors.

Education

The ultimate mission of most education programs is to obtain the student's total commitment to relevant information. To get that commitment, the student must first pay attention to the presentation. The student's behavior reflects his or her understanding of the material, and often the ability and desire to apply the information.

"There's no substitution for knowledge."
– W. E. Deming

Thus, the basic "ABCs" of effective education represent the sequence: Attention, Behavior, Commitment. This process is naturally easier said than done. Just consider the minimal commitment among students to many education and training programs.

In terms of safety, education that relies on lectures or videotapes will be fortunate to get past the attention state of learning unless it builds exercises into the process. Only through exercises that motivate relevant behavior among the learners can we hope for commitment. This is summarized eloquently by the well-known Confucian Principle:

"Tell them and they'll forget, demonstrate and they'll remember, involve them and they'll understand."

Motivation

The basic "ABCs" for behavior change involve: Activator-Behavior-Consequence.

"Activators" are often designed specifically to encourage certain behaviors or discourage others. They include signs, memos, lectures, demonstrations, policy announcements, vision statements, goal-setting exercises, incentives, and disincentives.

However, the power of activators to influence behavior is determined by consequences. For example, safety goals will lose their motivational impact on behavior unless time and effort are taken to recognize successes and correct failures (the consequences). Safety policies will not drive behavior change without enforcement consequences. Incentives will not increase the frequency of safe behaviors if the rewards promised do not actually follow the desired behavior. And people will not submit safety suggestions that are not followed up with a reasonable reaction. Whether it's goals, policies, or incentives, you need to follow up with appropriate consequences.

Action is fueled by relevant consequences.

Evaluation

Measurement is key to effective management. Therefore, evaluation is critical to effective safety management. It can provide both direction and motivation for safe work policies, practices, and processes. In other words, the feedback you get from an evaluation can pinpoint particular aspects of your organization's culture that need attention.

The "ABCs" of safety evaluations target three categories of safety factors: Attitudes, Behaviors, and Conditions.

Attitudes reflect what employees "feel" about safety in their work area and in the plant as a whole. To assess safety attitudes, you need to measure employees' perceptions or subjective opinions, usually through "climate surveys" or through interviews of individuals or groups.

Evaluations of behaviors and conditions are more objective and reliable than attitude surveys. You can obtain this information from systematic observation and recording of ongoing work practices, environments, and equipment. Optimally, these evaluations (or audits) are carried out periodically by the workers themselves with no fear of reprisal for undesirable reports.

One way to get workers more involved in evaluations is to make them aware of the outcome of their effort, such as safety work orders being issued to fix unsafe environmental conditions reported by the workers.

In collaboration with several corporate safety committees, I have developed and field-tested a number of evaluation forms to audit:

- Attitudes (including lifestyle, personality, and things such as mental distractions and "daydreaming" that cannot be observed);
- Behaviors (including group measures of compliance with personal protective equipment policies, and individual one-to-one assessments of safe versusat-risk work practices);
- Conditions (including audits of equipment, tools, and housekeeping).

What is Measured?	How is it Measured?	What is the Score?
Injury-related Accidents	Near-hit reports	Frequency & type of near-hits
	Injury reports	Number & type of injury producting incidents
	Worker Compensation Costs	Monetary expeditures
Environment	Observation of worksite	Percentage of safe conditions per opportunity
	Housekeeping Audit	Percentage of items in proper location
Behavior	Direct observation	Percentage of safe behaviors per opportunity
	Corrective action survey	Number of items corrected for safety
Attitudes Perceptions Person States	Questionaire	"Safetyscore" reflecting overall safety attitude, perception or person state
	Interview	Statements of specific and general attituddes about safety
Knowledge	Questionaire	Percentage correct
	Interview	Statements indicating awareness of a hazard or safety procedure
Opinions	Questionaire	Opinion Score
Participation	Direct observation Attendence Records	Number of participants per opportunity

There are many ways to evaluate safety performance.

Companies whose hourly workers collaborate in obtaining comprehensive and frequent audits of attitudes, behaviors, and conditions reach new levels of safety excellence.

Attitudes

Some attempts to get workers involved in evaluating ongoing work behaviors (especially through one-to-one auditing) meet with strong resistance. Some employees believe such an evaluation will be used against them. This can happen where there might be a lack of trust between management and hourly workers, or a lack of group cohesion between workers.

The "ABCs" of attitudes are: Affect, Behavior, Cognition. In other words, an "attitude" is a strongly held belief or feeling which involves personal emotion (affect); and it influences what we do and say (behavior), and how we think or talk to ourselves (cognition).

A person's attitude can be changed by targeting affect, behavior, or cognition. But the change process is not easy and is usually slow. In the first article in this chapter I explained why it's most cost-effective to start with behavior, and I specified some behavior change strategies for "acting a person into a new way of thinking."

All of the principles reviewed here can be applied to managing safety in your organization. However, implementing management strategies based on principles of human behavior obviously takes time and resources, and so often these are not available. The last "ABC" lesson of this article points out the need to change our daily management activities.

More specifically, managers spend their time Administrating, Building the Business (implementing innovations), and Catering to Crises. Obviously, continuous improvement in safety management and the achievement of a Total Safety Culture requires more of "B" and less "A" and "C".

Notes

1. Skinner, B. F. (1953). *Science and human behavior.* New York: Free Press; Skinner, B. F. (1974). *About behaviorism.* New York: Alfred A. Knopf.
2. Bem, D. J. (1972). Self-perception theory. In L. Berkowitz (Ed.), *Advances in experimental social psychology*, Vol. 6 (pp.1-60). New York: Academic Press.
3. Schachter, S., & Singer, J. E. (1962). Cognition, social, and physiological determinants of emotional state. *Psychological Review, 69*, 379-399.
4. Valins, S. (1966). Cognitive effects of false heart-rate feedback. *Journal of Personality and Social Psychology, 4*, 400-408.
5. Skinner, B. F. (1971). *Beyond freedom and dignity*. New York: Alfred A. Knopf.
6. A complete description of this 17-year field study is reported in Geller, E. S., Hickman, J. S., & Pettinger, Jr., C. B. (2004). The Airline Lifesaver: A 17-year analysis of a technique to prompt the delivery of a safety message. *Journal of Safety Research, 35*, 357-366.

7. More details on these strategies for increasing personal responsibility for safety are available in Geller, E. S. (1998). *Beyond safety accountability: Trainer's guide.* Neenah, WI: J. J. Keller & Associates, Inc.
8. More details about the Ford safety-belt program are published in Geller (1985). *Corporate safety-belt programs.* Newport, VA: Make-A-Difference, Inc.
9. More information on this commitment strategy is given in Cialdini, R. B. (2001). *Influence: Science and practice*, Fourth Edition. New York: Harper Collins College Publishers; and Zimbardo, P. G., & Leippe, M. R. (1991). *The psychology of attitude change and social influence.* New York: McGraw-Hill, Inc.
10. Parsons, H. M. (1974). What happened at Hawthorne? *Science, 183,* 922-932.
11. Covey, S. R. (1989). *The seven habits of highly effective people.* New York: Simon and Schuster.
12. Freedman, J. L. (1965). Long-term behavioral effects of cognitive dissonance. *Journal of Experimental Social Psychology, 1,* 103-120.
13. Lepper, M., & Green, D. (1978)(Eds.). *The hidden cost of reward.* Hillsdale, NJ: Erlbaum.
14. Kohn, A. (1993). *Punished by rewards: The trouble with gold stars, incentive plans, A's, praise, and other bribes.* Boston, MA: Houghton Mifflin.
15. Deming, W. E. (1991, May). *Quality, productivity, and competitive position.* Four-day workshop presented in Cincinnati, Ohio, by Quality Enhancement Seminars, Inc.
16. Covey, S. R. (1989). *The seven habits of highly effective people.* New York: Simon and Schuster.
17. Cameron, J., & Pierce, W. D. (1994). Reinforcement, reward, and intrinsic motivation: A meta-analysis. *Review of Educational Research, 64(3)*, 363-423; Eisenberger, R., & Cameron, J. (1996). Detrimental effects of reward: Reality a myth? *American Psychologist, 54(11)*, 1153-1166.
18. Kohn, A. (1993). *Punished by rewards: The trouble with gold stars, incentive plans, A's, praise, and other bribes.* Boston, MA: Houghton Mifflin.
19. Daniels, A. C. (2000). *Bringing out the best in people: How to apply the astonishing power of positive reinforcement*, Second Edition. New York: McGraw-Hill, Inc.; see also Daniels, A. C. (2001). *Other people's habits: How to use positive reinforcement to bring out the best in people around you.* New York: McGraw-Hill, Inc.
20. Deming, W. E. (1985). Transformation of western style of management. *Interfocus, 15(3)*, 6-11.
21. Norman, D. A. (1988). *The psychology of everyday things.* New York: Harper Collins Publishers.
22. Norman, D. A. (1988). *The psychology of everyday things.* New York: Harper Collins Publishers; Reason, J. T., & Mycieslka, K. (1982). *Absent minded? The psychology of mental lapses and everyday errors.* Englewood Cliffs, NJ: Prentice-Hall.
23. Heinrich, H. W. (1931). *Industrial accident prevention.* New York: McGraw-Hill.
24. Reported in Bird, Jr., F. E., & Davies, R. J. (1996). *Safety and the bottom line.* Loganville, GA: Institute Publishing, Inc.

CHAPTER THREE

The *Coaching* of People-Based Safety™

Introduction

"I can't expect you to spend the time and effort needed to follow the points given in this 'Coaching' chapter of *People-Based Safety™: The Source* until you truly appreciate the power of conversation," writes Dr. Geller. "Did you ever think your efforts to prevent injury in the workplace, at the home, and on the road are determined by conversation more than anything else?" (*Part 1*)

And the ability of coaching conversations to make a difference comes down to your approach, your tone (*Part 2*). Too many safety-related conversations are confrontations. So people tune out instead of turn on to safety. To draw people in and engage them in safety, your conversation should be based on empathy (*Part 3*). Show sincere understanding and appreciation for other people's circumstances.

Interpersonal communication is the critical intervention step of safety coaching, as Dr. Geller says. But there's more to it than that. Coaching characteristics (*Part 4*) include caring, observing, and analyzing. Your mission, in a nutshell, is to help. There are many ways to help (*Part 5*), including sticking to the facts, placing trust above accuracy (especially with behavioral observations), and making smart use of empowerment and giving people a choice.

One of the most important things a coach can do is simply sit down, zip the lip, and listen closely to what the other person is saying (*Part 6*). "If we want people to listen to our advice and accept our guidance, we have to slow down and resist the quick response," writes Dr. Geller. "It takes time to understand a problem or situation from another person's perspective instead of our own."

It also requires optimism and focus (*Part 7*). Many one-on-one coaching sessions are not constructive but destructive. It's the old habit of turning safety conversations into confrontations. Remain focused on what's truly important when coaching about safety issues, attitudes, or behaviors – you want the other person to trust you really care about improving or supporting their well-being.

Trust is crucial to prove you're not playing the "gotcha game" when you're coaching. One way to do this is to facilitate conversations where coworkers give each other safety feedback (*Part 8*). Your coaching role here is as facilitator. Employees talking to each other are likely to keep feedback to the point, on time, appropriate, and certainly real – four keys to delivering effective feedback.

Sometimes people freeze up when it's time to give feedback, so it's up to you as coach to break the ice (*Part 9*). How? "Ask someone for feedback on your performance, show appreciation when it's given, and you boost the likelihood your own advice will be accepted when given to other person," writes Dr. Geller.

Don't be a coach who practices what Dr. Geller calls "depressed learning" – pointing out mistakes and failures. Catch people doing the right thing for safety and let them know about it (*Part 10*). Be prepared: Many people get so little recognition from others they're caught completely off guard when it does come their way. They don't know how to act. So they might claim they don't deserve it, or see some hidden agenda at work. Your job as coach is to model how to receive recognition (*Part 11*). Remember, we all crave a little recognition. It's human nature.

And sometimes as coach, your job will be to deliver more than just "a little" recognition. But don't think you own all the great ideas for celebrating safety successes (*Part 12*). Ask people how they want to celebrate as a group. Challenge them to go beyond tangible rewards. As Dr. Geller writes: "You want a meaningful and memorable event that can serve as a steppingstone for greater achievements."

Dave Johnson, Editor
Industrial Safety & Hygiene News

PART 1

Coaching Is Conversing

Did you ever think that your efforts to prevent injury in the workplace, at the home, and on the road are determined by conversation more than anything else?

How we talk to ourselves (intrapersonal communication) and to others (interpersonal communication) is the most powerful determinant of safety excellence, I believe. In fact, I'm convinced the dramatic success companies experience with behavioral safety is essentially due to an increase in the quality and quantity of interpersonal conversation about safety. This process in turn improves intrapersonal conversations, increasing one's sense of personal control and optimism regarding his ability to prevent occupational injuries.

I'd like to convince you of the power of conversation. I can't expect you to spend the time and effort needed to follow the points given in this chapter of the The Source: People-Based Safety™ until you truly appreciate the power of conversation. So I hope you'll consider the following points.

Building Barriers

Almost everyone has seen how a lack of communication can escalate a minor incident into major conflict. Here's an example: You see a coworker and say, "hello"; yet she passes by without reacting. Maybe she didn't see you or

Person-to-person conversation has no substitute.

had other thoughts on her mind. Still, it's easy for you to assume the person is unfriendly or doesn't like you. So the next time you see this person, you avoid being friendly. You might even talk about that person's "unfriendliness" to others. I think you can see how the barriers start to build.

This is only one of many situations that can stifle interpersonal communication, and lead to negative feelings and judgments. The result? Perhaps perceptions of conflict, or an unpleasant relationship, lowered work output, and reduced willingness to actively care for another person's safety.

Resolving Conflict

If the lack of conversation can initiate or fuel conflict, it's not surprising the occurrence of conversation can prevent or eliminate it. "Let's talk it out," as the saying goes. Of course, it's the quality of that conversation that will determine whether any perceived conflict is heightened or lessened. Later, I address this issue of quality. Here I only want to show how the quality of conversation can make or break interpersonal conflict, which in turn enables constructive or destructive relationships.

Bringing Intangibles to Life

What are love, friendship, courage, loyalty, happiness, and forgiveness? Sure, you can describe behaviors that reflect these concepts, but where is the true meaning? I think we derive the meaning of these common words from our conversations. Think about how we "fall in or out of love" depending on how we talk to ourselves and others. We can convince ourselves we are happy through our self-talk, and this inner-conversation is obviously influenced by what we hear others say about us.

We define another person's friendship, courage, or loyalty by talking about that individual in certain ways, both to ourselves and to others. Our mental scripts and verbal behavior are powerful – giving useful meaning to concepts that define the very essence of human existence. And when groups, organizations, or communities communicate to define these concepts, we develop a "culture." Perhaps it's fair to say that culture is conversation – both spoken and unspoken.

Defining Culture

Does the term "unspoken conversation" make sense? I'm referring to customs or unwritten rules we heed without mention. For example, we might realize the "teacher's pets" sit in the front row, or the boss doesn't want to hear about a "near miss," or the real purpose of the safety incentive program is to stifle reporting of OSHA recordables. We might also know characteristics that bias certain managers' performance appraisals, from gender and seniority to ability on the golf course.

It might be understood that a male with high seniority and a low golf handicap is more likely to get the special training assignment, but such prejudice is certainly not expressed. If it were, a productive conversation would be possible – one that could reduce conflict and bias. The bottom line: Spoken and unspoken words define cultures and sub-cultures. And these cultures can change, for better or worse, through interpersonal and intrapersonal conversation.

Defining Image and Self-Esteem

Public conversation defines public image, whether referring to an individual or an organization. Sometimes, though, different groups talk about an individual or organization in different ways. As a result, we get mixed messages and an inconsistent public image. The image of our president changes, depending on whether you're listening to Democrats or Republicans. The safety image of an organization can vary, depending on who is doing the talking. Safety professionals might question the achievement of "zero injuries," while the public would not doubt this company's elite ranking.

How we talk to ourselves both influences and reflects our self-esteem. It's probably fair to say that our mental script about ourselves is our self-esteem.

Public conversation defines image.

We can focus our self-talk on the good things people say about us or on critical statements we've heard about us. The result is a certain kind of self-talk we call "interpretation." Such intrapersonal communication can negatively or positively affect how we feel about ourselves. In other words, our self-esteem can go up or down according to how we talk to ourselves about the way others talk about us. The next chapter on "The Thinking of People-Based Safety™" offers much more on the important topic of self-talk.

Making Breakthroughs

In his provocative book *Leadership & the Art of Conversation,*[1] Kim Krisco defines a breakthrough as going beyond business-as-usual and getting more than expected. This requires people to realize new possibilities, commit to going for more, and then make a concerted effort to overcome barriers. How is this done? You guessed it – through conversation.

Expect barriers and resistance to change, warns Krisco. And the greater the change, the greater the resistance. But remember, most barriers to change are interpretations or people's self-talk about perceived reality. Conversation, both interpersonal and intrapersonal, enables us to overcome the barriers that hold back the accomplishment of breakthroughs.

I hope I've convinced you that the status of safety in your organization is largely determined by how safety is talked about, from the boardroom to the breakroom. And whether we feel responsible for safety and are committed to go for a breakthrough depends on our interpretation or mental script on safety conversations.

Given the power of conversation to resolve conflict, achieve breakthrough, and define image, self-esteem, and culture, we need to direct this powerful tool to

Talking Points

Conversations we have with ourselves and others have the power to:

- Initiate or fuel conflict.
- Defuse or eliminate conflict.
- Shape self-esteem.
- Shape public image.
- Increase or decrease safety motivation.
- Shape an organization's safety image.
- Define work cultures, including safety cultures.
- Raise or lower production output.
- Improve or hinder safety performance.
- Achieve safety breakthroughs.

improve safety. But how do we maximize interpersonal and intrapersonal conversations? What kinds of conversations are more likely to provoke and maintain improvements? I'd like you to consider the following seven strategies for improving safety-related conversations between people. Each of these seven techniques can get employees more involved in safety, and improve your overall level of workplace safety performance.

Applying the methods can also improve how you talk to yourself – your "self-talk." The payoff? Increased self-esteem and perceptions of empowerment, which are essential for increasing our willingness to actively care for the safety and health of others.

> *Conversation Checklist*
>
> To get the most from safety conversations:
>
> - Listen attentively.
> - Emphasize positive actions you've observed.
> - Draw out responses from the other person.
> - Get them to tell you, in their own words, what they ought to be doing in order to be safe.
> - Ask questions with a sincere and caring demeanor.
> - Act as if you don't know the answer, even though you think you do.
> - Shift the focus to future ways of improving safety.
> - Seek a verbal commitment to embrace those ideas.
> - Bring the conversation back to the present by developing an action plan to achieve the improvements you desire.

1) Don't Look Back

Let's begin by considering how easy it is for conversations to dwell on past events, especially negative experiences. Think of safety meetings that dwell on past failures. To improve safety, we need to move conversations – both our "self-talk" and conversations with others – from recounting the past to focusing on future possibilities. From there we can develop an action plan.

So how do you pull this off? Say you approach someone about getting more involved in safety and they reply, "I offered a safety suggestion three years ago and it went nowhere." Where do you take the conversation from here?

This is really a matter of leadership, as discussed in Kim Krisco's book. Leaders help people move their conversations from the past to the future and then back to the present (where you begin by developing an action plan). To direct the flow of a conversation in this manner, you first must recognize and appreciate what the other person has to say. Then shift the focus toward the future. Remember, you're approaching this person to discuss possibilities for safety improvement and specific ways to get started now.

2) Seek Commitment

Your goal in this kind of conversation is to get a commitment from the other person. Safety-related conversations are productive when someone commits to taking a specific action.

A verbal commitment also tells you that something is happening on an intrapersonal level, within that other person. The person is becoming motivated. Now you can proceed to talk about how that commitment can be supported, or how to hold the individual accountable.

3) Stop and Listen

Be careful when you try to change behavior in others. Sometimes a passion for safety can lead to an overly directive approach. You know from personal experience, and clinical psychologists have shown, that it's better to give advice in a nondirective manner, especially over the long term.

Think about it: How do you respond when someone overtly tells you what to do? You might follow the instruction, especially if it comes from someone with the power to control consequences. But will you be motivated to make a permanent change?

Conversations that can be interpreted as "adult-child" confrontations may not work. Sure you mean well, but other people might not see it that way. Play it "safe." Try to be more nondirective.

Let me explain what I mean here: The theme of nondirective psychotherapy is active listening. The objective is to get clients to reveal their concerns, problems, and solutions on their own terms. The therapist's role is to be a passive catalyst, enabling and facilitating a conversation that is directed and owned by the client. I'm not suggesting safety leaders become therapists, but we can take some useful lessons from this nondirective approach.[2]

4) Ask Questions First

Instead of telling people what to do, try this: Get them to tell you, in their own words, what they ought to be doing in order to be safe. You can do this by asking questions with a sincere and caring demeanor. Avoid at all costs a sarcastic or demeaning tone.

But first, point out certain safe behaviors you noticed – it's important to emphasize positives. Then move on to the seemingly at-risk behavior by asking, "Is there a safer way to perform that task?" You might, in fact, find your presumptions to be imperfect. The "expert" on the job might know something you don't know.

By asking questions, you're always going to learn something. If nothing else, you'll hear the rationale behind taking a risk over choosing the safer alternative. You might uncover a barrier to safety that you can then help the person overcome.

Remember, it's only natural to offer a rationale for taking a risk. It's a matter of protecting one's self-esteem. Let it pass, and remind yourself when someone owns up to his or her mistake – even under a cloud of excuses – your nondirective approach is beginning to draw the person out and bring about the change you desire.

Safety directives can be perceived as confrontations.

5) Use Words Wisely

But what if the person doesn't give a satisfactory answer to your question about safer alternatives? What if the individual doesn't seem to know the safest operating procedure? Now you need to shift the conversation from nondirective to directive. You need to give behavior-focused advice.

In this case, start with the phrase, "As you know," as my friend John Drebinger advises.[3] Open the conversation with a phrase that implies the person really does know the safe way to perform but for some reason just overlooked it (or forgot) this time. This could happen to anyone. Such an opening can help prevent others from feeling their intelligence or safety knowledge has been insulted.

6) Beware of Bias

Every conversation you have with someone is biased. You can't get around it. From personal experience, people develop opinions and attitudes that influence the words we hear, how we interpret those words, and what we say in response. Every conversation influences how we process and interpret the next conversation.

Personal biases can cause people to tune you out. By asking for their input upfront, you reduce the likelihood they will later tune you out. It's the principle of reciprocity: By listening first, you increase the odds the other person will listen to you without a "tune-out" filter.

Don't let your prejudices about a speaker limit what you hear. Do you ever listen less closely to certain individuals, perhaps because the person seldom has anything useful to say or because you think you can predict what they'll say? Tell yourself you're not listening to someone, rather you're listening for something. You're not listening reactively to confirm a prejudice – you're listening proactively for clues or possibilities to solve a safety issue.

Pay close attention to body language and tone in conversations. I'm sure you've heard many times that the method of delivery can reveal as much, or more, information as the words themselves. Listen for passion, commitment, or caring. If nothing else, you can learn whether the messenger understands and believes the message. And perhaps you'll learn a new method for delivering a message yourself.

7) Plant Words to Improve Self-Image

Above I discussed how conversation influences both public and self-image:

Two people have two perspectives.

- How we talk about others influences perceptions within a group.
- How we hear others talk about us shapes our own self-image.
- And how we talk to ourselves about these viewpoints can make them a permanent feature of our self-image or self-esteem.

Want to change how others perceive you? Change the conversations people are having about you. If you suspect, for example, colleagues consider you to be forgetful and disorganized, you could mention certain self-management strategies

Conversation can elevate or lower self-esteem.

you've been using lately to improve memory and organization. Of course, you need to actually practice these techniques. If you focus on new positive qualities rather than past inadequacies in your conversations with others and with yourself, you'll surely improve your self-image and self-esteem.

There's a process at work here: Planting words in conversations can improve your own self-image and confidence as someone who can facilitate safety improvements. Telling others of your increased commitment encourages more effective safety conversations. Then use these seven strategies to improve interpersonal conversation. Commend yourself when you do. In this way, intrapersonal and interpersonal conversations work together to cultivate a Total Safety Culture. And interpersonal conversation reflects thinking – the theme of the next chapter in this People-Based Safety sourcebook.

PART 2

Converse, Don't Confront

Safety-related conversations often come across as confrontational. One person tells another he or she is working unsafely and needs to do something about it. This points out that people expect the worst when safety feedback is offered. If you confirm those expectations, you'll have trouble being an effective safety coach. Here are five ways to avoid potential problems:

1) Stress that feedback is necessary

Repeat after me: Practice does not make perfect. We can practice the wrong way of doing something over and over and develop a bad habit. Only with specific behavior-based feedback can we improve and eventually "make perfect." Even when our behaviors give us natural feedback, such as in sports, we still need coaching. Sometimes coaches will demonstrate a better way, so we can learn by watching them.

Remember, risky behaviors are naturally followed by reinforcing consequences such as comfort, convenience, or efficiency. That makes it easy to develop risky habits. Coaching with the right kind of behavioral feedback is the best way to help people practice the right way and develop safe habits.

Feedback makes it possible to improve.

2) Be positive

How do you feel when someone asks: "May I give you some feedback?" Do you really expect the incident to be rewarding? Most people do not. Based on my experince, feedback is more often linked with "reprimand" than "praise."

Your first feedback session really needs to be positive and constructive to set the tone and change those expectations. In general, the context of how feedback is delivered is crucial. The nature of the conversation or group discussion surrounding a feedback session determines whether such a process will be appreciated, supported, and sustained.

3) Use "trial-and-success learning"

It's popular to believe the best way to learn is by making mistakes. If we believe we learn more from our mistakes, and we act on this belief, we'll be ineffective coaches.

Behavioral scientists have shown quite convincingly that we learn more from focusing on our successes than our failures. Edward Lee Thorndike demonstrated this at the beginning of the twentieth century.[4] He discovered that cats, dogs, fish, chickens, monkeys, and humans solved problems through a process he called "trial and accidental success." At first, his subjects tried various behaviors seemingly at random. When a behavior resulted in no gain, the behavior was less likely to occur again. But when a behavior was followed by success, the behavior was much more likely to be repeated. The subjects learned to solve the problems with greater and greater ease by discovering which behavior worked and then repeating that behavior.

> *5 Myths about Feedback*
>
> - Practice makes perfect.
> - Feedback is viewed as positive.
> - We learn more from our mistakes.
> - Give positive feedback in public.
> - Feedback should always follow behavior.

It's ironic that descriptions of Thorndike's work referred to "trial-and-error learning." But Professor Thorndike knew better. We do learn something from feedback about our mistakes. We learn what not to do. But it's the positive feedback from our successes that produces the most learning.

And positive feedback is good for our attitude. It helps us feel good about ourselves and the task at hand. Feedback influences more than behavior. So if we want people to feel good about safety-related behavior, we better offer more positive than negative feedback.

4) Be careful with public praise

Whether positive or negative, individual feedback should not be delivered publicly without the recipient's permission. Many people feel embarrassed when receiving special attention in a group context. They might fear harassment by their peers. You know the jealousies that can surface: "Why did you deserve that special recognition? Have you been kissing up to management again?"

It can be useful to give group feedback publicly. Since individual responsibility is diffused or dispersed across the group, there's little risk of individual embarrassment or peer harassment. But it's critical for this group feedback to be more positive than negative. It should be presented in terms of achievement rather than failure. Remember, we want people to look forward to the next feedback session.

5) Sometimes give feedback first

If you're already motivated to do your best, when do you want feedback in order to improve? When do you want the coach to remind you of specific behavioral steps to perform? It often makes sense to give individual feedback immediately before the next opportunity to perform the target behavior.

Jason DePasquale and I conducted rigorous field research that found teenagers who were learning to drive increased their safe driving practices significantly only when they received specific behavioral feedback before their driving session. During baseline observation, our research assistants rated several driving behaviors of students as "safe" or "at-risk" on a critical behavioral checklist. After these baseline observations, one group of 14 drivers received specific behavioral feedback at the end of their driving session; student drivers in another group received it immediately before the next session. Only this latter group improved their driving safety, as measured by our research assistants' use of the checklist.[5]

I hope you can see from these five steps the importance of dispelling some common myths about feedback. These myths can actually hinder safety improvements. Set the record straight and you help enhance understanding and buy-in for a behavioral feedback process.

PART 3

Coach with Feeling

Using conversations to improve safety performance is the theme of this chapter on "The Coaching of People-Based Safety." Here, I focus on the highest level of conversation you can have – empathic coaching.

It's a difficult level to attain but one that can do wonders to facilitate mutual learning and behavioral improvement. Leaders who demonstrate empathy – sincere understanding and appreciation for other people's circumstances – are more likely to be followed. And their directions, based on an empathic diagnosis of the situation, are more effective.

Conversations at this level are not efficient, but they are effective. They require patience. It takes time to learn, mostly through questioning and listening, what it's like to be in the other person's situation. Then the objective shifts to designing an action plan that fits the circumstances. This requires mutual understanding. Everyone who is taking part in the conversation must have the same feeling for what the circumstances are. Then, if everyone states their commitment to follow through with the plan, you've had a most effective conversation.

This is easier said than done, you might say. You're probably right. But the payoff can be great: When we show more empathy in our conversations, we have more impact on improving attitudes and behaviors. When we show others, through empathic listening, that we really understand their position, we maximize the chance of progress.[6]

Empathy can be rewarding.

Achieving Empathy

Here's how to achieve an empathic level of awareness and appreciation:

• Take off your blinders. Minimize the reactive filters that bias conversations. They are barriers to listening intently and proactively to another person.

• Ask more questions. This is how you truly understand the other person's position and eventually diagnose the problem.

• Listen for more than words. Not only must we hear every word, but we must also be sensitive to feelings, passion, and commitment. This comes across as much in body language and manner of expression as in words themselves. Listen for more than words when workers give evaluations of their at-risk behavior and offer recommendations for self-improvement. Listen for feelings or emotions that reflect concern for errors and commitment to change.

When we show more empathy in our conversations, we have more impact on improving attitudes and behaviors.

• Use your imagination. When you observe another person's work practices, try to view the situation from that individual's perspective. When you listen to someone explain why he or she took a risk or got injured, try to see yourself in the same predicament. Imagine what defense mechanisms you might use to protect your ego or self-esteem.

• Weigh alternatives. When you consider action plans for improvement, try to view various alternatives by putting yourself in the same "steel-toed shoes" of the other person.

Empathic coaches understand the other person's perspective.

We need to approach our safety coaching conversations with an empathic mindset. We want to learn what motivates someone to risk their safety; we want to put ourselves in their place. From that understanding we can derive an action plan that we would be willing to follow. You can do this by bringing empathy to your safety conversations.

Empathy – Not Sympathy

Empathy is not the same as sympathy. Don't confuse the two, though dictionary definitions are similar. *The New Merriam Webster Dictionary* (1989) defines sympathy as "the capacity for entering into and sharing the feelings or interests of another" and empathy as "the capacity for experiencing as one's own the feelings of another."

My *American Heritage Dictionary* (1991) defines empathy as "identification with and understanding of another's situation, feeling, and motives" – in contrast to sympathy as "a feeling or expression of pity or sorrow for the distress of another person."

We sympathize when we express concern or understanding for another individual's situation, but we empathize when we identify with another person's situation and realize what it's like to be in the other person's shoes.

An Empathic Coach

Last fall I witnessed a most unusual and effective tennis lesson. Later, I realized how empathy was at the heart of this success story.

Frank, my longtime tennis opponent, had a strong forehand that had weakened considerably. It got so that I expected to win every set, and he expected the same outcome. Eventually, he lost interest in our regular competition, and I lost a regular tennis opponent.

Then Josh Williams, a friend and associate at Safety Performance Solutions, stepped in to help. Josh played varsity tennis for four years at Kalamazoo College in Michigan, and subsequently taught tennis professionally at John Newcome's Tennis Resort. When Josh arrived at my tennis court, I asked him if he wanted to watch Frank and me rally for a while so he could assess the problem. Numerous tennis instructors use this approach. They observe a student hit a tennis ball numerous times and then provide direct feedback by verbalizing and demonstrating certain behavioral changes. Then they watch some more and give specific feedback.

But Josh declined my idea. Instead, he took my side of the court and began rallying with Frank. He didn't say anything about any problem, just "Nice shot" a number of times to commend good performance.

At one point, Josh stopped rallying and asked Frank where he thought he was having difficulty. Convinced he knew his problem, Frank discussed the way he grips his racket when shifting from a backhand to forehand stroke. Frank does hold his racket differently than most, using what's referred to as a Western grip instead of the more common Eastern grip.

Josh agreed with Frank's diagnosis and asked him to rally some more balls. This time Josh used the same Western grip as Frank and mimicked his forehand stroke. In this way, Josh could understand exactly how it felt to be in Frank's tennis shoes. When switching from a backhand to forehand stroke, Josh changed his grip exactly as Frank in order to appreciate the difficulty Frank was experiencing.

Josh truly empathized with Frank's situation, and as a result he provided more relevant advice. And because Josh demonstrated genuine understanding and appreciation of Frank's problem, his advice was readily accepted.

PART 4
The Coaching Process

Achieving a Total Safety Culture requires employees to observe their coworkers and look actively for ongoing behaviors that can increase or decrease the odds of personal injury. Observers need to recognize and promote safe behaviors and correct at-risk behaviors in a way that will be accepted by the individual observed.

I call this "actively caring safety coaching." Let's review the basic characteristics of effective safety coaches.

The coaches of winning athletic teams practice basic observation and feedback processes, and follow most of the recommendations discussed here. In other words, the best team coaches observe the behaviors of their players, record their observations in systematic fashion (on a team roster, behavioral checklist, or on videotape) and then offer specific behavioral feedback (both correcting and supporting) to the team members.

Often, this behavioral feedback is given both individually (in one-on-one communication) and in group sessions (by reviewing videotapes of the team competition). The most effective coaches give this feedback so the team members learn from the exchange and are motivated to continuously improve.

The five letters of the word COACH can be used as a mnemonic to remember the basic characteristics of the most effective coaches, whether coaching for a winning athletic team or for a work group seeking safety performance.

Coaches observe carefully and then give behavior-based feedback.

A win/lose mindset conflicts with interdependency.

"C" for Care

Know I care and you'll care what I know. Safety coaching starts with caring. Safety coaches genuinely care about the health and safety of their coworkers, and they act on such caring. In other words, they "actively care."[7] And people are more likely to accept their advice when a safety coach's words and body language reflect caring.

Many people are unwilling to coach or to be coached for safety because they consider safety a matter of individual or personal responsibility. This is reflected in the verbal or mental statement, "If Susan and Chuck want to put themselves at risk, that's their problem, not mine." Thus, for some individuals a change in personal perspective or attitude is needed to facilitate the occurrence and acceptance of safety coaching. Everyone needs to consider safety coaching a shared responsibility or an interdependent opportunity to prevent injuries throughout their work culture. This calls for a shift from a win/lose individualistic to a win/win collectivistic frame of reference.[8]

Most employees are willing to adopt a collectivistic or team approach when it comes to work quantity and quality. In other words, people are more willing to give each other feedback about work performance than safety performance. Coaching for production is part of the job; coaching for personal safety is meddling. Workers need to realize the safety-related behaviors need as much (probably more) interpersonal observation and feedback as any other job activity.

Pointing out a company's injury record for a certain period of time can convince people to accept safety coaching as a shared responsibility. Although they might not have been injured, others were hurt on the job, and everyone obviously cared about that. With an overarching caring attitude, people are ready to learn what they can do to make a difference. The answer is to become an actively caring safety coach. The coaching must be behavior-based, and the process begins with behavior-based observation.

"O" for Observe

Safety coaches observe the behavior of others objectively and systematically. They look for both safe and at-risk behavior. Actions that "go beyond the call of duty" for the safety of another person should be especially noted.

The coach must know exactly what behavior is desired and undesired. This is an obvious requirement for athletic coaching. It's often advantageous (usually essential) to develop a checklist of safe and at-risk behaviors in your workplace and rank these in terms of risk. Obviously, workers themselves are the best source of information for developing a behavioral checklist. Risk rankings also can be derived from injury records and reports of "near misses."

Observer: **Date:**

Target Behavior	**Safe**	**At-Risk**
load appropriate		
hold close		
use legs		
move feet — don't twist		
smooth motion — no jerks		
Comments (use back if necessary):		

% Safe Observations:

$$\frac{\text{Total Safe Observations}}{\text{Total Safe Observations + At-Risk Observations}} \times 100 = \_\_\_\_\%$$

A critical behavior checklist can increase safe lifting.

"A" for Analyze

Safety coaches spend time interpreting their observations. They need to understand why certain behaviors are occurring.

Coaches realize, for example, that certain at-risk behaviors occur because they are directed by activators such as work demands, at-risk examples set by peers, and inconsistent or mixed messages from management. They also know that at-risk behaviors are often motivated by one or more consequences (comfort, convenience, work breaks, and management or peer approval). This is the ABC principle (activator-behavior-consequence) that shapes behavior.

Safety coaches realize the way they observe, analyze, and communicate can activate safe behaviors (through instructions, reminders, individual and group discussions) and motivate repeated safe behavior (through verbal feedback, recognition, and group celebrations).

Activator →	**Behavior** →	**Consequence**
Discussion/ Consensus	Drive the Speed Limit	Thank-You
Lecture/Film	Buckle Up	Self-Approval
Policy	Lock Out Power	Peer Approval
Demonstration	Put On PPE	Smile
Directing Feedback	Use Equipment Guards	Motivating Feedback
Goal Setting	Give a Safety Talk	Prize or Reward
Pledge Signing	Clean Up a Spill	Reprimand
Incentive	Remind Others to Work Safely	Penalty
Disincentive		
Safety Sign		

Intervention strategies are classified by the ABC Model.

"C" for Communicate

Interpersonal communication is the critical intervention step of safety coaching. Everyone wants to improve, but at the same time many people resist giving and receiving the kind of communication that is critical to beneficial change. The "same old routine" is familiar, nonthreatening, secure, and relatively easy. Change-focused communication sometimes threatens personal confidence and competence.

Some people perceive feedback that implies personal change as an indictment of their current work style, job skills, or diligence. This reaction is most likely to happen when someone is being asked to dramatically change, and when current risky procedures have been followed for years.

To overcome this type of resistance, effective safety coaches steer clear of disruptive dramatic communication (or conflict) and emphasize incremental "fine tuning." They also promote change by accentuating the positives. Several articles in this chapter offer advice on giving effective feedback communication to facilitate desirable change in ourselves and others.

Safety coaches look for opportunities to recognize or support "small win" safety improvements in work practices and conditions. Certainly at-risk behavior needs to be corrected, but effective coaches realize people do not like to be criticized and are apt to reject or deny a totally negative communication about the need to change.

Before suggesting a need for specific change, the safety coach attempts to communicate in a positive (or at least neutral) way by finding something nice to say about the situation (if only to state sincere concern for the safety of an important member of the workforce).

"H" for Help

Actually "help" summarizes the mission of a safety coach. The goal is to help an individual prevent an unintentional injury. The key is to get that person to accept feedback. How? Let's use the letters in the word HELP as reminders:

"H" for humor: Safety is certainly a serious matter, but sometimes a little humor can increase interest and decrease resistance. It can help diffuse a stressful situation.

Coaching requires a sharp eye and careful listening.

"E" for esteem: People who feel inadequate, unappreciated, or unimportant are not likely to go beyond the call of duty to benefit the safety of themselves or others. Thus, coaches choose their words carefully (emphasizing the positive over the negative) in an attempt to build or avoid lessening another person's self-esteem.

"L" for listen: One of the most powerful and convenient ways to build self-esteem is to listen attentively to another person. The person can interpret this active listening as a reflection of self-worth ("I must be valuable because my opinion is appreciated"). And after a coach actively listens, his or her message is more likely to be heard and accepted.

"P" for praise: Praising another person for a specific accomplishment is another powerful way to build self-esteem. If the praise targets a particular behavior, the odds of the behavior occurring again increase. This is the basic principle of positive reinforcement. It motivates people to continue their safe work behaviors and to look out for the safety of their coworkers.

Building a Culture

To summarize, safety coaching is a key process for developing a Total Safety Culture. As more workers effectively apply the principles of coaching discussed here, the entire workplace moves closer to a Total Safety Culture.

Obviously, training and practice are essential to developing safety coaching skills. It's also critical that the entire organization embrace and support interpersonal coaching for safety improvement. This might require a dramatic change in how a company approaches safety (from fault finding to fact finding; from a focus on punishment for safety violations to a focus on recognition and support for safety achievements; and from a fatalistic perspective to a "make a difference" attitude).

A large-scale safety coaching process can require time and resources, but the long-range outcomes will be well worth the effort.

Start small and build confidence and optimism by recognizing the "small wins" that lead to the ultimate goal – a workplace of employees who coach each other consistently and effectively to increase safe work practices. In the process they increase their own and others' sense of self-esteem, empowerment, and belongingness.

PART 5

Ten Coaching Guidelines

Let's consider ten guidelines for implementing an effective safety coaching process throughout an organization. These guidelines were gleaned from a decade of Safety Performance Solutions (SPS) helping organizations develop and sustain an effective behavioral observation and feedback process. The guidelines were developed and refined from studying the trials and tribulations of over 100 SPS clients. I'm convinced they reflect the state-of-the-art in safety coaching.

1) Teach principles

There is a difference between education and training. Education explains "why" and training shows "how." Motivation to learn what to do – the procedures – can come from understanding the underlying rationale – the principles. Before people are trained on how to conduct behavioral observation and feedback, they should be educated on the philosophical foundations of People-Based Safety. Then participants can appreciate the procedures that make the principles practical.

When participants learn and accept the principles behind a safety initiative, they can help to define and refine tools and techniques applicable for their work groups. Such involvement in designing process steps facilitates empowerment and ownership – the next guideline.

Without education, training can feel degrading.

2) Empower employees

Genuine empowerment is not given. It is enabled and then released from people when they feel ownership. But ownership does not come easy, and it doesn't happen overnight. It's not the same as compliance.

We often comply with rules, regulations, and operating procedures without ownership. In this case, we perform because someone is holding us accountable. Such behavior is other-directed. Ownership, on the other hand, facilitates internal control, self-accountability, and self-directed behavior.

People who get involved in designing, implementing, evaluating, and refining a process acquire a special degree of ownership. Their contributing behaviors are self-directed. These behaviors occur consistently because participants hold themselves responsible, not because someone else is holding them accountable.

3) Give 'em a choice

Choice, involvement, and ownership go hand in hand. Each supports the other two. More of one influences more of the others.

Choice is motivating. Research has shown that even insignificant choice benefits commitment and human performance. For example, people have shown improved performance when they select aspects of a task that are actually irrelevant to effective completion of the task.[9]

So how much choice is optimal? Our systematic evaluation of numerous successful behavioral safety coaching (BSC) programs indicates that too much choice can actually be detrimental. We found that safety coaching programs labeled "completely voluntary" were generally not as successful as BSC programs introduced with the explicit expectation that everyone will get involved to some degree.

Command and control without choice stifle creativity.

Also, BSC programs that incorporated an accountability system to track involvement obtained the most participation and success. I hasten to add that all of the most successful BSC programs included some element of choice throughout process development, implementation, and continuous improvement.

Maintain an effective balance. Provide structure and direction, but accompany your advice with opportunities to select among alternative action plans.

4) Facilitate supportive managers

Whether considering BSC or another type of safety program, a "hands off" policy does not work. Let's face reality. People give priority to those aspects of their jobs that get attention from supervisors and managers. People do what they believe they need to do in order to please those who control their monetary compensation for successful job performance.

Yes, self-directed, responsible behavior is best, but often behavior must start as other-directed. Before people can appreciate the natural supportive consequences of BSC, they usually need to be held accountable for carrying out the observation and feedback procedures. Plus, supervisors can do a number of other things to encourage and support BSC:

- Allocate time to discuss process activities and results at group meetings.
- Contribute to group discussions of BSC procedures and results.
- Help schedule and coordinate opportunities for BSC activities, such as observation and feedback sessions.
- Request systematic observation and feedback for certain tasks.
- Use the observation data to identify environmental hazards and barriers to safe behavior.
- Help remove hazards and barriers identified in the behavioral observation and feedback process.
- Request periodic briefings on data from the BSC process, such as amount of participation, percent safe behavior, number of coaching sessions performed, percentage of safety suggestions accomplished, and results of special BSC intervention efforts.
- Recognize individuals and teams for notable BSC participation.
- Organize and support group celebrations of special safety achievements.

5) Go easy on punishment

The last two bullets refer to the use of recognition and group celebrations to support BSC activities and accomplishments. This guideline specifies the avoidance of negative or punitive consequences. I've discussed the disadvantages of traditional enforcement procedures in the prior section on "The Acting of People-Based Safety". Here I emphasize that connecting negative consequences to any aspect of an employee-driven (and management-supported) BSC activity can kill the entire process. Punishment stifles feelings of trust, empowerment, ownership, and commitment.

The data from a behavioral observation and feedback process reveal at-risk behaviors and environmental hazards that need attention. It can also demonstrate less-than-optimal participation in a critical safety-related procedure. Such negative results, or specification of improvement needs, can provoke an enforcement mindset and suggest a need for punitive consequences. Please retreat from this traditional approach.

I am not recommending elimination of all punishment or "discipline" applications, even though most of these are not corrective and can do more harm than good. If you want to use negative consequences to motivate compliance, do so at your own risk. But be sure to administer your enforcement policy independently of all BSC activities.

Your workforce must believe the data from their BSC process cannot be held against them. Finding low participation or at-risk behavior is not cause for punishment – it pinpoints opportunities for improvement. Open and frank conversation about areas of concern is much more likely than punishment to increase mindful commitment to change and to activate peer support for specific improvement targets.

6) Stick to the facts

At first, peer-to-peer observation and feedback can feel awkward. From the start it's critical to emphasize that the observer (unlike a typical athletic coach) is not responsible for correcting behavior. The observer merely completes a critical behavior checklist (CBC) and shows the observee the results.

The two workers might discuss environmental or system factors that discourage safe behavior and encourage risk taking. They might consider ways to remove barriers to safe behavior. The coach might give positive words to recognize certain safe behaviors, but no direct disapproval of any at-risk behavior is offered.

This is nondirective coaching. There is no peer pressure. Only self-accountability matters here. Any change in behavior is self-directed, provoked by the results of an anticipated application of a CBC.

7) Place trust above accuracy

"Anticipated" means the recipient of an observation and feedback session knows it's coming and can prepare for a good showing. Observations are not random and the results are not really representative of a worker's daily routine. The CBC data are biased toward the positive.

If this leads to overly positive results, why announce observations in advance?

Well, imagine workers sneaking around and completing CBCs on the sly. You then have a "gotcha" program that undermines trust, involvement, and ownership. The lower "percent safe" scores might be more accurate, but at the expense of the cooperation needed to achieve an injury-free workplace.

Even when they know they are being observed, workers still take certain risks. The BSC process holds people accountable to perform their jobs as safely as they know how. When they learn ways to be safer under these circumstances, workers truly add new behavioral patterns to their knowledge base.

Still, organizations most successful at BSC progress from announced to unannounced observations. This shift should occur only when workers realize the process is truly for their own benefit.

There are creative ways to facilitate the transition from announced to unannounced observations. One organization distributed hard hat stickers workers could display to indicate their willingness to be observed. Eventually, every employee at this facility had the sticker pasted on their hard hats.

8) Avoid paralysis by analysis

The benefits of BSC extend far beyond analyzing CBCs. In fact, it's likely most records of behavioral observations are biased and unreliable. They are typically obtained under unnatural conditions. Observations are often announced beforehand, and there is a tendency to overlook at-risk behavior, especially when feedback follows an observation.

Observation and feedback sessions provide useful data to compare across the same work group and between different work teams. But don't take the absolute values of these numbers too seriously. Above all, the process is more powerful than the outcome.

One-to-one BSC demonstrates peer support, develops interpersonal trust, and helps to cultivate the kind of learning-oriented organization that brings out the best in people. The process teaches workers they can be "unconsciously incompetent" and they need feedback from others to improve. This leads to interdependency – people contributing diverse talents and relying on each other to make the whole workplace greater than the sum of its parts.

9) Refine your process

With experience, behavioral coaches become more adept at noticing the subtle features of safe versus at-risk work practices, beyond the obvious use of personal protective equipment. This enhanced coaching expertise needs to be reflected in your revised CBCs.

Continually assess the behavioral and attitudinal impact of your BSC procedures. Evaluating people's opinions and attitudes about a BSC process requires conversations with both participants and nonparticipants. These should occur in both group and individual one-to-one sessions.

10) Focus on people factors

This article focuses on BSC, but keep in mind People-Based Safety principles can be applied to many other domains of occupational safety, including ergonomics, training, recognition and celebration, hazard identification, and corrective action, to name a few. In each of these cases, people-based reflects a particular approach toward handling the human dynamics of the effort. Observation and feedback are components of an interpersonal coaching process that applies certain research-supported tools derived from behavioral science.[10]

Beyond BSC

For many readers these ten principles may seem to reflect common sense. Consider, however, that numerous safety programs have not adhered to these guidelines, resulting in less than optimal participation.

Through experience and feedback, common sense is informed and evolves into continuous improvement. For those who don't view these guidelines as common sense, I hope this presentation has informed your common sense and influenced your behavior. I also hope you see these principles of program implementation relevant for more than BSC. Indeed, these guidelines can be applied to develop, administer, and refine any organizational process that involves your entire workforce.

PART 6

Slow Down and Listen Up

Here are four techniques to help you relate to coworkers' concerns. You're eating lunch and a coworker sits down and begins complaining about his job, his supervisor, and the company in general. Then, he tells you he's going to quit. How should you react? This person is obviously unhappy, perhaps ready to do something drastic and impulsive. What do you say? This situation is not rare these days. The "lean and mean" atmosphere in American industry has increased stress and distress in the workplace, leaving many employees worried about job security. Disgruntled workers at all levels of an organization are apt to vent their discontent and frustration to a friend or perhaps to anyone who will listen.

So now you're on the receiving end of a barrage of cynical and disturbing statements. A troubled coworker might do something extreme. His attitude could influence behavior that puts him and others at risk of personal injury.

So it's critical to react appropriately. You could defuse a volatile state of mind and possibly prevent a serious injury, or you could make a bad situation worse. What will it be?

Here are some guidelines for how to respond to these situations. Many readers will recognize these principles from workshops or seminars on basic communication skills. Even so, it's worthwhile to refresh our memories and boost our personal motivation to apply these guidelines. It's not always easy to be a good listener – what I call "actively listening" – but this is one way we actively care for safety and health.

Opportunities for active listening may be on the decline.

Typical Reactions

When someone says, "I'm quitting," "I'm going to get even," or "Wait 'til I get my hands on him," these emotional threats bring out the adult counselor in us. Usually we're ready with "quick-fix" advice. This advice comes from a selective interpretation of what we hear filtered through our personal views. So we proceed to tell the person what he or she should or should not do. Often, we preface this unsolicited counseling with phrases like "If I were you," or "When I was in a similar situation, I..."

Another common reaction to signals of distress is to probe for more details. We take a radical statement like "I'm going to quit" at face value and follow it by asking, "Why?" We're trying to quickly get to the bottom or "root cause" of the person's problem because we think we'll be able to solve their distress if we know more about it. So we interrogate the individual, true detective style, with specific questions in order to evaluate the situation and provide advice.

We have a lot of practice with this questioning/counseling style, so much that it becomes a natural communication pattern. Think about your interactions with family members at home. Sometimes we know a family member, such as a young child, well enough to probe, evaluate, and counsel. But I bet this approach often misses the mark, even at home. Your verbal investigation often silences the other person, especially teenagers, and your premature guidance is frequently irrelevant and resisted.

Our initial interpretation and early advice are apt to be wrong and discarded because they are distorted and one-sided. We're talking about "autobiographical bias." You see, how we try to evaluate and guide others is based on our own experiences. We use "selective perception" to put what someone says into our personal frame of reference. We respond to what's relevant to us and base advice on our past experiences and biases.

This kind of reaction to another person's problem is likely to be off the mark. Even if the well-intentioned advice is appropriate, it's not likely to be accepted because it probably comes across as biased. It might even be perceived as cold, uncaring.

If we want people to listen to our advice and accept our guidance, we have to slow down, resist the quick response. It takes time to understand a problem or situation from another person's perspective instead of our own. This requires active listening. We need to grasp the other person's biased viewpoint before making interpretations and suggestions. We need to keep our own ego in check, allowing the other person to share their true perceptions and feelings. Premature probing, evaluating, and advising – a rush to judge, if you will – will probably cut the person off from revealing private thoughts and emotions.

It's possible, even likely, that initial statements from a troubled coworker do not reflect the real problem. To say, "I'm quitting," is a broad reaction, and might even be an over-reaction to get your attention. Much more information is needed for you to possibly understand what's going on and offer useful and acceptable advice.

Keep in mind, people are usually reluctant to reveal their deeper emotions

– even to family members – although we can't really help unless there is such self-disclosure. To show you really care – to actively care – you need to reach a deeper level of understanding. And this requires you to be an engaged, empathic listener.

"Seek first to understand."
– Stephen Covey

Dale Carnegie wrote about the value of active listening more than 50 years ago in his classic book, *How to Win Friends and Influence People.*[11] His wisdom is reflected in the writing of many contemporary authors, including Stephen Covey's fifth habit of highly effective people, "Seek First to Understand... Then to be Understood."[12] Carnegie, Covey, and others offer the same basic strategies for active listening; if you've had any training in effective communication, you've received the same advice.

I'd like to review these guidelines with four easy-to-remember words, each beginning with the letter "R." In these "lean and mean" times of frustration and anxiety, we all need to be teachers and users of actively listening principles:

Repeat

This is the easiest technique to use. Simply mimic or repeat what you hear in the same words. This clarifies that you heard correctly, and most importantly, prompts the person to say more. Remember that the purpose of active listening is to motivate the other person to say more so you can truly understand the problem.

So if a coworker tells you he is quitting, you might repeat, "You're quitting?" This shows you're attentive and interested and waiting for more information. Hearing how drastic the statement sounds, the person might reply, "Well, at least I feel like quitting." Then what would you say? Following this repeat technique, you would say, "You mean you feel like quitting?" Or you might use different words to echo the same meaning. This is the next active listening technique.

Rephrase

Instead of mimicking what you hear, you might rephrase the words. In our example, you might say, "You mean you don't like working here anymore?" By putting the statement in your own words, you show genuine interest while also asking for more information. You're also checking for understanding. If you can rephrase the statement correctly, you have accurately received and interpreted what's been said.

It's possible your coworker miscommunicated or you misperceived something. Your rephrasing gives the other person a chance to explain. This is what you want – more disclosure of the problem.

Suppose he clarifies, "Well, it's not that I don't like working here; it's just that my supervisor gets me so frustrated at times, I feel like quitting." Now he has revealed a more specific aspect of the problem. What do you say next?

You could use the repeat strategy and return with, "Your supervisor gets you frustrated?" Or you could attempt to rephrase with something like, "You mean your supervisor gets you so angry that your motivation to work is sapped?" Perhaps this statement calls for the next "R" of active listening – ratification.

Ratify

Here you demonstrate affirmation or support for the individual's statement by confirming your understanding. Offer words that show empathy for what is being said, and this in turn encourages more explanation. In our example, you might ratify your appreciation of the statement by saying, "I know the feeling; I've been frustrated with my supervisor at times and wonder whether my job is worth it."

At this point, you might be tempted to jump in with probing questions to find out more about the frustration, the supervisor, or the situation. What did your supervisor do that got you so upset? Why are you so frustrated that you want to quit?

Resist the temptation to get into gossipy details. More active listening could reveal problems beyond the supervisor. Perhaps it's not the supervisor *per se*, but a particular job assignment. Or the problem might stem from interactions with another employee, or a family member, or from feelings of personal inadequacy, including a perceived loss of confidence, self-esteem, or personal control.

The bottom line is that a person's distress signals can come from many sources, and these will probably not come to the surface quickly in one-to-one communication. And if the relevant causes of a problem are disclosed, it's unlikely you could give advice that is both useful and acted upon. Usually, the best we can do is listen actively with repeat, rephrase, and ratify strategies in order to get the problem out in the open.

Ultimately, we want the person to express his true feelings.

Reflect

When people reflect their inner feelings about a situation, they are at the personal root of the problem. Such self-disclosure can lead to insight into the true cause of the problem for both the speaker and the listener, and suggest strategies for intervention. However, even with outer layers of the onion peeled away, it's usually better to let the speaker consider various solutions.

If you've been an actively caring listener, you might eventually get the ultimate reward for your sensitivity, patience, and emotional intelligence. The speaker will ask you for specific advice. When you hear words like, "What do you think I should do?" you have mastered active listening. You have shown that you actively care, and now your direction will likely be most relevant, understood, and accepted. Actually, a better description for this highest level of listening is "empathic listening."

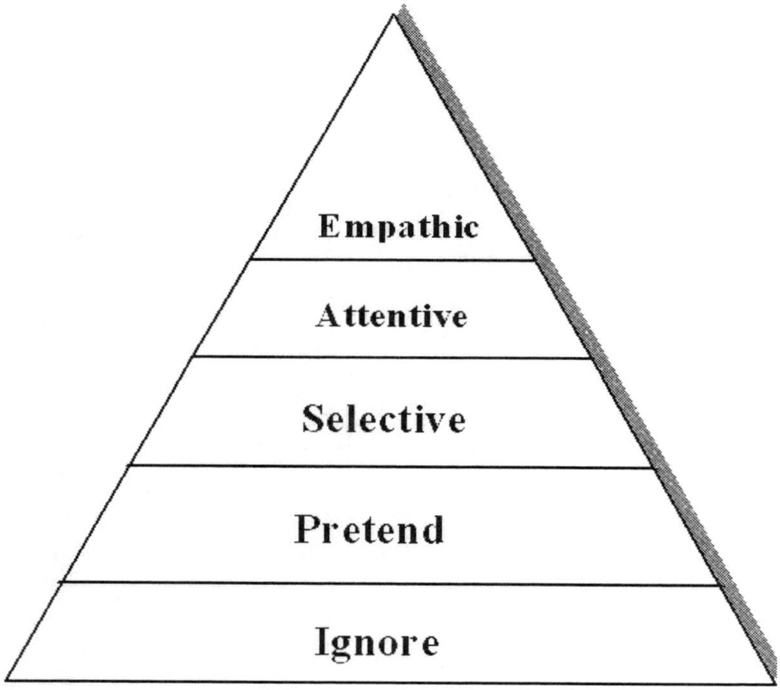

Listening occurs at one of five levels.

PART 7
Stay Positive and Focused

The key process underlying the success of behavioral safety coaching (BSC) is interpersonal observation and feedback. After appropriate education and training, workers follow these steps:

1) A list of critical safe and at-risk behaviors is derived for particular work areas or for an entire work site;

2) Critical behaviors are defined precisely and operationally so all participants can observe them objectively and reliably;

3) A critical behavior checklist (CBC) is developed to record safe and at-risk behaviors;

4) Observers use the CBC to observe and evaluate the work practices of individuals or groups;

5) Observers share the results with the people they observe in one-to-one coaching sessions and at group meetings;

6) Participants periodically discuss successes and failures with their observation and feedback procedures to continually improve the process;

7) Participants develop intervention techniques to decrease the resistance and increase long-term involvement in the process.

This is only a brief overview. More details are given earlier in this chapter. But this basic framework allows even readers who have not participated in BSC process to understand two common mistakes that crop up in BSC.

Personal Experience

Let me describe these mistakes by relating a personal experience. I recently met with a group of line workers who had been implementing a BSC process for about a year. Reaching an all-time low in recordable injuries, management considered this program successful. In fact, part of my visit was to discuss a broader implementation plan.

But these workers were not satisfied. Many one-on-one coaching sessions were constructive, but many were not. Some workers were quite negative about one-on-one observation and feedback. So while injuries were on the decline, several safety coaches were seemingly discouraged and "burning out" on the whole process.

During our discussion, I realized a basic reason for the increasing disinterest in BSC:

1) Too often the BSC sessions were more negative than positive.

This is a common mistake that can be made in coaching. For example, one individual explained that he recently approached a coworker who was working without the proper personal protective equipment (PPE) and asked if he could conduct a behavioral observation. After receiving reluctant approval, he proceeded to fill out his checklist. Since it included many more checkmarks in the "at-risk" than "safe" columns, the feedback session with this employee was necessarily more negative than positive.

I suggested the way to ensure a positive feedback session would have been to ask the worker if you could return in about ten minutes to conduct a behavioral observation. This would have given the employee ample time to find the appropriate PPE and put it on for the observation.

Take the confrontation out of coaching to get workers more enthused about participating in the process.

Then the evaluation would have more "safe" than "at-risk" checks, and the coaching session could be more positive than negative. This could increase the acceptability of the entire BSC process.

The group's immediate reaction seemed to be confusion or outright disagreement. One employee remarked, "If we did our observations that way, we'd never get true data." This basic misconception about using a CBC is the second common mistake I see in behavior-based coaching:

Feedback is often more negative than positive.

2) Workers get so involved in completing their observation checklists, tallying results, and posting group percentages that they lose sight of the primary purpose of the process.

I explained that safety coaching is not done to obtain "true" measures of safe versus at-risk behavior. In fact, results would only be acceptable as "true" by the scientific community if two observers independently observed the same work process and scored their checklists exactly the same for 85 percent or more of the categories.

The primary purpose for participating in a BSC process is to support safe behavior, reduce at-risk behavior, and thus prevent injuries. Yet it's easy to get caught up in the numbers. I've seen observers continue to complete their CBC while the person they were observing continued to perform at-risk behavior. Of course, it is easier to check columns than step in to change behavior, especially if the one-on-one feedback is perceived as negative.

The most important information to track in BSC is amount of participation. The number of CBC cards turned in is more diagnostic than the number of "safe" versus "at-risk" columns checked per card. To be sure, comparing the percentages of safe behaviors across CBC categories helps pinpoint problem areas. But degree of participation is far more predictive of outcome success (or injury reduction) than individual percentages of safe behavior.

It's essential that safety coaching is positive and nonthreatening. This builds confidence, group cohesion, and interpersonal trust – leading to increased participation. This is key to making a difference with BSC.

PART 8

How to Give Feedback

How do you use interpersonal feedback to improve safety? There are many issues to consider, so here you'll find a list of 20 guidelines to help you use and deliver feedback effectively. It's a critical tool for influencing the type of behavior you want to see in the workplace.

1. Feedback can be positive or negative, and can influence the quality and frequency of performance.

2. When you want to motivate the frequency of a particular behavior, try to deliver appropriate feedback immediately after the target behavior.

3. Safe behavior should be followed by positive feedback (or praise) to support that behavior and increase the odds it will occur again.

4. At-risk behavior should be followed immediately with negative feedback to stop the behavior and reduce the chance of recurrence.

5. When you see an at-risk behavior, you should usually do more than just attempt to stop it. Give specific direction for improving the behavior to make it safer.

6. Direction for changing behavior (i.e., directive feedback) is most influential when it occurs just prior to an opportunity to perform the behavior. So take note of the corrective action needed to make a certain behavior safer, and when an occasion arises for that behavior to occur again, offer instruction at this time – as an activator.

7. Sometimes at-risk behaviors – incorrect lifting, running down stairs – begin and end too quickly for you to intervene. You might not be able to step in, but the right corrective feedback can help prevent future risks. If a situation calls for a sequence of at-risk behaviors, corrective feedback following one behavior will serve to direct the next behavior.

8. If the opportunity for another at-risk behavior is delayed, feedback is more powerful if given later, preceding an opportunity to be safe or at-risk. Delaying such correction is also less embarrassing for the performer.

9. It's not necessary for you to tell the person about the prior at-risk observation, just remind him or her to perform the upcoming behavior in a safe manner. Then, statements like "Remember to avoid twisting," "Don't forget to use the handrail," and "I'm sure you'll buckle up and use your turn signal" come across as friendly and caring reminders rather than "gotcha" indictments.

10. Safety feedback needs to focus on specific behavior.

11. Feedback needs to be given with straightforward and objective words. Ambiguous and subjective language that tries to judge internal states of mind is not useful and can be counterproductive. For example, statements like, "It seems you're careless, lazy, unenthusiastic, unaware, disorganized, or out of touch" only add resentment and lessen acceptance of the behavioral message.

12. When you give positive statements, watch for the use of "but." Rather than giving pure praise or appreciation, we often feel obligated to add a negative (or corrective feedback) statement to balance the communication. Such mixed messages can weaken your feedback. Some people hear only the positive, some hear only the negative, and others discount both messages.

13. It's more effective to make your specific behavior-focused feedback "short and sweet." Rather than combining both positive and negative feedback in one exchange or overloading a person with several behaviors to continue or change, focus your advice on one area of performance.

14. It's much better to give people brief and specific feedback messages over weeks or months than to give people fewer but longer feedback sessions with mixed and potentially confusing motivators and directives.

15. Motivational feedback to increase or decrease the frequency of behavior should follow the target behavior as soon as possible. On the other hand, when the purpose of behavioral feedback is to shape the quality of a response, it often makes sense to give such direction as an activator (preceding the next opportunity to perform the target behavior).

Remember, the ABC model of behavior change reflects the basic principle that behavior (B) is directed by activators (A) and motivated by consequences (C). Activators precede our actions and are most apt to influence the quality of our performance (how we do things); consequences usually influence the quantity of our performance (how often we do things).

16. Receiving feedback about errors (a consequence) can be perceived as punishing and frustrating if an opportunity to correct the observed errors is not available in the near future. When the person eventually receives an opportunity to correct the behavior, the advice might be forgotten. By giving corrective feedback as close as possible to the next opportunity for the behavior to recur, you increase its directive influence and reduce the potential negative effect of catching a person making a mistake.

17. Feedback should fit the situation. Specific and well-timed feedback must be appropriate for the needs, abilities, and expectations of the person on the receiving end. It should be expressed in language the performer can understand and appreciate, and it should be customized for the performer's abilities at the particular task.

When people are learning a task, directive feedback needs to be detailed and perhaps accompanied with a behavioral demonstration. In such learning situations, it's important to match the advice with the performer's achievement level. Don't give more advice than the individual can grasp in one feedback session.

Often at-risk behavior is performed by experienced workers who know how to do the job safely, but they have developed poor habits or are just taking a risky shortcut. It could be insulting and demeaning to give these individuals detailed instructions about the safe way to complete their job. In these situations, it's appropriate to give brief corrective feedback as a reminder to be safe and set the right example for others.

18. Giving good feedback requires up-to-date knowledge of the performer's abilities regarding a certain task. It also requires specific knowledge about the safe and at-risk ways of performing the task. This is a prime reason why the most effective safety coaching usually occurs between coworkers on the same work team.

19. Feedback will be ineffective if it's viewed as a way of exerting top-down control, or demonstrating superior knowledge or motivation. The only reason for giving safety feedback is to reduce personal injury.

20. The "gotcha" perspective associated with safety often interferes with a manager's sincere attempt to correct at-risk behavior.

When the boss wants to see me, I expect the worst.

Corrective feedback is often perceived as most genuine or "real" when it occurs between coworkers on the same work team. These individuals know most about the situation and the person, and thus have sufficient information and opportunity to give the best feedback.

These guidelines can be summarized by the word "SOAR." Effective feedback delivery must be Specific, On time, Appropriate, and Real. This is how you can "soar" to success using interpersonal feedback.

I think it's important for me to reiterate that there is special value in coworkers giving each other safety feedback. Coworkers' comments are less likely to come across as a "gotcha" indictment of performance, and more in the spirit of the "brother's / sister's keeper" idea. Plus, fellow employees are more likely to be present when immediate feedback is necessary. And they can best shape a message – probably without even giving it much thought – to the expectations, abilities, and experience level of the recipient. Finally, encouragement or especially corrections from a coworker are more apt to be taken as a sign of true caring.

PART 9

Ask for Feedback

We just reviewed 20 guidelines on how to deliver feedback on safety issues. But for feedback to be effective, you must give it regularly. And for many people this is not easy, particularly when it comes to safety. Compared with production, safety is usually perceived as personal. We might feel comfortable discussing personal issues with family members but not with coworkers. When coworkers choose not to use personal protective equipment, that's their own business.

So how do we increase willingness to give and take safety feedback? I suggest starting by consistently asking others what they think of your own safety performance.

When you ask someone for feedback and show appreciation when it's given, you boost the likelihood your own advice will be accepted when given to other persons. Show a desire to improve your own performance through feedback and you teach others by example. If you ask questions that direct the observer to give specific, timely, appropriate, and real feedback, you are teaching an excellent tool for safety improvement.

Don't "Fish" Around

Merely asking "How did I do?" after performing a certain job assures timely advice, but the reaction you get might not be specific enough. In fact,

*Ask for **corrective** feedback.*

this kind of question might come off as though you're "fishing" for a compliment – especially if your performance was pretty good, which is usually the case when a person asks for feedback.

It's quite rare for people to ask for feedback when they know their performance was inferior or below average. Ironically, this is when feedback is most instructive. But if you don't ask for specific details, it's possible you'll never learn how to improve. Another barrier to getting better is that your friends and coworkers are most reluctant to offer advice when it's really most needed. They don't want to hurt your feelings.

My advice is to ask for feedback often, and in such a way that it invites correction. Begin by asking for comments after you've done something well. Then show sincere appreciation for what you hear. This allows friends and co-workers to build up your "emotional bank account," making it easier for them to make "withdrawals" when you ask for feedback following a below-average performance.

But as I mentioned, be careful when you start out asking for comments about good performance, or you risk appearing insincere. One way around this is to use a ten-point rating scale. After you ask, "How did I do?" follow up with – "Please, give my performance a rating from one to ten, with one being completely inadequate and ten being perfect." This opens the door for specific feedback. People might give you an "8" or "9," even "9.5," but probably not a perfect "10." So now you ask, "What can I do to come closer to a 10?"

Since you've already received fairly high rating, it's easier for your friend or coworker to follow up with some corrective feedback to help you reach your goal. And here's another benefit of using this system: Perhaps you'll convince your friend to be a more careful observer of your performance next time, in order to help you achieve that "perfect 10." Overall, this interpersonal communication cultivates the kind of interdependency that enables ongoing continuous improvement.

The Extra Edge

Feedback gives us the insight we need to take performance to a higher level. You see, some of our behavior is naturally followed by consequences we can use to better ourselves. When we hammer a nail, type a word, shoot a basketball, or organize our work area, we observe natural consequences that give us feedback about how we did. But even in these situations an observer could give us specific advice that helps us get from a "9" to a "10" on that rating scale.

We might put the basketball in the hoop or hit the nail on the head, but a careful and knowledgeable observer can tell us about our form in a way that improves our accuracy or reduces the probability of a cumulative trauma disorder like carpal tunnel syndrome. Again, we'll only get this precise and invaluable feedback if we invite others to observe us and then show genuine interest in hearing what they have to say.

So many everyday behaviors go unaccounted for; nothing is said about them, yet they add up. Ultimately, they contribute to safety records or just how we perceive someone. Reflect for a moment on how simple behaviors – a limp fish or crushing Superman handshake – influence our positive or negative perception of people. Yet if we never learn what they really think, we go on repeating potentially detrimental behavior.

This can be particularly damaging when it comes to safety. Think about the numerous safety-related behaviors we perform every day without any feedback. Usually, the environment does not give us natural feedback in this regard. Careful observers could tell us how to make small adjustments to reduce the possibility of an injury. But just as you're reluctant to give others personal advice about something like their handshake, people are apt to feel uncomfortable making specific suggestions about a coworker's risky behavior.

So take it upon yourself to open up the lines of communication. Ask others for specific feedback about your own safety performance. But don't settle for generalities like, "You did fine." Shoot for specifics. Show you're really serious about safe work habits. It's likely you'll learn something yourself, and you'll teach others the value of feedback – one step in improving overall workplace safety.

PART 10
How to Give Recognition

How many times have you heard: "We can't learn unless we make mistakes." This might make us feel better about the errors of our ways, but nothing could be further from the truth. Behavioral scientists have shown convincingly that success – not failure – produces learning.[13]

Just look at our own experiences. A pleasant consequence gives us direction and motivation to continue the behavior. We know what we did to receive the reward, and we're motivated to earn another.

A negative consequence following a mistake only tells us what not to do. It provides no specific direction for problem-solving. And overemphasizing a mistake can discourage us from continuing the learning process.

Learning occurs most smoothly and is most enjoyable when there are no errors. Mistakes disrupt the teaching/learning process and can lead to a negative attitude, especially if negative social consequences follow. Even subtle reactions to an error – disappointed faces or verbal tone – can increase feelings of despair and turn a person off to the entire learning process.

Positive recognition can be rare.

The antidote to this kind of depressed learning is to provide positive consequences for correct behavior. And the most powerful positive consequence to support a learning process is social recognition – the theme of Part 10. Here are seven guidelines for giving quality recognition:

Be on Time

People need to know what they did to earn your appreciation. Then they are motivated to continue that behavior. So, timely recognition is important. If it's necessary to delay recognition, when you do give it, relive the behavior or activities that were noteworthy. Talk specifically about the performance. Don't hesitate to ask the recipient to recall aspects of the situation and the desirable behavior.

Get Personal

Recognition should not be generic, fit for anyone in any situation. It should be customized. This happens naturally when recognition is linked to individual performance under designated circumstances.

It's tempting to say "we appreciate" rather than "I appreciate," and to refer to company gratitude rather than personal acknowledgment. But speaking for the company can come across as impersonal and insincere. Of course it's appropriate to reflect value to the organization when giving recognition, but the focus should be personal.

Take It to a Higher Level

Adding a universal attitude like leadership, integrity, trustworthiness, or actively caring to your recognition statement obviously makes what you're saying more rewarding. This is called reflecting a higher-order characteristic, a potent way to boost self-esteem and make recognition most memorable. But it's important to state the specific behavior first, and then link it to the positive attribute it reflects.

Go One on One

It's customary to recognize individuals in front of a group. Just think of the award ceremonies at the Olympics. Many managers take the lead from sporting events and give their individual recognition in group settings. But many people feel embarrassed when singled out in front of a group. There might be accusations of "sucking up to management."

Replace negative gossip with positive gossip.

In athletic events the participants' performance is measured fairly, and the winner is objectively determined. Behavioral safety recognition is also objective, but it is usually impossible to assess everyone's safety-related behaviors and obtain a fair ranking for individual recognition. So, praising a person in public can be seen as favoritism by individuals who feel they did equally well but did not get praised. Plus, this ranking sets up a win/lose atmosphere – perhaps appropriate for sporting events but not in workplaces that need everyone actively caring for the safety of others to eliminate injuries.

Recognizing teams of workers can be done in a group setting. Since individual responsibility is diffused or dispersed across the team, there's minimal risk of individual embarrassment or peer harassment.

Remember, though, team achievement rarely results from equal performances by all team members. It's important to deliver private recognition to those who went beyond the call of duty for the sake of their team.

Let It Sink In

In this fast-track age, we all try to communicate as much as possible when we finally get in touch with a busy person. When you recognize a person's special safety effort, don't tag on a bunch of unrelated statements, even a request for additional behavior. This comes across as, "I appreciate what you've done for safety, but I need more." Resist this temptation. Give your rewarding words a chance to be internalized so they become part of the person's own long-term self-motivation for safe behavior.

Don't Misplace the Focus

If a material reward accompanies social approval, words of appreciation can become less significant. This, in turn, lessens the impact on one's self-reinforcement system. Tangibles can add to the quality of interpersonal recognition if they are delivered as tokens of appreciation. But they must not be viewed as a payoff for the safety-related behavior – only as a symbol of going beyond the call of duty for safety.

Spread the Word

Sometimes people are suspicious of praise when it's delivered face to face. Is there an ulterior motive? Perhaps a favor is expected in return. Or maybe the recognition is seen merely as an extension of a communication exercise.

Suppose I tell you that someone else in your work group told me about the superb job you did leading a safety meeting. Chances are you'll consider the recognition genuine because I was only reporting what someone else said. This secondhand recognition also can build a sense of belonging or group cohesion among individuals. Gossip can be beneficial – if it is positive.

PART 11

How to Receive Recognition

Many people get so little recognition from others, they're caught completely off guard when it does come their way. Not knowing what to do, they might claim they don't deserve it, or see some hidden agenda at work. Naturally, this kind of response is a turnoff for anyone trying to be encouraging, perhaps inhibiting them from trying again. Which is unfortunate, because sincere recognition for safe behavior provides direction and motivation, and improves attitudes toward safety in general.

Remember, consequences influence behaviors, making it crucial for us to react appropriately when we're praised. This is how we nurture positive reinforcement throughout the workforce. Here are five basic guidelines for receiving recognition:

Don't Deny It

We've all seen the awkward denial. You tell someone they've done a nice job and they act as though they didn't hear you. Or they say something like, "It really was nothing special." The most common expression I hear following my recognition or "thank you" to a university student is, "No problem."

It's okay to take pride in our small accomplishments. After all, the vision of a Total Safety Culture depends on everyone going beyond the call of duty. Really, numerous people deserve recognition daily for the little things they do. When your effort gets noticed, just accept it, and keep in mind your genuine appreciation increases the chance more recognition will be given to others.

Pay Attention

Listen intently when someone praises you. Obviously, you want to learn what you did right. Plus, you can evaluate how well the recognition is given.

If it doesn't pinpoint a particular behavior, you might ask the person about it. This helps improve his method of giving recognition. But don't come off as being critical. Show genuine appreciation for the special attention. After all, it's not easy for many people to go out of their way to compliment others.

Take It In

Go ahead – treat yourself, revel a bit in your recognition. It doesn't come your way that often, and you know the times your extra effort hasn't been acknowledged.

You need to listen actively to every word of praise not only to show you care but also to make an impression upon yourself. Don't hesitate to relive this moment later by talking to yourself. This self-recognition motivates you to continue going beyond the call of duty for safety.

Return the Favor

Smile, make eye contact, say "thanks," in general be sincerely appreciative when someone praises you. Again, how you react can determine whether similar recognition is apt to occur again.

I find it natural to add, "You've made my day" to the "thank you" because it's the truth. When someone goes out of their way to offer me quality recognition, they have made my day. And I'll often relive the moment when I need a boost another day.

Payback is a form of reciprocity.

Sometimes it's possible to do even more to ensure the flow, the give-and-take of quality recognition through the workplace. Reward the person for recognizing you. You might say, for example, that you really appreciate the pinpointing of a particular behavior and the praise.

We need to embrace the concept of reciprocity. Research has shown that when you're nice to others, as when giving special praise, you increase the likelihood they'll reciprocate by showing similar behavior.[14] You might not be the one benefiting from it, but someone will.

Genuine acceptance of quality recognition activates the reciprocity norm. And the more this happens, the more we'll see interpersonal communication consistent with the vision of a Total Safety Culture.

Ask for It

If you feel you deserve recognition, why not ask for it? OK, so the feedback might be less genuine than if it were spontaneous, but you many receive some words worth reliving later for self-motivation. And perhaps most important, you'll remind the other individual in a nice way that he or she missed an opportunity to actively care. This could be a valuable learning experience.

I promote self-recognition among my research students by telling them they can request a standing ovation at any time during class or group meetings. All they do is state specifically the behavior they feel deserves recognition and then ask for standing applause. This isn't the best recognition – it's not private, personal, and one to one. Naturally, many people feel inhibited. But when a request is made, the experience is always positive for everyone.

There's always a solid rationale – earning an exemplary grade or receiving an acceptance letter from a graduate school or an editorial board for a professional journal, for example. The actual ovation is fun and feels good, whether on the giving or receiving end. Plus, we all learn something about the power of behavior-based recognition, even when it doesn't follow all of the quality principles. You can feel it.

William James, the first great American psychologist, wrote "The deepest principle in human nature is the craving to be appreciated."[15] Giving and receiving recognition well is how we fulfill this basic need. Plus, I don't think there's a better way to cultivate a Total Safety Culture.

PART 12

How to Celebrate Safety Success

Surveys of safety professionals by *Industrial Safety & Hygiene News* show worker morale to be a top concern. "Lean and mean" downsizing has indeed shaken spirits in many organizations, leading to apathy, helplessness, and less willingness to look out for the safety and health of others. What can we do to respond?

Giving and receiving quality recognition, as discussed above, are prime ways to boost morale. Here I want to talk about celebrations. When done correctly, safety celebrations can be an antidote for sagging morale. They can motivate teamwork, build a sense of belonging, and boost our desire to actively care for others. The key is the phrase "when done correctly." Here are guidelines you can follow:

Lean and mean downsizing can be overwhelming.

Don't Celebrate Cheating

It's quite common for companies to give employees a dinner after a particular number of weeks or months pass with no recordable injury. This kind of achievement is certainly worth celebrating, but let's be sure the record was reached fairly. If people cheat to win – not reporting injuries, for example – the celebration won't mean much.

I like the idea of celebrating the success of process activities. The behaviors needed from employees to warrant a celebration can be specified. For example, a group might decide to celebrate after completing a designated number of safety audits, investigating a given number of "near-hit" reports, finishing a particular training series, or completing a certain number of one-on-one safety coaching sessions. In these cases, an achievable goal is set and progress monitored. When the goal is reached, a celebration is clearly earned.

Focus on the Journey

Most safety celebrations I've seen give far too little attention to the journey – the processes that contribute to reaching the milestone. Typically, the focus is on the end result, like achieving zero injuries for a certain period of time. When you pinpoint processes instrumental to reaching a safety milestone, you give valuable direction and motivation. Participants learn what they need to do to continue a successful journey.

Success is a journey, not a destination.

Plus, employees who are responsible for the behaviors identified as contributing to the safety outcome receive a special boost. They feel effective, in control, and optimistic. This reinforces their internal "scripts" for later self-motivation.

But perhaps the most important reason for acknowledging journey activities is that it gives credit where credit is due. The people and actions that made the difference are endorsed.

Recipients Should Be Participants

Speeches from top management often kick off safety celebrations. There might be charts comparing past and present records. Sometimes a motivational speaker or humorist gives everyone a lift and some laughs. Certificates and trinkets might be handed out. But rarely do participants discuss the processes they supported in order to achieve success.

In your typical safety celebration, managers give and employees receive – certainly an impressive show of top-down support. But the ceremony is more memorable and beneficial as a learning and motivational experience when employees play a bigger role. Management should listen more than speak. And employees should talk more about their experience than listen to managers' pleasure with the bottom line.

Relive the Experience

Management's primary role in a safety celebration should be to facilitate discussions of activities that led to success. The best safety celebration I ever observed was planned by employees and featured a series of brief presentations by teams of hourly workers. Numerous safety ideas were shared. Some workers showed off new personal protective equipment, some displayed graphs of data obtained from environmental or behavioral audits, some discussed their procedures for encouraging near-hit reports and implementing corrective action, and one group presented its ergonomic analysis and redesign of a workstation.

Even the after-dinner entertainment was employee-driven. A skit related to safety issues. A talent show had entrants from all levels of the organization, including top managers. There was no need to hire a band – a number of talented musicians were found in the workforce of 600. (Luckily they didn't find a drummer, allowing me to sit in and relive my rock-and-roll gigging from the '60s.)

Don't Ignore Failures

The work teams in this celebration discussed both successes and failures, displaying positive results and recalling disappointments, dead ends, and frustrations. Pointing out the highs and lows made their presentations realistic and underscored the amount of dedication needed to complete their projects and contribute to the celebrated reduction in injuries.

You justify a celebration by showing how difficult it was to reach the goal. Pointing out hardships along the way reflects the fact that luck was not involved. Many people went beyond the call of duty to contribute and collaborate.

Make It Memorable

One week after the safety celebration I've described here, each participant received a framed photograph of everyone who attended the event. That picture hangs in my office today, and every time I look at it I'm reminded of the time several years ago when management did more listening than talking in a most memorable and educational safety celebration.

Tangible rewards have this effect. They reinforce the memory of an occasion and promote its value. Ideally, the memento should have a safety theme or slogan and be something that can be displayed or used in the workplace – coffee mugs, caps, or shirts, for example. When delivering these keepsakes, it should be noted that they were selected "to remind us how we achieved our real reward – fewer injuries on the job."

Treat others as they want to be treated, not as you want to be treated.

Go One on One

In every group, some individuals take charge and champion the effort, while others sit back and "go with the flow." In fact, some people exert less effort when working with a group than when working alone. Behavioral scientists call this phenomenon "social loafing."[16]

When you recognize the champions of a group effort one on one, you let them know you realize the importance of their leadership. This adds to the motivation received from the earlier group celebration and increases the likelihood of their continued leadership.

Here's a closing thought for you: When I mentioned to my graduate students I was writing an article on how to celebrate, one of them quickly responded, "That's easy, a $100 bottle of cognac, a $6 cigar, and a special friend." I had to tell him, of course, that my focus was on a different kind of celebrating. But it occurred to me that everyone has their own way of enjoying success. And when it comes to group celebration, we often inadvertently impose our prejudices on others.

When people ask people how they want to celebrate as a group, challenge them to go beyond tangible rewards. The celebration shouldn't be seen as a payoff. You want a meaningful and memorable event that can serve as a steppingstone for greater achievements.

Notes

1. Krisco, K. H. (1977). *Leadership and the art of conversation.* Rocklin, CA: Prima Publishing.
2. More information on the nondirective approach to interpersonal conversation is available in Rogers, C. R. (1961). *On becoming a person: A therapist's view of psychotherapy.* Boston, MA: Houghton Mifflin; and in Rogers, C. R. (1980). *A way of being.* Boston, MA: Houghton Mifflin.
3. John Drebinger provides more practical advice for effective safety communication in his book: Drebinger, Jr., J. W. (1998). *Master safety communication.* Galt, CA: Wulamoc Publishing.
4. Thorndike, E. L. (1911). *Animal intelligence: Experimental studies.* New York: Hofner; Thorndike, E. L. (1932). *Fundamentals of learning.* New York: Teachers College Press.
5. DePasquale, J. P., & Geller, E. S. (2001). Intervening to improve driving instruction: Should behavioral feedback be delivered before or after a training session? *International Journal of Behavioural Safety, 1,* 1-14.
6. This relates directly to Stephen Covey's Habit 5 of highly effective people, "Seek first to understand, then to be understood." Covey, S. R. (1989). *The seven habits of highly effective people.* New York: Simon & Schuster.
7. Geller, E. S. (1991). If only more would actively care. *Journal of Applied Behavior Analysis, 24,* 607-612; Geller, E. S. (1994). Ten principles for achieving a Total Safety Culture. *Professional Safety, 39(9),* 18-24; Geller, E. S. (1996). *The psychology of safety: How to improve behaviors and attitudes on the job.* Boca Raton, FL: CRC Press.
8. Triandis, H. C. (1977). *Interpersonal behavior.* Monterey, CA: Brooks/Cole; Triandis, H. C. (1985). The self and social behavior in differing cultural contexts. *Journal of Personality and Social Psychology, 96,* 506-520.
9. Geller, E. S. (1996). *The psychology of safety: How to improve behaviors and attitudes on the job* (Chapter 14). Radnor, PA: Chilton Book Company; Monty, R. A., Geller, E. S., Savage, R. E., & Perlmuter, L. C. (1979). The freedom to choose is not always so choice. *Journal of Experimental Psychology: Human Learning and Theory, 37,* 170-178; Perlmuter, L. C., Monty, R. A., & Kimble, G. A. (1971). Effect of choice on paired associate learning. *Journal of Experimental Psychology, 91,* 47-53.
10. For more on these guidelines for effective safety coaching, see Geller, E. S., Perdue, S. R., & French, A. (2004). Behavior-based safety coaching: Ten guidelines for successful application. *Professional Safety, 49*(7), 42-49.
11. Carnegie, D. (1936). *How to win friends and influence people* (Revised Edition). New York: Galahad Books.

12. Covey, S. R. (1989). *The seven habits of highly effective people.* New York: Simon & Schuster.
13. Chance, P. (1999). *Learning and behavior,* Fourth Edition. Pacific Grove, CA: Brooks/Cole Publishing Company.
14. Berkowitz, L., & Daniels, L. R. (1964). Affecting the salience of the social responsibility norm: Effect of past help on the responses to dependency relationships. *Journal of Abnormal and Social Psychology, 68,* 275-281.
15. James, W. (1890). *The principles of psychology*. New York: Holt.
16. Latané, B., Williams, K., & Harkins, S. (1979). Many hands make light the work: The causes and consequences of social loafing. *Journal of Personality and Social Psychology, 37,* 822-832.

CHAPTER FOUR

The *Thinking* of People-Based Safety™

Introduction

What can be worse for safety than "just not thinking"? Yet it's easy to cruise through our routine-filled days on autopilot. The "Thinking" component of People-Based Safety puts considerable emphasis on the need for mindfulness (*Part 1*) and the risks that arise when minds turn off to safety (*Part 2*).

One type of mindless thinking – sticking to ill-informed viewpoints and attitudes (premature cognitive commitment) – is a serious barrier to the teamwork and interdependency needed for a Total Safety Culture.

So how do you ratchet up thoughtful mindfulness for safety? Dr. Geller contends a behavior-based observation and feedback process makes both the observed and the observer more mindful of the many environmental and behavioral facets of the work process that could cause personal injury.

Your leadership style, of course, can turn minds on or off to safety (*Part 3*). Leaders who exhibit "confident uncertainty" can empower workers to come up with their own solutions for safety and health. As a trainer and coach, allow people to use their minds to figure out how to adapt a safety principle for a particular situation.

What you're doing in these cases is giving people a choice. Traditional safety has relied too much on control, too little on freedom of choice. Having a choice, having to decide, makes you think – it makes you mindful (*Part 4*). This is a key precept of People-Based Safety.

Giving people a choice, getting them to think for themselves, is key to solving one of safety's biggest challenges: How to work safe when no one is watching. In effect, you're teaching people how to mind their own business (*Part 5*).

People-Based Safety gives you a number of principles and tools to guide people's thinking about safety and injury prevention:

- Using the mind's eye (*Part 6*) – mental imagery or visualization – can motivate us to assume increased personal responsibility for the safety of ourselves and others.

• We all need a belief system (*Part 7*) to guide us. Three essential beliefs: 1) We are competent – trained and equipped to work safely; 2) We are confident our abilities and strategies will work; and 3) We believe our competence and confidence will indeed improve our safety, and the safety of our coworkers.

• Ease up on safety's old "command and control" strategies and use indirect persuasion (*Part 8*) – allow the workforce to have substantial control and authority over desired safety procedures. Increasing choice, ownership, and empowerment builds internal motivation and thought processes that maintain long-term safety mindfulness.

• Make employees mindful of the conflict between what they sometimes say about safety ("Sure, I'm all for it") and what they do (take risks to save time, etc.). Creating internal tension (*Part 9*) that's uncomfortable can produce positive behavior change.

The "Thinking" component of People-Based Safety would not be complete without examining how personality shapes safety beliefs and behaviors (*Part 10*).

Why focus on personality? Writes Dr. Geller: "Over the years in safety, we've tackled the so-called low-hanging fruit by focusing on recognizable risks that can be observed, measured and controlled. But even more injuries can be prevented if personality factors are adequately addressed."

But when focusing on personality, it's important to distinguish between personality traits – more or less determined by the time a person reaches adolescence and often the result of a mixture of genetics and early experiences – and states – which fluctuate according to behavioral context or climate (*Part 11*).

"Success seeking" is a state of mind you want to encourage to counter entitlement thinking (*Part 12*), the bane of many a safety leader. Instead of taking personal responsibility for safety, some people believe safety is management's obligation and the safety department's job. Success seekers expect the best, and take matters into their own hands to reach their goals.

Dave Johnson, Editor
Industrial Safety & Hygiene News

PART 1

The Need for Mindfulness

How many injuries occur because people were "just not thinking"? How often do we get into a work routine involving a sequence of behaviors we perform unconsciously? We take our mind off the process and put ourselves on automatic pilot.

People sometimes move through daily regimes with little thought, alertness, or creativity. The more mundane and commonplace the activity, the more likely a person will use an unconscious script to guide behavior – with an accompanying lack of awareness. Social psychologists warn that this mindless activity leaves us vulnerable to sales pitches, authoritative directives, and injuries.[1]

Mindless activity is fine if all the habitual behaviors are safe, but what if a risky shortcut is interspersed in the behavioral sequence? What if an environmental event, such as a forklift truck speeding around a corner, requires us to immediately adjust our behavior? Our lack of awareness, or our mindlessness at the time, will prevent prompt reaction. Without even realizing it, our mindless work practice puts us at risk for injury.

So how do we become more mindful of behavioral routines that could lead to injury, either to ourselves or to others?

Mindlessness can be dangerous.

The Power of Synergy

It's useful to write down the distinct steps of a job and reflect on the possibilities of an at-risk behavior and injury at each step. Perhaps this was already done in the job safety analysis (JSA) of your job. But that JSA could be long forgotten. A lot has happened since, and maybe you weren't even involved in conducting the analysis. This is about your awareness of the critical safe and at-risk behaviors involved in your daily work practices.

Optimal mindfulness of complex activities is not something you achieve on your own. It requires the interpersonal support of others. A good example of group consciousness-raising is the development of a critical behavior checklist (CBC). Everyone in the group contributes. This has several benefits:

- Mindfulness is spread across several individuals at once;
- People become mindful of the varied safe steps of a certain job;
- Everyone also becomes more aware that maximum mindfulness and protection from injury occur when people look out for each other.

Mindfulness about specific safety-related behaviors is increased prominently when a work team develops a CBC.

An Exercise in Mindfulness

How about this group exercise for a safety meeting? Pass out a raisin to everyone at the meeting and ask participants to place the raisin on their tongues. Then, request each person to close their eyes and very slowly chew on their raisin, attending to every aspect of the raisin: its shape, texture, and taste. The aim is to become aware – or mindful – of every aspect of this single raisin-eating experience.

Why would you want employees at a safety meeting eating raisins?

Psychotherapists use this raisin-eating exercise to help people reduce their adverse reaction to stressors. In fact, this is a common stress-reduction exercise for heart patients who need to decrease their blood pressure. The exercise reminds me of frequent advice my mother gave me whenever she saw me rushing around to accomplish an overload of tasks: "Don't forget to stop and smell the roses."

So you might use the raisin exercise as a stress-reduction technique. By having participants slow down to experience the process of eating a single raisin, they learn how to intentionally slow down their thinking and body processes and put themselves in a state of relaxation. The experience can also help people appreciate value in "stopping to smell the roses." In addition, I believe this exercise has special benefit for safety. It can teach people the difference between mindful and mindless work practices.

Observation Etiquette

At the October 1998 Behavioral Safety Now Conference in Dallas, a panelist stated that it's OK to conduct behavioral audits without an employee's permission. In fact, he indicated that his consulting teams often find situations where unannounced observations are especially beneficial. I had to disagree. I have not found a single situation that gives greater advantage to secretive rather than announced behavioral audits. I sincerely hope this brief article on mindfulness helps you see it this way, too.

Unannounced observations might give a more realistic picture of the at-risk behaviors occurring while someone works, but such audits run the risk of reducing interpersonal trust and giving the impression that behavior-based safety is a negative "gotcha" program. And from a behavior-change perspective, observations without permission cannot raise safety mindfulness. It's likely the mindfulness developed and increased from an open and voluntary behavioral observation process is critical for behavior change and injury prevention. To get the best from such a process, we need to be mindful of what it takes to develop and maintain an atmosphere of interpersonal trust and "actively caring."

But even more mindfulness occurs when a CBC is used.

Imagine one coworker approaching another who is hard at work and asking, "Is this a good time for a behavioral audit?" Whether the answer is yes or no, some amount of safety mindfulness is raised. Now consider the impact of the actual observation process on job-specific awareness. After volunteering to be observed, the worker is now mindful of every aspect of his or her job. The employee not only thinks about the specific items on the checklist but tries to be cognizant of every possible safety-related behavior of the task.

The Importance of Trust

In the right context, the observed employee actually shows off his individual ability to work safely. This is mindfulness at its best. It is initiated by an observation process that includes several key elements: communication is open and direct, the focus is on behaviors, and the observation is only conducted with permission. This helps to build the proper context – an atmosphere of interpersonal trust and mutual actively caring.

The individual feedback portion of this behavioral coaching process is

The individual feedback portion of this behavioral coaching process is certainly important. It supports the safe decisions a coworker makes, and provides an opportunity to improve the safety of a job. Feedback also makes both employees, the observed and the observer, more mindful of the many environmental and behavioral facets of the work process that could cause personal injury. I'm convinced this increased mindfulness is one of the most influential outcomes of a behavior-based observation and feedback process, contributing significantly to its remarkable injury-prevention success.

PART 2

When Minds Turn Off

Have you ever suffered from "premature cognitive commitment"? I'd like to explore this concept, taken from Ellen J. Langer's book, *Mindfulness*,[1] as a follow-up to the previous article on how to increase mindful behavior to prevent injuries.

I've come to really appreciate the term because it makes me mindful of the various ingredients of such mindless activity:

First, it's premature – occurring before adequate diagnosis, analysis, and consideration.

Second, it's cognitive – a thinking process that influences our perceptions, attitudes, and behaviors.

Finally, it's a commitment – a relatively permanent opinion or mindset that filters or biases the information we receive, and shapes how we act.

In other words, we commit ourselves to an initial impression without the benefit of critical thinking, and that opinion determines how we process and respond to subsequent information. This is an important concept to grasp because premature cognitive commitment contributes significantly to much of the conflict that arises between people. It's a barrier we must overcome to develop the teamwork and interdependency needed for a Total Safety Culture. Being aware of how we all fall prey to premature cognitive commitment is the first step is overcoming this barrier to safety.

Our past affects our thinking.

Interfering with Safety

Here are three ways premature cognitive commitment can hurt our safety efforts:

First, it can interfere with constructive learning. For example, I've found it difficult to teach behavioral safety principles and methods to people who have a preconceived notion that attitude or culture change must come first or that targeting safety-related behavior blames employees for a management problem.

Second, a biased mindset is especially detrimental to constructive learning and sound decision making when it is used to form global stereotypes. In fact, this is a primary contributor to prejudice and hate crimes. Dr. Langer extends this kind of mindlessness to our preconceived ideas of broad concepts such as intelligence, love, caring, respectability, excitement, fatigue, family, and aging. Adopting specific categorical definitions for these concepts not only biases perceptions, attitudes, and behaviors, but also leads to wasted potential.

Consider, for example, how a narrow meaning of "intelligence" (such as a score on a college entrance exam) can limit opportunity or self-image. Or how a detailed safety policy can thwart the customization and ownership of a generic safety mission.

This leads to the third effect – when we adopt narrow and premature definitions and concepts, we limit choice and personal control. For example, people who attribute the cause of an injury purely to the victim's carelessness or to a particular environmental hazard reduce the range of preventive solutions. When we become committed to a single-minded explanation (think of the urge to find quick fixes for safety problems), we are not open to information that runs counter to it. Dr. Langer and her colleagues showed this to be the case even when the contrary information was provided by experts.

Increasing Mindfulness

So how can we shift from the mindlessness of premature cognitive commitment to increased mindfulness in ourselves and others? Earlier, I explained how a behavior-based observation and feedback process can help us become more mindful of environmental hazards and at-risk behaviors. An open and above-board system for auditing work tasks increases mindfulness for both the person doing the observing and the person or persons being observed. This method relates to one of Dr. Langer's key recommendations for making people more mindful – get them to pay more attention to how they are trying to accomplish something (such as a safety goal), as opposed to focusing only on the outcome of that process (the safety record).

There are many examples of how we take a process for granted and direct our focus to the outcome. Dr. Langer reminds us that, starting in kindergarten, the focus of schooling is on the final result. Students in my university classes seem obsessed with their grades and seemingly lose sight of the important purpose of their "higher" education. Rather than focusing on the critical thinking and problem-solving processes related to a particular theory or research finding, students memorize the facts and formulae needed to perform well on an exam.

Likewise, travel is often seen as only a means to an end. The journey can be viewed as unimportant, so long as the destination is reached.

Safety professionals readily see the fallacy in this logic. How you complete a journey can determine whether you reach the destination in one piece. Again, the focus is on how you do it. Orient your people to the process – the steps needed to ensure safety every day. Emphasize their involvement in deriving corrective action plans from ongoing reports of environmental/ behavioral audits, near hits,[2] first-aid cases, property-damage incidents, and occurrences of recordable and lost-time injuries.

When employees see how these successive steps or "small wins" lead to an outcome such as a reduced injury rate, their sense of mindful control is enhanced. They see the outcome as hard won through their control of the process. And by continuing to improve people's mindful attention to the process, injuries can be reduced even more.

What is Premature Cognitive Commitment?

- Mindless thinking
- Prejudice
- Mindset
- Paradigm
- One-sidedness
- Bigotry
- Discrimination
- Pigheadedness
- Just plain bias

How Does it Hurt Safety?

- Interferes with constructive learning
- Leads to single-minded explanations
- Reduces a sense of personal control
- Blocks teamwork and interdependence

So, keep tracking outcomes, of course, but facilitate and reinforce discussions of the ongoing processes needed to prevent injuries. Conversations about safety processes keep people mindful of what they must continue doing in order to keep themselves and others safe.

PART 3

Benefits of Mindfulness

Being mindful benefits four key elements of effective safety.

Training – loosen up

Did you ever think about how your style as a safety trainer can encourage either mindlessness or mindfulness? Dr. Langer made this case: When facts are presented unconditionally as an absolute truth, alternative ways of thinking about something are stifled.[3] She backed this up with an interesting study. A collection of objects was introduced in an ordinary, unconditional way to one group, as for example, "This is a dog's chew toy." For the second group, objects were introduced conditionally with the extra phrase "could be," as in, "This could be a dog's chew toy."

After the objects were introduced, the groups were asked to complete some survey forms. Then the experimenter announced the survey could not continue because the wrong instructions had been given and no spare forms were available. Then several subjects suggested the rubber chew toy could be used as an eraser to correct the flawed forms. Interestingly, this resourceful idea came only from the conditional group, those told, "This could be a dog's chew toy."

Do you discuss safety rules as unconditional mandates? Or do you focus on safety principles that imply certain guidelines but can be customized? It's obvious which approach stimulates more creativity and ownership among individuals and work teams. The uncertainty of the second approach allows people to use their minds in figuring out how to adapt a safety principle for a particular situation. In turn, they feel like they own the solution they came up with, and they will be committed to mindfully follow the personalized procedures.

Leadership – let your guard down

Here's a related way to promote innovation and initiative: As a leader, display a degree of "uncertainty." Dr. Langer suggests a leader should show confidence that a particular job will get done but without being certain of the best way to do it. Again, this allows employees room to be mindfully alert, creative, and self-motivated. Workers are less afraid to make mistakes and more willing to suggest ways to improve a process.

As a safety leader, you should confidently expect employees to take appropriate precautions to prevent injuries. But you shouldn't pretend to know exactly how they should do this. After all, employees are the real safety experts. They know what hazards need to be eliminated or avoided, and what safety-related behaviors need to occur more or less often. Most likely, they are also effective at encouraging safe behaviors and discouraging at-risk behaviors. I hope you see how a leadership quality of "confident uncertainty" can empower workers to go beyond the call of duty for safety and health.

Teamwork – note the differences

We tend to give global labels for people – student, patient, homosexual, union representative, safety professional, athlete, or homeless person. Each label influences how we view people, judge them, and react to their communication with us. You can see the effect this can have on teamwork, which often makes or breaks safety efforts. Mindless labeling, or premature cognitive commitment, leads to stereotyping, prejudice, interpersonal conflict, and sometimes even hate crimes.

Now here's a twist: Dr. Langer suggests the key to reducing prejudice is to make more – not fewer – distinctions between people. When people become more mindful of the many differences among individuals, and how these differences can vary according to time, place, and the people involved, it becomes harder to stick labels on people. It becomes impossible to view people and their behavior as black or white, normal or abnormal, masculine or feminine, safe or unsafe.

Stereotyping is mindless and unfair.

In this case, an employee should not be labeled "safe" or "unsafe" at a particular job. It helps teamwork and overall safety efforts to realize each person works at his own level of safety, and that level can fluctuate dramatically from one situation to another.

Involvement – give 'em a choice

The degree of personal control you give people helps determine their level of participation in efforts to improve workplace safety and health. People mindful of having personal control are more likely to actively care.

In a seminal study, Dr. Langer and her colleagues[4] gave one group of elderly residents in a Connecticut nursing home the opportunity to care for a houseplant and to make a number of minor decisions about their daily routines. A year and a half later, these residents were more cheerful, alert, and active than a similar group who were not given these choices. The most remarkable result: less than half as many of the residents in the "choice group" had died compared with those in the other group.

> ### *Be mindful of...*
>
> 1) Using conditional rather than unconditional statements when training, assigning jobs, or stating expectations;
>
> 2) Showing confidence as a leader but displaying some degree of uncertainty regarding exactly how a job should be safely completed;
>
> 3) Making more distinctions between individuals and avoiding global categorization of people and events; and
>
> 4) Becoming more mindful of our daily choices we so often take for granted.

Dr. Langer suggests we can be more motivated to take charge by becoming more mindful of the many choices we actually make during ordinary activities. What time we get up in the morning, what we wear, what we eat for breakfast, how we get to work – there are alternatives and options for all of these routine, almost mindless decisions. Becoming more mindful of how we shape our days can increase our perception of personal control and our motivation. You can apply the same thinking to even the most routine jobs, and people can become more mindful of actions and attitudes that could be safer, more useful, and more productive.

Understanding mindful versus mindless behavior has many benefits. It gives us insight into individual perceptions and interpersonal conflict. When we listen to conversation based on mindless labeling or see mindless behavior, we understand how it leads to nonproductive relationships and at-risk behaviors. By diagnosing a situation more accurately, we can develop an effective intervention process. At the very least, we become more aware of our own mindlessness and can begin work on changing ourselves. You can always build on awareness – on mindful activity.

Benefits of Being Mindful

- People mindful of having personal control are more likely to actively care and be involved.
- Teamwork and overall safety are helped when you realize each person works at his or her own level of safety.
- Leaders who exhibit "confident uncertainty" can empower workers to come up with their own solutions for safety and health.
- Focusing on safety principles that can be customized instead of mandates allows employees to take the initiative and ownership of processes.

PART 4

Choice Makes You Mindful

Once I visited an ExxonMobil Chemical facility of 350 employees where it was really brought home to me how the "power of choice" can make a difference in safety.

The notion that "choice increases involvement" relates to many motivational theories supported by psychological research.[5] Essentially, when people believe they have personal control over a situation, they are generally more motivated to achieve and get more involved.

On the other hand, when we lose that sense of personal control, we experience "distress". This is a debilitating state and can lead to burnout or what is called "learned helplessness."[6]

The bottom line is this: Personal control increases motivation and decreases the possibility of stress turning to distress or burnout.

The ExxonMobil Chemical facility serves as an excellent example of how this important sense of control can be increased. The facility initiated an actively caring observation, feedback, and coaching process in 1992 and since then has reaped amazing safety benefits for their efforts.

Personal control increases motivation and decreases stress.

When it's important, we like to be in control.

The Payoff

In 1994, for example, 98 percent of the work force had participated in behavioral observation and feedback sessions, documenting a total of 3,350 coaching sessions for the year. A total of 51,408 behaviors were systematically documented on critical behavior checklists, of which 46,659 were safe and 4,389 were at-risk.

Such comprehensive employee involvement in a behavioral observation and feedback process has led to remarkable outcomes. At the start of their process in 1992, the plant safety record was quite good – 13 OSHA recordables for a total recordable incidence rate (TRIR) of 4.11. The plant improved to five OSHA recordables in 1993 (TRIR=1.60), and in 1994 it had the best safety performance in ExxonMobil Chemical, with only one OSHA recordable (TRIR=0.35). Since then, this company has reached zero or injury-free for several years.

I've seen numerous companies improve their safety performance substantially with processes based on the principles of People-Based Safety, but this plant holds the record for getting everyone involved and obtaining exceptional results. I'm convinced a key factor in this outstanding success was the employee's "choice" in the development, implementation, and maintenance of the process. These people own their behavioral observation and feedback process because they have applied people-based principles their way.

Here's what I mean:

There is no best way to implement a behavior observation and coaching process; rather, the principles and procedures need to be tailored to fit the work culture. And the most efficient way to make this happen is to involve employees in customizing the process.

At this ExxonMobil Chemical facility, the entire work force learned the relevant people-based principles detailed in Chapters 2 and 3 of this book by participating in ten one-hour small-group sessions spaced over a six-month period. The sessions were facilitated by other employees who had received more intensive training.

Taking Ownership

During these group sessions, employees discussed specific strategies for implementing a plant-wide behavioral monitoring and coaching process. They also entertained ways to overcome barriers to total participation and sustain the process over the long term. Eventually, they designed a process that includes employee choice at its very core. Although some specifics of the process have changed since its inception in 1992, the choice aspect remains a constant.

This is how the ExxonMobil Chemical process played to the power of choice: At the start of the implementation, employees scheduled a monthly behavioral observation and feedback session with two other employees who serve as observers. That is, they selected the task, day, and time for the coaching session, as well as the two individuals who would observe their performance and give them immediate and specific feedback regarding safe and at-risk behaviors. Employees chose their observers (and coaches) from anyone in the plant.

At the start of this process, the number of volunteer safety coaches was limited to about 30 percent of the work force as potential safety coaches. Why? It was a matter of personal choice. This freedom facilitated employee involvement, ownership, and trust.

At first, some employees did not have complete trust in the process and resisted active participation. Some tried to "beat the system" by scheduling their observation and feedback sessions at inactive times when chances of an at-risk behavior were minimal, such as watching a monitor or completing paperwork.

Most employees were certainly mindful and "on their toes" when the observers arrived at the scheduled times. They were primed for constructive feedback and advice from the observers they had selected. Still, many people – whether observing or being observed – were surprised that many at-risk behaviors occurred in situations where employees knew the safe operating procedures and knew they were being observed.

After experiencing and trusting the process, most employees at this facility scheduled their coaching sessions during active times when the probability of an at-risk is highest. Frequently, the observed individual pointed out an at-risk behavior necessitated by the particular work environment or procedure – a difficult-to-reach valve, a hose-checking procedure too cumbersome for one auditor, a walking surface made slippery by an equipment leak, or a difficult-to-adjust machine guard.

Many employees have chosen to use their observation and feedback process to demonstrate that some at-risk behaviors are necessitated by equipment design or maintenance and by environmental conditions or operating procedures. This has often led to improvements in conditions or procedures. Today, almost 15 years since the facility started this behavioral coaching process, the periodic observation and feedback sessions are unannounced, and every employee serves as an observer and a coach.

Familiar Feelings

If you reflect on your own life circumstances, you'll quickly see how a sense of choice or personal control makes you more motivated, involved, and committed. We've all experienced the pleasure of having alternatives to choose from and feeling in control of those factors critical for success. How sweet is the taste of success when we can attribute it to our own doing.

Of course we're not always in control of critical events or ongoing circumstances. This contributes to those familiar feelings of frustration, discomfort, and distress that come from being at the mercy of circumstances or other people's decisions.

The message is clear. Give people the power to choose safety procedures consistent with the right principles and the result will be motivation, involvement, and ownership. This might require management changes. Be ready to relinquish some top-down control; abandon a desire for the "quick fix"' change; switch from focusing on outcomes to recognizing process achievements; and give people opportunities to choose, evaluate, and refine their means to achieve the ends. The result will be perceptions of personal control and self-effectiveness – notable distinctions of an empowered work force.

We can't control everything.

PART 5

Minding Your Own Business

When we work alone, we need to hold ourselves accountable, and that takes a sense of personal responsibility. How do we do it? What will make us go out of our way for our own safety?

Interpersonal safety coaching isn't relevant here. But the very essence of behavior-based safety is used for a process I call safety self-management. It's a way of getting people to act themselves into feeling more personally responsible for their own safety, to actively care about workplace safety and health when no one is around to hold them accountable. Here are ten techniques for managing your own safety:

1) Observe and record your own behavior

Managing your own safety starts with self-knowledge. Develop a checklist with a number of critical safety-related behaviors to observe while you work. Every time an opportunity for a particular target behavior occurs, simply judge whether your behavior was safe or at-risk, and mark the "safe" or "at-risk" column of your checklist. At the end of a day or week, total up the number of safe and at-risk occurrences for each behavior to calculate a "percent safe" score. An "overall percent safe" can be calculated from these totals. Then chart your performance on a graph to track daily or weekly fluctuation.

Lone workers hold themselves accountable.

Recording and charting "percent safe" scores will significantly improve your personal safety because it gets you involved; you become accountable to yourself. Still, you'll discover that a few at-risk behaviors occur more frequently. They become the targets of your self-management process.

2) Analyze the activator-behavior-consequence sequence

As explained in Chapter 2, a key principle of People-Based Safety™ is that actions are directed by activators or events preceding behavior and are motivated by consequences or events following behavior. During your self-observation and recording process, note activators and consequences relevant to the behaviors on your checklist. You might be able to remove activators or consequences that encourage or reward at-risk behavior. Or you might be able to add activators or consequences to increase certain safe behaviors.

3) Take control of activators

Posters, signs, and other reminders are the most popular activators for safety. But only a small portion of the many activators we see each day actually influences our behavior. We're often in a state of information overload where we either don't notice or ignore many activators. Still, we can place a few activators in strategic locations as reminders. Or we can tell ourselves to pay attention to certain activators that encourage safe behavior or discourage particular at-risk behavior.

The most powerful activators make us aware of the consequences of our actions, either positive or negative outcomes. Sometimes a picture is all you need. Then write your own caption to make the activator more personal and compelling. Personally written or spoken statements are activators that both instruct and influence your perception and beliefs.

Strategically placed activators can be critical reminders.

4) Cue your own performance

If you say to yourself, "I buckle up to set a safe example; my behavior could influence anyone who sees me, especially a family member; and I don't want anyone to think I'm irresponsible about personal safety," you are likely to buckle up. Notice that this self-dialogue includes specific instructions, and expresses a belief about the value of setting an example that provides a strong rationale for performing safely. Note, too, how your beliefs influence your perception or interpretation of personal events.

Observations can shed light on your true beliefs. What does it say about your safety beliefs if you catch yourself speeding, or taking a calculated shortcut? You might find you're not being entirely truthful when you say safety is one of your core values. Perhaps you'll discover an inconsistency between something you value and the way you act. This can motivate you to make a behavioral adjustment.

5) Reward yourself

Research shows that individuals who reward themselves are more likely to sustain a self-management process and improve their own performance.[7] Three factors determine the effect of these rewards: selection, delivery, and timing.

First, personalize your reward. The possibilities are endless. We could be talking about opportunities to exercise, eat certain foods, spend money, attend an entertaining event, watch television, or say to yourself with pride, "I did it." It's a matter of giving yourself an opportunity to do something enjoyable after you've done something that is less fun but important for your own improvement.

Base your rewards on specific behavior, not affirmations or good intentions. Observe your behavior systematically and reward yourself according to the criteria you define. The reward should come as soon as possible after the target behavior occurs.

6) Set SMART goals

Rewards should be directed at a "SMART" goal – one that is Specific, Motivational, Achievable, Relevant, and Trackable as explained in Chapter 2. At first, give yourself rewards to recognize small steps of progress toward the goal. During the early stages of self-management it's often useful to reward yourself for just participating in the process. In one self-management project, for example, a woman rewarded herself by adding $1 to her vacation fund each day she completed her self-observing and recording. Later she only rewarded herself when her target behavior improved. Continuous improvement occurred by successively requiring more behavior for the $1 reward.

Eventually, one SMART goal was reached, and then another, more challenging SMART goal was set.

7) Chart progress and celebrate your success

SMART goals are potent self-motivators because they are stated in a way that enables you to objectively monitor your own progress. When a specified level of achievement is reached, you should celebrate. It can be a personal celebration, perhaps as simple as giving yourself a pat on the back. Better yet, give yourself one of those opportunities for some personal pleasure.

Involving other people in your celebration is even more effective. Tell others about your efforts at managing your own safety and invite them to help you celebrate. If you tell others that you intend to improve certain target behaviors, the likelihood that you will actually improve increases.

8) Make a commitment

When you publicly commit to doing something, you create both internal and external pressures to follow through. So make a formal commitment to improve your own safety. You can do this by:

- Signing and publicly displaying a simple promise card that states your intention to participate in a self-management process and reach a certain safety-improvement goal; or
- Signing an interpersonal contract with a friend or coworker that specifies the safety-related behavior you wish to improve and includes a brief outline of your plan for accomplishing this goal.

There are numerous benefits of involving others in your self-management work. They can hold you accountable to initiate and maintain your efforts and encourage you to keep going. Plus, they can make a celebration more reinforcing.

9) Enlist social support

You can get invaluable encouragement from a work culture where employees trust each other's abilities and intentions and feel a sense of belonging and interdependency. You'll be more willing to accept personal responsibility for your own safety when you believe your coworkers genuinely want you to improve.

When you take control of managing your safety, you create a supportive social context for yourself. You look for others who might appreciate your personal commitment and enlist support from supervisors, coworkers, friends, or family members who you know care.

10) Use imagery

Mental imagery is using your "mind's eye" to picture situations without actually being there. It's a way to anticipate and prepare for events. It can be used to direct behavior (as an activator), and to motivate behavior (as a consequence). In fact, mental imagery can be very useful in increasing personal responsibility for safety in the absence of a formal self-management project. In the next part of this chapter, I talk more about this safety improvement technique.

PART 6
Using Our Mind's Eye

Mental imagery is using our "mind's eye" to picture situations without actually being there. It's something we do every day.

When we look forward to a particular event, for instance, we use imagery. Picturing pleasant consequences can lead to excitement, even an emotional high. In contrast, imagining negative outcomes can evoke fear. In fact, one of the most effective ways to relieve distress or anxiety is to visualize yourself in a serene and relaxing setting (like lying on a sandy beach and hearing the calming rhythm of the ocean waves, and feeling the warm sun and cool breeze). On the other hand, your vacation on a sandy beach can be ruined by a mental image of work stressors.

When you think about the behavioral steps or procedures needed to complete a task, you're using mental images to rehearse the job. Before their performances, athletes practice their sport mentally, actors run through their lines and stage positions in their mind's eye, surgeons mentally rehearse the steps of a complex operation, and musicians imagine playing or singing the right notes on key and on time. Public speakers often practice their lines mentally just prior to their actual delivery.

Research has shown significant benefits of mental rehearsal, whether

A mental image can ruin a vacation.

practicing an athletic skill, an occupational task, or a script of dialogue.[8] It's not clear whether the mental rehearsal actually strengthens the correct behavior or merely increases one's motivation to perform at a higher level. We don't know why mental rehearsal improves performance, only that it does. The more vividly individuals can imagine themselves performing desired behaviors, the greater the beneficial impact of this technique on actual performance. Now what does all this mean for safety and injury prevention at home and in the workplace?

Making the Connection

I could not find any research on the effects of imagery on safety-related behavior. But given the variety of performance behaviors that have benefited from this practice, it's obviously a useful tool to prevent injury. We can mentally rehearse images to anticipate and prepare for tasks. Imagery can direct our behavior (as an activator) or motivate our behavior (as a consequence). For safety self-management you can use imagery to:

- Clarify your safety goals.
- Enhance your motivation to choose the safest behavior.
- Build your self-efficacy, personal control, or optimism.
- Rehearse safe acts and actively caring behaviors.
- Reward yourself for success at self-management.

Imaging consequences motivates behavior.

Your imagery can activate a chain of safe operating procedures, as well as motivate action. Motivation comes from imagining potential consequences following safe versus at-risk behavior. For example, visualizing a possible injury from using a chainsaw can motivate the use of personal protective equipment. The image can also suggest the safe behavior needed to avoid injury, making it directing and motivating.

It's often more useful to create a mental picture of positive consequences resulting from your safe actions. Focusing on positive outcomes can increase your confidence in being successful, as well as increase your desire to reach your goals.

Here's how to use mental imagery to manage your own safety:

- See yourself performing the appropriate safe behavior with ease and convenience;
- Visualize avoiding specific negative consequences with the safe behavior;
- Imagine feelings of accomplishment following the safe behavior;
- Take an active rather than passive perspective;
- Share your imagery with others to get their support and perhaps increase their safe behavior.

It's important to be active in your image. Don't sit back and watch a movie starring yourself. Imagine yourself acting within the complete activator-behavior-consequence (ABC) framework. First, see the activators in the situation that cue your desired behavior. Then visualize yourself actually performing the safe acts. Finally, imagine positive feelings from setting the safe example and acknowledging safety as a value.

Before mentally picturing this ABC sequence, I find it quite motivating to visualize the negative consequence of getting hurt. Reaching for a skill saw, I imagine getting a finger caught in the blade. I imagine the ringing in my ears getting worse after not using hearing protection. All too often I imagine one of my two daughters in a vehicle crash. Such negative imagery might be too morbid for you, but it sure motivated me to assure my family believed in vehicle safety belts and always used them.

I like to share my motivating imagery with others, too. In fact, one reason personal testimonies of injuries or near hits are powerful motivators is because listeners can get a powerful mental image. They can readily visualize the speaker in the precarious situation described, especially if the presenter gives a passionate and realistic delivery. Even more motivating is when listeners imagine themselves or a family member in the place of the speaker. Of course, it's essential to focus on the specific behaviors that can be performed to avoid the injury or near hits discussed.

People can have contrary images.

My point here is that it can be useful to share personal experiences in ways that conjure up a motivating image. Sometimes, though, people imagine a situation differently. The figure illustrates what I mean, and it shows again how imagined consequences can influence ongoing behavior. In this case, the passenger should share her image with the driver. But this might not change the driver's behavior, if his imagery paints a contrary picture. I see a possibility for interpersonal conflict, don't you?

To Summarize

The right kind of mental imagery can motivate us to assume increased personal responsibility for the safety of ourselves and others. We can rehearse mentally the safe way to complete a job, and thus increase the likelihood the job will be accomplished both safely and efficiently.

We can also teach others how to use mental pictures to prevent injuries. Let's encourage personal testimonials of injuries or near hits that could have been prevented by certain action. We need to hold ourselves accountable for using and teaching this effective safety self-management technique.

PART 7

Build Your Belief System

Do you try to influence self-efficacy, response-efficacy, and outcome-expectancy to improve safety in your workplace? What?

Let me explain these psychological terms because they determine whether a person feels empowered. First, when you promote "can do" self-talk toward safety, you're promoting self-efficacy. Numerous studies have shown that people with strong "can do" thinking demonstrate greater ability and motivation to solve problems at work. And they have better health and safety habits.[9]

But it's not enough to convince yourself and others we "can do" safety. People must believe their safety plan will be effective. This is called response-efficacy.

Finally, people must believe safety is worth the effort. This is outcome-expectancy.

So how do you instill these three keys to safety participation in your self and others?

Building Skills

As discussed in the prior chapter, The Coaching of People-Based Safety, interpersonal feedback is critical for skills building. People-based coaching builds confidence and competence by detailing specific steps for: 1) observing and analyzing another person's behaviors; 2) delivering supportive and corrective feedback; 3) developing an improvement plan; and 4) obtaining commitment for change and follow-up.

But effective safety

Negative thinking can lead to negative behaviors.

coaches need more than these skills to possess that "can do" thinking of self-efficacy. People may be competent, but not confident in their coaching abilities. It takes practice and feedback over time to develop the sense of mastery that usually leads to self-efficacy.

Please note that self-efficacy is not the same as self-esteem, though these beliefs tend to influence each other. Self-esteem reflects a general sense of self-worth, as in, "I am valuable." Self-efficacy refers to feeling successful or competent at a particular task. Self-esteem remains rather constant across situations. Self-efficacy is task-focused and can vary markedly from one circumstance to another.

But even when employees have both self-efficacy and adequate skills to execute their safety plan, they won't do it unless they believe their plan will work – response-efficacy.

Proving the Payoff

It's not enough to know what to do and have the confidence to do it. You can have the skills and self-efficacy to perform safety coaching, for example, but you will not actually coach on a regular basis unless you believe the coaching process actually improves safety. So how do you convince yourself and others a certain safety technique will pay off?

The most common approach is to use statistics that show significant improvement as a result of a particular safety strategy. But people don't necessarily relate to these numbers. It's better to get more personal when trying to "sell" the value of a safety process to a work force.

Research on risk perception, for example, has shown that people get more concerned or outraged about an issue when individual case studies are used in lieu of group statistics.[10] That's why politicians like to point out specific individuals in their audiences when trying to gain support for a particular issue or plan.

Personal testimonies provide a powerful image. Listeners can relate to an individual's story and put themselves in the same situation. Two kinds of testimonies can increase response-efficacy: 1) a personal account of an injury that could have been prevented by the safety technique; and, 2) an anecdote about someone who avoided injury by using the particular strategy or safety process.

But Is It Worth It?

We might believe we can do something for safety. We also might believe that what we do will have a positive effect. But we won't get involved unless we also believe the outcome is worth working for.

In safety, for example, a group might believe their safety record is good enough, given that they see very few coworkers getting seriously injured. The potential gain from an inconvenient safety process might seem too small to justify the amount of extra effort required.

Remember, too, that most people see the probability of getting hurt as minuscule. As a result, the need to participate in a safety effort can seem insignificant.

Consequences keep us going – I've mentioned this many times throughout this book. One of B. F. Skinner's most important legacies is the principle that we motivate ourselves to do or not do something by anticipating what positive consequences we expect to gain from our participation – and/or what negative consequences we expect to avoid.[11]

So to build outcome-expectancy – the belief that the consequences are worth your effort – I suggest again "selling" with a case study rather than statistics. You could show, for example, the details of a single injury that occurred in your plant. Explain how an intervention like the one being taught could have prevented that incident.

Part of your "selling" should be to get people to see the bigger picture.

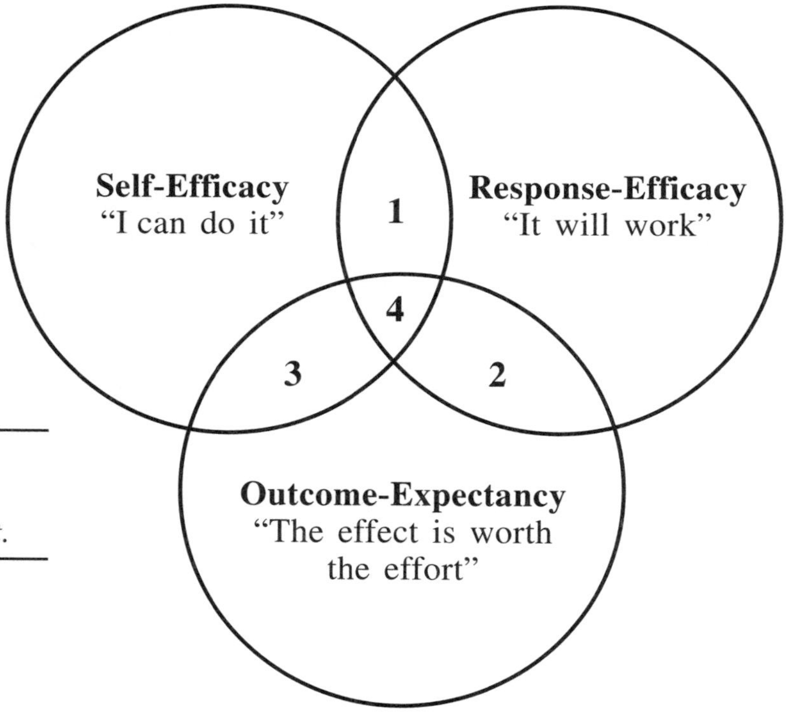

Three beliefs determine empowerment.

1. I can do it and it will work.
2. I'm motivated to make it work.
3. I can and want to do it.
4. I want to make a difference.

Move them away from the individualistic "it-won't-happen-to-me" mindset. You want to develop systems thinkers who take a wider view, and recognize that someone will benefit from large-scale participation in your safety process.

Appeal to people's caring for themselves, their families, and their coworkers. When people see the bigger picture and adopt a "collective community" perspective, they realize their participation in a safety process will eventually benefit someone in their workplace. And you'll find this belief – that it is meaningful to work for the potential benefit of others – in turn fuels self-efficacy and response-efficacy.

Pop psychologists and motivational speakers are right. Beliefs and self-talk are important in determining success. But we need to go beyond self-affirmation or self-confidence and self-talk to meet the challenges of workplace safety. Inspiring the three beliefs I've discussed in this article – both in yourself and others – defines true empowerment. They are key to maximizing participation, personal responsibility, and success in a safety process.

About "Self-Efficacy"

There is empirical and theoretical support for the assertion that believing you can do something is the first step toward doing it. The academic term for this belief is "self-efficacy," and it has been the topic of many research articles and theoretical proposals. Most notable is Albert Bandura's 1997 book titled, simply, *Self-Efficacy*.[12] Here, in 604 pages of fine print, the author makes a strong case for self-efficacy being the most central and critical concept in applied psychology. The main features of this concept are self-efficacy, response-efficacy, and outcome-expectancy.

PART 8
Thinking and Long-Term Behavior Change

Why do people often revert to risky ways after being lectured about safety? Why do the goggles come off or the earplugs come out after you leave the area?

This is one of safety's ongoing challenges: How do you sustain safe behavior without constant supervision? I want to compare direct versus indirect approaches to influence behavior – and I hope to convince you that the indirect approach is usually more effective.

The Direct Approach

Advertisers use direct persuasion by showing us people using their products and enjoying positive consequences or avoiding negative ones. They apply the ABC contingency of behavior analysis to sell their wares. The activator ("A") announces the availability of a reinforcing consequence ("C") if the purchasing behavior is performed ("B").

Advertisers also apply research-based principles from social psychology to make their messages more persuasive. Social scientists have shown advantages in using highly credible communicators, so we see sales pitches often given by authority figures.[13]

But these attempts at direct persuasion do not ask for a significant change in behavior. Normally, the purpose of an ad message is to persuade a consumer to select a certain brand of merchandise. This boils

The ABC Model is used to sell.

down to merely choosing one commodity over another.

Safety-related behavior is usually more inconvenient and requires more effort than switching brands at a supermarket. It often requires a significant adjustment to an ingrained routine at work, at home, or on the road.

Here's my point: Direct persuasion is frequently not the best approach to increase safety-related behavior or promote long-term participation in a safety process. Direct attempts to persuade people to make challenging changes in their lifestyle usually yield disappointing outcomes. Communication strategies have generally been unsuccessful when designed to persuade smokers to quit smoking, drivers to stop speeding, bigoted individuals to cease prejudicial behavior, homeowners to conserve water, or sexually active people to use condoms.[14]

I can quote rigorous research to support each of these failures of direct persuasion. But you probably don't need research results to convince you the direct approach has its limits when applied to safety. Your own experience has likely been the best teacher here.

The problem with direct persuasion is that it's direct. It comes across as someone else's idea. And it can give the impression the desired behavior is primarily for someone else's benefit.

The Indirect Approach

These days many safety professionals have learned from experience the best way to increase safety involvement is to allow the workforce to have substantial control and authority over desired safety procedures. Increasing choice, ownership, and empowerment reflect indirect persuasion. You're not telling people what to do in order to remain safe. Rather, you're giving people the knowledge, tools, and resources to implement a particular process that will help keep them safe.

The problem with direct persuasion is that it's direct. It comes across as someone else's idea.

I realize all of this empowerment stuff is easier said than done. But surely you see advantages to this way of motivating long-term participation. It enables a reciprocal relationship between behavior and self-perception, which facilitates self-persuasion and increases the probability of a sustained effort.

Research has shown safety participation and performance can be improved by creating a link between overt behavior and self-perception. Remember, how we behave influences how we think about and define subsequent behavior. This is self-directed behavior, and it can persist without external control.

Self-persuasion is more likely to occur when the motivational strategy is less direct, less obvious. For example, behavioral research has shown that compliments are more powerful when they are more indirect than direct.[16] Have you ever been flattered by someone's compliment and thought, "That person is only trying to get something from me"? But if a friend shares with you what another person said about your special talents it tends to have more influence on your self-perception. Why? Because the direct approach is tainted by the possibility of an ulterior motive.

Indirect persuasion deviates significantly from the standard direct and top-down method of obtaining compliance with safety regulations. Both approaches might be equally effective at motivating behavior change, but the indirect approach will be far more successful at enhancing the kind of internal dialogue or thinking needed to maintain behavior when people have only themselves to hold them accountable.

PART 9

Create Internal Tension

Focusing on awareness is the typical educational approach used in safety to change behaviors and attitudes. For example, you raise awareness by giving employees a clear and persuasive rationale about the need to wear safety glasses and hearing protection in certain work areas.

It's also common to combine awareness and commitment. Employees receive the convincing rationale and then publicly sign a pledge card, for instance, promising to wear PPE under specified circumstances for one month.

You would expect more PPE use with the awareness-plus-commitment approach than with awareness alone. When people make a public statement to do something, they encounter both personal and social pressures to follow through. The power of public commitment is tied to the consistency principle – a tool of influence lying deep within us, directing our actions (and reflecting) our motivation to be and appear consistent.

Now evidence suggests that a third method, combining commitment and the "hypocrisy effect," is most influential in bringing about desired changes. In this case, people publicly commit to a certain safety action (to wear safety glasses and earplugs, for example). Then they list situations when they should wear eye and hearing protection but don't, such as when mowing the grass in their back yards.

Here I explain the hypocrisy effect and why you should test it in your safety efforts.

Examining the Evidence

Let's start with the empirical evidence. Elliot Aronson, one of the world's most honored social psychologists, and his students conducted a series of experiments to demonstrate the power of combining commitment with a procedure that reminded participants of their hypocrisy – inconsistencies between their commitment and their prior behavior.[17] Targeted behavior in these experiments focused on AIDS prevention, water conservation, and resource recycling.

Participants first made a public commitment to take a certain course of action and then completed an exercise that reminded them of their failures to perform according to their commitment. In all three studies, the hypocrisy exercise led to more desired behavior – use of condoms, shorter showers and more recycling – than awareness or commitment approaches.

Explaining the Effect

How can the hypocrisy effect be explained? Why does this kind of intervention influence more behavior change than standard awareness and commitment procedures?

Let's return to the consistency principle. Given a person's desire to keep his words in line with his actions and vice versa, having people remind themselves of an inconsistency between what they say they will do and what they actually do leads to internal conflict or tension. Social psychologists call this "cognitive dissonance."[18]

This internal tension is not a pleasant state. It challenges one's personal integrity. How do you reduce this tension and restore a sense of integrity? Easy – simply change your behavior to make it consistent with your commitment.

You might want to use a hypocrisy exercise the next time you attempt to motivate people to follow certain safety procedures. Remember, evoking internal tension by reminding people their personal commitment is inconsistent with their past actions leads to more desired behavior change than a standard awareness or commitment intervention.

Three Methods for Changing Self-Talk and Behavior

1. **Awareness** – employees receive a clear and persuasive rationale about the need to wear safety glasses and hearing protection in a certain work area.

2. **Awareness + Commitment** – employees receive the convincing rationale and then publicly sign a pledge card, promising to wear this PPE under specified circumstances for one month.

3. **Commitment + Hypocrisy** – employees publicly sign the pledge card to wear safety glasses and earplugs and then develop a list of situations in which they should wear this PPE but don't, such as when mowing the grass in their back yard.

Stirring Up Feelings

I'm sure you can think of various ways to use this technique to increase participation in safety-improvement efforts. Simply ask people to commit publicly to do something for safety, and then ask them to think of times when their behavior has been inconsistent with their commitment. Your objective is to stir up self-talk of being hypocritical or inconsistent.

Of course, you need to obtain the initial commitment, and that could be a challenge in some situations. However, I've found it easy to get people to state openly that they hold safety as a "core value." It's common for workers to admit that the greatest reward for supporting a safety initiative is to go home in one piece and to see their coworkers do the same.

Safety must be a core value, not just a priority. Try facilitating a discussion that leads to participants publicly voicing their commitment to safety as a core value. This might be enough to establish a context for the hypocrisy effect. Next, ask people who claim safety as a value to make a list of things they do in their work areas that are inconsistent with holding safety as a value.

Testing Ideas

Many questions arise from this exercise:

- Should the list of inconsistencies be private or public?
- Suppose it's possible to create group tension by obtaining group consensus that safety is a value, and then listing specific behaviors observed by group members that are inconsistent with safety as a value. Would this exercise lead to a group hypocrisy effect? Would team members be motivated to reduce collective tension by adjusting their personal and interpersonal behaviors? And would this group exercise be more efficient and effective at improving safety-related behavior than the individual approach used in the research literature?
- How long will the beneficial behavioral impact of the hypocrisy effect last?

Since no safety research has tested the hypocrisy effect, we are left with critical empirical questions with no answers. These questions can't be answered until intervention ideas such as I've described here are attempted and evaluated. So what's holding you back? Test the hypocrisy effect, and document your findings. We have so much to learn about ways to prevent workplace injuries.

PART 10
Thinking and Personality

During my 35 years of university teaching, I've noticed some students possess a "need to achieve," while others portray a "need to avoid failure."

Failure avoiders study only minimally to avoid failure and are not "happy campers." Those who "work to achieve" enjoy my class much more. They view it as an opportunity to earn a good grade, even an opportunity to learn.

This dichotomy of working to achieve versus working to avoid failure is based on classic research conducted in the 1950s and 1960s by Richard Atkinson and David McClelland.[19] Atkinson's original theory identified four types of individuals: success seekers, overstrivers, failure avoiders, and failure accepters. All four exhibit personality states that influence your self-talk and the outcome of your safety efforts.[20]

Success seekers are the most desirable participants in your safety improvement plans. These individuals show the highest levels of self-efficacy, personal control, and optimism and are more likely to actively care for the safety and health of others. With the high expectancy for success and low fear of failure, success seekers respond to setbacks with optimistic persistence, self-assurance, and a sense of personal control.

It's generally better to be an overstriver than a failure avoider or failure accepter, but the high fear of failure among overstrivers leads to self-doubt. These individuals experience high levels of distress, low perceptions of personal control, and unstable self-esteem.

As you can imagine, failure avoiders have low expectations for success and thus avoid challenges. They are unsure of themselves and are overly anxious and pessimistic about the future.

Optimists plan for success.

Failure accepters are actually better adjusted than failure avoiders. Their acceptance leads generally to apathy, not anxiety. But from an organizational perspective, failure acceptors are least desirable – they have simply given up.

So how would you classify yourself in terms of these four person states? How would you categorize your coworkers? Would you place some people in one category with regard to safety, but in another category when it comes to production or quality? Have you seen people, perhaps yourself, change from one state to another as the result of certain work experiences? Keep in mind that environmental conditions, work contexts, and company cultures determine the number of safety success seekers in an organization.

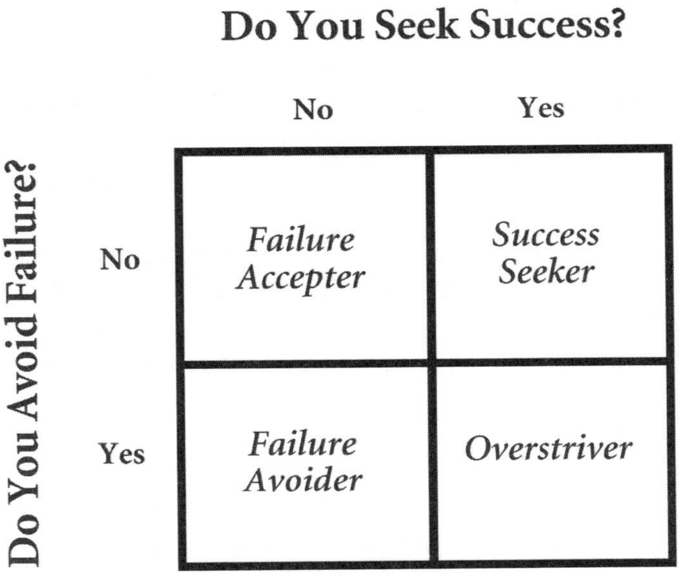

Thinking success or failure affects attitude and behavior.

It's obvious we need to find ways to facilitate success-seeking thinking. The more safety success seekers in your organization, the greater the probability of achieving and maintaining an injury-free workplace. Let's consider ways to increase the number of safety success seekers in a work group.

All About Loss

Traditional safety programs emphasize failure avoidance over positive achievements:

• When the key indices are the number of recordable lost-time injuries, the focus is on avoiding failure.

• Safety rewards or financial bonuses based on "days without an injury" make failure avoidance a primary motivator.

• When companies are ranked according to their OSHA-recordable injury rates, a reactive failure-avoidance stance takes precedence over success seeking.

• If lost-time injuries seem to arouse the most attention to safety, avoiding failure is promoted.

• If management considers "injury investigation" the key job responsibility of the company safety pro, avoiding failure gets priority status.

• When managers summarize safety performance with injury statistics and loss-control numbers, they put clear and obvious emphasis on avoiding failure.

No wonder a failure-avoiding state is often the prominent motivation of workplace safety. And if failures (or injuries) keep occurring in spite of people's best efforts to avoid them, a mindset of "failure acceptance" can develop. Of course, this apathetic and helpless perspective stifles participation in any safety-improvement effort.

Achievement-Based Accountability

The obvious antidote is to focus on safety achievement rather than injury avoidance. Easier said than done, I admit. With quality production, positive consequences are inherent with ongoing work activities. People can usually see evidence of achievement when contributing to the production of a quality commodity or service. Plus, the scoring system for the productivity side of an organization is typically given in achievement terms. Not so for safety.

The only way to put an achievement spin on safety is to define proactive things to do for injury prevention, and then hold people accountable for achieving them. An achievement-based accountability system should put more focus on positive consequences for accomplishment, from interpersonal recognition to group celebrations. Plus, your safety scoring system should be based on proactive measures – activities accomplished to prevent injury.[21]

Think failure and you're less likely to succeed.

Imagine the Alternatives

Imagine a safety meeting that begins with a presentation of various process accomplishments for injury prevention. You might discuss:

- The number of environmental hazards removed;
- Near-hit reports reviewed;
- Safety audits completed;
- Interpersonal observation and feedback sessions conducted;
- Safety suggestions received and implemented; and
- Percentage of safe behaviors observed per work team.

Moreover, imagine the meeting facilitator asking participants to state publicly what they have done for safety since the last meeting. Imagine that work teams are not ranked according to negative-based injury records, but are recognized for what they do to prevent personal injury. And imagine the safety portion of a performance appraisal including a checklist of safety accomplishments rather than total recordable injury rate.

With these transitions from traditional safety, it's not difficult to imagine cultivating an achievement mindset toward safety – and increasing the number of "safety success seekers."

Who Are You?

Those four states (success seeker, overstriver, failure avoider, and failure accepter) were derived from a two-dimensional matrix that categorized people according to whether they work to succeed or avoid failure in a particular situation.

When we work primarily to achieve success, we are 1) "success seekers" as opposed to 2) "failure avoiders" who are motivated by fear of failure. As 3) "overstrivers" we are driven to avoid failure by working in overdrive to succeed. In this state, we are not "happy campers" but experience skepticism, low emotional control, high anxiety, and unstable self-esteem. The 4) "failure accepter" is a person who expects failure regardless of personal effort and is resigned to apathy or indifference

Do you know people who are failure avoiders or failure accepters with regard to workplace safety? How would you classify yourself? Does your classification vary according to the environmental context or the individuals on your work team? Are there more safety success seekers in situations where there is more positive participation for safety?

Wouldn't It Be Nice?

Midway through my safety leadership presentation for NASA (at Langley Air Force Base), my PowerPoint screen went blank. The audience was silent as I tried to solve the problem. As a computer technician reached the front of the room, I noticed the power cord from my laptop was not plugged in. The battery could support only the first 45 minutes of my talk.

When I plugged in the cord, the slide show started up at the very point it had stopped. The audience clapped enthusiastically. I couldn't help but thank everyone for recognizing my success at solving a problem. I also thanked them for not criticizing or complaining when the screen went blank. Then I acknowledged the key point I've just made here. Wouldn't it be nice if in safety we gave more attention to solving safety problems than to reacting negatively after an injury occurs? If we did, we'd increase the number of safety success seekers in our organization and come closer to achieving and sustaining an injury-free workplace.

PART 11

Traits vs. States

I want to make an important distinction between one's propensity to get injured on the job (injury proneness) versus one's willingness to participate actively in safety improvement processes.

Why focus on personality? Over the years in safety, we've tackled the so-called low-hanging fruit by focusing on recognizable risks that can be observed, measured, and controlled. We've used strategies such as ergonomics, machine guarding, and behavior-based safety. But even more injuries can be prevented if personality factors are adequately addressed.

The link between personality and safety has long been a subject of investigation. Piles of research in psychology show that personality factors influence behavior.[22] In the 1950s, researchers avidly sought what they called the "accident prone" personality. Methods of study varied dramatically, and potential explanations for why some people seemed to suffer more injuries than others ranged from chance or "bad luck" to innate personality characteristics or traits. Each of these explanations and their accompanying methodologies were flawed, leading to studies that produced inconsistent or ambiguous results.

Certain personalities suggest injury proneness.

So data linking the control of injuries with personality factors were often misinterpreted, creating miscommunication and confusion among researchers and leading many to scoff at the concept of injury proneness.

The Problem with Proneness

Injury proneness is determined largely by internal or dispositional factors that are difficult to assess reliably. Injury proneness is more likely a trait (relatively permanent and difficult to change) than a state (such as a passing mood). Personality traits are more or less determined by the time a person reaches adolescence and are often the result of a mixture of genetics and early experiences.

Strategies to change one's personality traits will usually be ineffective. Still, by gaining an understanding of these traits, job training can be tailored and job duties redefined to accommodate and capitalize on individual differences.

Personality states on the other hand can be addressed more directly. For example, situations controlled by the management of an organization and by relationships with managers and employees can influence a person's willingness to contribute his time and effort toward a safety improvement process. In this case, we're talking about a personality state that fluctuates according to behavioral context or climate.

Here's the bottom line: it makes more sense to design environmental and behavioral interventions to get more people involved in a safety-improvement campaign than to attempt to change an individual's personal proneness to get injured.

The figure at right depicts this distinction between propensity for injury and willingness to participate in an injury-prevention effort. The labels given the four categories defined by the 2 x 2 matrix reflect the relative risk of injury to four different personality types. Where would you place yourself?

The safest individuals are those who are not injury prone and do whatever they can to prevent an injury. The most unsafe employees are those who do not take precautionary measures and are injury prone. Appropriate intervention strategies can move an "externally at-risk" individual into the

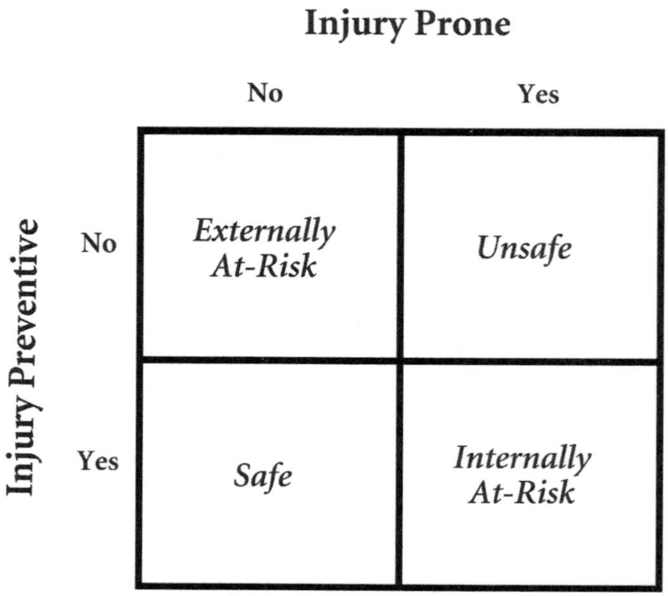

Personality affects injury proneness and injury preventiveness.

safe category, but it's unlikely an external technique can be successful in advancing an "internally at-risk" person to the safe classification.

Working with Personality States

Let's consider a few personality characteristics regarding this classification system. As a personality trait, anxiety probably influences both injury proneness and injury preventiveness. Plus, certain situations can activate an anxiety state and increase the probability of the kind of thinking and behavior that puts people at risk for personal injury.

It makes more sense to intervene to get people involved in safety (focusing on personality states) than to try to change an individual's injury-proneness (based on personality traits).

This change in state would presumably affect every participant in that setting and would not be considered injury proneness as a unique personality factor. In this case, the at-risk state could be eliminated by alterations of external or situational variables. We call this an injury preventive intervention. An anxiety state could also increase the perceived need for prevention and motivate intervention participation.

So from a personality or safety-identity perspective, person states are most relevant for injury prevention. They can be changed by an intervention process, and they reflect one's willingness to participate in such a process.

In contrast, injury proneness is more relevant to personality traits than states, and is relatively immutable to external intervention.

Factors to Consider

Some personality factors have greater impact on injury prevention than injury proneness. The four success/failure categories I discussed previously in this chapter – failure accepter, failure avoider, success seeker and overstriver – influence people's motivational state and thus their desire to participate in a prevention effort.

Likewise, optimists and people who perceive a high level of personal control (termed "internals") are more likely to be injury preventive than pessimists and "externals" (or those with relatively low expectations of personal control).

Still, because of their greater expectations of personal control and positive outcomes, internals and optimists might take more risks and thus be relatively

Optimists participate in injury-prevention efforts.

injury prone. And so these personality factors can influence one's propensity for both preventing – and experiencing – personal injury, resulting in no net gain for safety.

Obviously, we've just cracked the surface in showing how the variety of personality characteristics can impact one's predisposition for personal injury and for voluntary participation in an injury-prevention program. The role of optimism and personal control were briefly mentioned, but numerous other personal dimensions are relevant, including belongingness, self-efficacy, introversion/extroversion, perceptions of invulnerability, conscientiousness, need for approval, impulsivity, and emotional intelligence.

I hope I have furthered your understanding of the role personality plays in your safety and health efforts. It's a complex subject but worth your attention. Understanding the differences between personality traits and states helps you best select targets for your safety interventions and to develop interventions to improve safety-related thinking and acting.

PART 12

Entitlement Thinking

I want to explore the perceptions of wage workers as they relate to safety thinking. Let me begin with my premise: The way most wage workers are compensated in U.S. industry encourages entitlement thinking. And this hinders acceptance of personal responsibility for optimizing performance, including safety.

Problems with entitlement thinking have occurred to me for many years, but I never linked wage contingencies to this human condition until reading a thoughtful book by William B. Abernathy.[23] What do I mean by "entitlement thinking" and how can such a mindset hinder safety performance?

The illustration below includes a brief assessment tool psychologists have used to measure degree of entitlement thinking in individuals. Research with this scale has shown entitlement thinking to be a relative stable personality trait that can predict specific behaviors.[24]

In the following section, please respond to the following nine items using the number that best reflects your own beliefs. Use the following seven-point Likert scale, ranging from 1 (strong disagreement) to 7 (strong agreement).

1. I honestly feel I'm just more deserving than others.
2. Great things should come to me.
3. If I were on the *Titanic*, I would deserve to be on the first lifeboat!
4. I demand the best because I'm worth it.
5. I do not necessarily deserve special treatment.
6. I deserve more things in my life.
7. People like me deserve an extra break now and then.
8. Things should go my way.
9. I feel entitled to more of everything.

These questions assess entitlement thinking.

Comforts Are Inevitable?

As a human dynamic, "entitlement thinking" is a belief that basic personal comforts are natural and inevitable, even owed to people. In other words, regardless of individual effort, people believe they deserve to have their basic needs met – they are "entitled."

Does this sound like Marxist communism or socialism?

Does this perspective seem contrary to the capitalistic work ethic on which American industry was founded?

While you might disagree that such entitlement thinking permeates our culture, it is reasonable to assume that this perspective can stifle personal responsibility to achieve peak performance. And we can't deny the existence of certain societal contingencies that encourage entitlement thinking. I'm not picking on welfare, retirement, or work compensation programs in this regard, although a case could be made that aspects of these social systems encourage entitlement thinking.

Instead, let's consider a much more serious and large-scale contributor to an entitlement perspective – the way many are paid for their work.

Entitlement Pay

Yes, the low minimum wage (currently $5.15 per hour) creates hardship for many workers.[25] But how about the fact that most wage workers are paid for their time, not for behavior or performance results?

It doesn't matter how well the worker performs; the compensation is the same. Furthermore, increases in one's hourly pay are more often based on time in service (or seniority) than contributions to organizational effectiveness.

As the trite expression goes, "You get what you pay for." Organizations compensate employees for their time, and that's what they get – time on the job. Now I'm reminded of Parkinson's law, experienced by most readers – "Work expands to fill the time available." Don't blame people for this. It's human nature to exert the minimum effort required to obtain desired consequences.

Some people are especially conscientious and go beyond the call of duty. They put in more time than they're paid for, and they do higher quality work than most within the allotted time. Organizations do reward some of these special performers for their dedication and ability to produce exceptional results. They get promoted. More often than not, this involves a transition to a management position in a new industrial setting.

How ironic – the performers achieving the best results at a particular job are promoted to a different job in a new organizational setting. And if these responsible industrial workers are less talented in their new position, it's OK. They still receive an increase in compensation for their time. They're entitled, regardless of their behavior or accomplishments.

Promotions can increase entitlement thinking.

How do the average, less-than-exceptional workers "earn" their pay increases? Of course, we know the answer, because we've all been there. Even if our behavior on the job remains the same, we're entitled to successive increases in pay, right? We call this a "cost-of-living" adjustment.

More irony – we give people a fixed increase in compensation for their time to compensate for inflation, which in turn is caused, in part, by steady increases in compensation. So in order to cover successive wage increases that cannot be absorbed by profits, companies reduce their workforce and outsource.

Entitlement Thinking and Safety

How does entitlement thinking influence participation in safety-related programs? This is a useful topic for conversation. It's likely group discussions will reveal a number of ways an entitlement perspective impacts safety at your facility.

Here are three possibilities:

1) Should employees receive prizes or a financial bonus based on injury statistics?

Such programs may simply reduce the reporting of injuries. But try removing this ineffective approach to motivating safety participation and you'll likely experience entitlement thinking. "You can't do that, we're entitled."

2) Are workers entitled to an optimal "fail-safe" work environment?

I've heard employees use such entitlement thinking as an excuse for not participating in a behavior-based safety process. "Why should we change our behavior when management has not given us the safe environment we deserve?"

Of course, it's important to remove as many environmental hazards as possible and to provide employees with the most comfortable and effective personal protection equipment (PPE) available. But it's often not economically feasible to make work settings "fail safe" and upgrade all PPE. Employees need to take personal responsibility to help themselves and others adjust their behavior so as to keep out of harm's way. Indeed, the safest environment in many situations would replace employees with robotics.

3) Shouldn't employees expect their local safety professional to handle all safety-related concerns and do whatever it takes to keep the organization injury-free?

I bet many safety pros have experienced and bemoaned this entitlement perspective. In a similar view, I've heard workers claim their compliance with safety rules and regulations is all the responsibility they need to accept for injury prevention.

What Can We Do?

In his book *The Sins of Wages*, Bill Abernathy describes a performance-based pay system to substitute for the traditional pay-for-time approach. For most readers, making this kind of change in their organization is beyond their domain of influence. Here are a few alternative strategies, which may be less effective yet are within the personal control of many.

Entitlement thinking is a belief that basic personal comforts are natural and inevitable, even owed to people.

Eliminate management by perception. Unfortunately, most performance appraisals are not objective measures of individual performance. Too often they are based on subjective opinions of such nebulous concepts as "enthusiasm," "self-motivation," and "conscientiousness." If these evaluations were more behavior-based and results-oriented, workers' payment for time would reflect what they actually do on the job. So we should ask for and use objective, performance-based appraisals.[26]

Eliminate management by exception. An easy but ineffective way to manage job performance is to look for mistakes and activate a corrective action plan.

This might direct workers' attention to what they are doing but not to the important stuff – what they are doing well. Plus, it can facilitate a failure-avoidance mindset. As I discussed earlier in this chapter, this mindset is detrimental to a person's self-confidence, personal control, and optimism and ultimately hinders their performance.

Bottom line: Use objective, behavior-based criteria to recognize those who perform well. Do this frequently and consistently. Also, help people experience the natural rewarding consequences of performing their job effectively and safely. This nourishes a success-seeking attitude that can starve entitlement thinking.

Notes

1. Langer, E. J. (1989). *Mindfulness.* Reading, MA: Perseus Books.
2. I use "near hit" instead of the more common term "near miss," because its literal meaning is more relevant.
3. Langer, E. J. (1989). *Mindfulness.* Reading, MA: Perseus Books.
4. Langer, E., & Rodin, J. (1976). The effects of enhanced personal responsibility for the aged: A field experiment in an institutional setting, *Journal of Personality and Social Psychology, 34,* 191-198; Rodin, J., & Langer, E. (1977). Long-term effects of a control-relevant intervention among the institutionalized aged. *Journal of Personality and Social Psychology, 35,* 897-902.
5. Geller, E. S. (1996). *The psychology of safety: How to improve behaviors and attitudes on the job* (Chapter 14). Radnor, PA: Chilton Book Company; Monty, R. A., Geller, E. S., Savage, R. E., & Perlmuter, L. C. (1979). The freedom to choose is not always so choice. *Journal of Experimental Psychology: Human Learning* (1971). Effect of choice on paired associate learning. *Journal of Experimental Psychology, 91,* 47-53.
6. Seligman, M. E. P. (1975). *Helplessness: On depression, development and death.* San Francisco: Freeman.
7. Watson, D. C., & Tharp, R. C. (1997). *Self-directed behavior: Self-modification for personal adjustment.* Seventh Edition. Pacific Grove, CA: Brooks/Cole Publishing.
8. Suinn, R. M. (1993). Imagery. In R. N. Singer, M. Murphey, & L. K. Tennent (Eds.), *Handbook on research in sport psychology* (pp. 492-510). New York: Macmillan; Suinn, R. M. (1997). Mental practice in sport psychology: Where have we been, where do we go? *Clinical Psychology: Science and Practice, 4,* 189-207.
9. Bandura, A. (1997). *Self-efficacy: The exercise of control.* New York: W. H. Freeman and Company; Seligman, M. E. P. (1991). *Learned optimism.* New York: Alfred A. Knopf.
10. Covellow, V. T., Sandman, P. M. & Slovic, P. (1991). Guidelines for communicating information about chemical risks effectively and responsibly. In D. G. Mayo & R. D. Hollander (Eds.) *Acceptable evidence: Science and values in risk management.* (pp. 66-90). New York: Oxford University Press; Slovic, P. (1991). Beyond numbers: A broader perspective in risk perception and risk communication. In D. G. Mayo & R. D. Hollander (Eds.). *Acceptable evidence: Science and values in risk management.* (pp. 66-90). New York: Oxford University Press.
11. Skinner, B. F. (1953). *Science and human behavior.* New York: Free Press.
12. Bandura, A. (1997). The power of self-persuasion. *American Psychologist, 54,* 875-884.
13. Hovland, C. I., & Weiss, W. (1952). The influence of source credibility on communication effectiveness. *Public Opinion Quarterly, 15,* 635-650.
14. Aronson, E. (1999). The power of self-persuasion. *American Psychologist, 54,* 875-884.

15. Bem, D. J. (1972). Self-perception Theory. In L. Berkowitz (Ed.). *Advances in experimental social psychology*. Vol. 6 (pp. 1-60), New York: Academic Press.

16. Allen, J. (1990). *I saw what you did and I know who you are: Bloopers, blunders and success stories on giving and receiving recognition*. Tucker, GA: Performance Management Publications.

17. Aronson, E. (1999). The power of self-persuasion. *American Psychologist, 54,* 875-884; Aronson, E., Fried, C., & Stone, J. (1991). Overcoming denial and increasing the intention to use condoms through the induction of hypocrisy. *American Journal of Public Health, 81*, 1636-1638.

18. Festinger, L. (1957). *A theory of cognition dissonance*. Stanford, CA: Stanford University Press.

19. Atkinson, J. W. (1964). An introduction to motivation. Princeton, NJ: Van Nostrand; McClelland, D. C. (1961). *The achieving society*. Princeton, NJ: Van Nostrand.

20. More details on this typology and its relation to industrial safety are given in Weigand & Geller, E. S. (2005). Connecting positive psychology and organizational behavior management: Achievement motivation and the power of positive reinforcement. *Journal of Organizational Behavior Management*. (in press)

21. For more on proactive measures see Geller, E. S. (2001). *The Psychology of safety handbook*. Boca Raton, FL: CRC Press; and O'Brian, D. P. (2000). *Business measurements for safety performance*. New York: Lewis Publishers.

22. Hough, L. M., & Ones, D. S. (2001). The structure, measurement, validity, and use of personality variables in industrial, work, and organizational psychology. In N. Anderson, D. S. Ones, H. K. Sinangil & C. Viswesvaran (Eds.), *Handbook of Industrial, Work, and Organizational Psychology* (Vol. 1) (pp. 233-277). London: Sage; Roberts, B. Lo. & Hogan, R. (2001). *Personality psychology in the workplace*. Washington, DC: American Psychological Assocation; Roberts, D. S. (2002). Integrating person factors into the OBM framework: Perspectives from a behavioral safety practitioner. *Journal of Organizational Behavior Management, 22*(2), 31-39.

23. Abernathy, W. B. (1996). *The sins of wages*. New York: PerfSys Press.

24. Campbell, W. K., Bonacci, A. M., Shelton, J., Exline, J. J., & Bushman, B. J. (2004). Psychological entitlement: Interpersonal consequences and validation of a self-report measure. *Journal of Personality Assessment, 83,* 29-45.

25. Ehrenreich, B. (2001). *Nickel and dimed: On (not) getting by in America*. New York: Henry Holt and Company, LLC.

26. Drake, J. D. (1997). *Performance appraisal: One more time*. Menlo Park, CA: Crisp Publications, Inc.; Murphy, K. R., & Cleveland, J. N. (1991). *Performance appraisal: An organizational perspective*. Boston: Allyn & Bacon.

CHAPTER FIVE

The *Seeing* of People-Based Safety™

Introduction

Why are people generally underwhelmed, asks Dr. Geller, by risks or safety hazards at work?

It's a matter of perception. Much of the "Seeing" chapter of *People-Based Safety™: The Source* helps you understand the truly remarkable power of perceptions. After all, "Behavior is determined by perceived, rather than actual, risk," writes Dr. Geller.

Increasing workers' perception of personal risk (*Part 1*) is one of the big challenges facing safety leaders. But first, you need to understand how perception works:

• Perceptions can fool us *(Part 2)*. Sometimes we actually are more likely to take risks if we feel protected by safeguards such as safety belts and air bags.

• Perceptions can motivate us *(Part 3)*. For example, people will "see" different meanings in safety mementos such as coffee mugs or baseball caps. It depends on how they relate to the story and emotions behind the memento. Some will be reminded of a personal, safety-related experience or lesson. "Seeing" or perceiving this meaning, they will be emotionally charged to act positively – and safely.

• Perceptions can influence participation in safety activities *(Part 4)*. Many employees want no part of a so-called "accident investigation" because they perceive it to be a witch hunt to find a person to blame for the incident.

• Our perceptive abilities are crucial to uncover the true causes of safety-related incidents *(Part 5)*. Traditional safety "puts the blinders on" and narrowly searches high and low for one root cause. We need a broader perspective. We need to "see" how a variety of possible environmental, behavioral, and personal factors combine interdependently to cause incidents.

• Perceiving a just world *(Part 6)* where people get what they deserve – good and bad – can lead us to blame the victim, a too common occurrence in safety. It can also lead to increased risk-taking, poor incident analysis, and apathy about safety activities.

• Sometimes we are impulsive with our perceptions *(Part 7)*. We rush to judgment based on a too-quick "reading" of a situation. Too often in safety, retraining or discipline is seen as the way to close the gap between the behavior you see and the behavior you want. Be cautious: Socrates said, "A prescription without diagnosis is malpractice."

• Sometimes we find ourselves in a state of "hyper-perception," which actually benefits safety *(Part 8)*. This state is triggered by anxiety. People who have an ongoing internal concern about the safety of themselves and others are more likely to see environmental hazards and remove them, writes Dr. Geller.

Of course, there are more systematic methods for being alert to hazards *(Part 9)*. One way to evaluate and prioritize risks in your workplace is to use "ESP." This takes into account the degree of exposure, potential severity, and probability of occurrence.

Once we grasp how perceptions can both sharpen or dull our ability to recognize risks and we familiarize ourselves with workplace risks using the ESP assessment, we can employ scanning and focusing techniques (*Part 10*).

We can also take steps to ease sensory overload at work (*Part 11*), freeing up our ability to recognize risks. In many workplaces, we are bombarded by messages, slogans, signs, posters, directions, and announcements to the point we simply tune out and turn off.

That's exactly what we can't afford to do at work. We need to take off our blinders (*Part 12*) and use all our relevant senses to recognize what we are doing and where we are doing it. Fully extend your antennae. Fully engage the present – at home, on the road, at work – and you'll make a mishap unlikely, writes Dr. Geller.

Dave Johnson, Editor
Industrial Safety & Hygiene News

PART 1

How We Perceive Risk

Why are people generally underwhelmed, or unimpressed, by risks or safety hazards at work? After all, the high degree of hazard exposure caused by a large work force and many hours of work makes it quite probable someone will eventually be injured on the job. Of course, the use of appropriate protective clothing or equipment can eliminate the possibility of injury in many cases. But many people don't appreciate the value of using personal protective equipment or following safe operating procedures. Why? Their perception of risk is generally much lower than actual risk.

A primary challenge of every safety professional is to increase workers' perceptions of personal risk. This is important because behavior is determined by perceived, rather than actual, risk. How can this be accomplished? Let's see what strategies might arise as we examine the factors that influence perceptions of risk in the workplace.[1]

A Matter of Choice

Hazards we choose to experience (like driving, skiing, and working) are perceived as less risky than hazards we feel forced to endure (like food preservatives, environmental pollution, and earthquakes). Of course, the perception of choice is also subjective, varying dramatically across individuals.

For example, people who feel choice over their residence location (they could move if they wanted to) would likely perceive less risk (and stress) from the nearby nuclear plant or seismic fault. Likewise, employees who feel more choice

Perception affects personal choice and control.

Driving is influenced by past perception.

regarding their place of employment generally perceive less risk in that environment. These individuals are typically more motivated and less distressed.

Familiarity Breeds Complacency

Familiarity is probably a more powerful determinant of perceived risk than choice. The more information and experience we have regarding a risk, the less risk we perceive. Recall how attentive you were to potential hazards when first introduced to the high-tech equipment of your workplace. Remember also how quickly your perceived risk was lowered as the situation became more familiar, and you often adjusted your behavior accordingly. When driving a car, for example, most of us quickly shifted from "both hands on the wheel and no distracting radio or conversation" to "one hand on the wheel, loud radio, and ongoing verbal interaction."

Power of Publicity

It's so easy to forget the familiar hazards of the workplace, and thus safety professionals spend a good deal of their time and effort reminding employees of risks (via memos, newsletters, safety meetings, and signs). On the other hand, professionals sometimes must counter the efforts of unusual, catastrophic, and memorable events, such as explosions and toxic contamination, broadcast by the news media and proliferated in movies. This dramatic publicity influences misperception of actual risk in the workplace.

Sympathy for Victims

Many people feel sympathy for victims of publicized accidents, even vividly visualizing their injuries as if they happen to themselves. By personalizing these experiences, awareness and perceived risk are increased.

This brings up an important point. Employees show much more attention and concern for occupational hazards when injuries or near hits are discussed from a case study approach than when presented in group or collective statistics. The average person can't relate personally to numbers; but a case study presentation gets our attention, especially when the presentation is given by the person who had the experience and when we know the individual. I have met many people who use case studies in lieu of convincing statistics to justify their risky behavior ("The police officer told Uncle Jake he would have been killed if he had been buckled up"; "Aunt Martha is 91 years old and still smokes two packs of cigarettes a day").

The fact that perceived risk is raised more easily with individual case examples than group statistics suggests a shift in presentation style or format for many safety professionals. Safety meetings and intervention strategies should focus on individual experiences rather than numbers. Thus, safety professionals should focus on individual experiences rather than numbers, and safety professionals should solicit personal presentations from victims.

This implies, of course, the company culture encourages self-disclosure and public reporting of close calls and injury experiences. Unfortunately, this approach is stifled by management systems in many companies that emphasize fault-finding rather than fact-finding, piecemeal rather than system approaches to injury investigation, and more enforcement and penalties than recognition and rewards to influence on-the-job behaviors.

Perceived Control

Hazards we can explain and control cause much less alarm than hazards that are not understood and are thus perceived as uncontrollable. Many employee education and training programs explain workplace hazards and give the impression they are controllable. Indeed, safety professionals often state a vision or goal of "zero injuries," implying complete control over the factors that cause injuries. Thus, in the process of convincing people the causes of occupational injuries are understood and controllable (enabling the prevention of all injuries), perceived risk is actually lowered.

Much more subjective risk, dread, and attention are associated with hazards whose ramifications are unknown and uncontrollable (for example, nuclear energy and weapons, radioactive waste, DNA technology, medical x-rays, saccharin, microwave ovens, and natural exposure to radiation, radon, asbestos, and various chemicals).

Perhaps it would be advantageous for safety professionals to admit and publicize that only two of the three types of factors contributing to workplace injuries can be managed effectively (environmental/equipment factors and employee behaviors). The inside, unobservable, and unknown world of people (their attitudes, expectancies, perceptions, and personalities) influence risk of personal injury dramatically, and these cannot be measured, managed, or controlled reliably.

The inside person factors make it impossible to prevent all injuries. Discussing the complexity of people and their integral contribution to most workplace hazards and injuries should increase both the perceived value of ongoing safety interventions, as well as the belief that total employee involvement to achieve a Total Safety Culture is extremely important.

Acceptable Consequences

The benefits of risky work behaviors are obvious to all (from individual comfort, convenience, and work pace to increased group output). The costs of risky work behaviors are improbable and delayed, and thus are generally perceived as less important than the immediate benefits. As a result, risky work practices are often accepted and not perceived to be as risky as they actually are.

Sense of Fairness

Many people believe in a just and fair world, implied by the statement, "What goes around comes around." In other words, we get what we deserve. When hazards or injuries seem unfair, as when a child is molested or inflicted with a deadly disease, special attention is given. This increased attention results in more perceived risk. Thus, it's relatively easy to obtain financial contributions or voluntary assistance for programs that target vulnerable populations (learning-disabled children).

Workplace injuries, on the other hand, are perceived as fair. They are indiscriminately distributed among employees who take risks, and thus deserve what they get. This perception naturally lowers the outrage we feel when someone gets injured on the job. And it can make it difficult to get support for safety programs.

All the factors mentioned here affect whether people react to workplace hazards with alarm, apathy, or something in between. Taken together, they shape personal perceptions of risk and illustrate why the cultivation of an injury-free workplace is so challenging. This justifies more resources for occupational safety and health, and supports the need for strategies to motivate continual employee involvement in the achievement of a Total Safety Culture.

PART 2

Perceptions Can Fool Us

Are we more likely to take risks if we feel protected? Do safety belts, air bags, and antilock brakes lead to more risky driving, for instance? This is one of the most controversial questions in the field of safety.

It's an issue many safety professionals ignore or deny. Obviously, the notion that personal protective equipment could encourage risky behavior is extremely repugnant. But we need to explore this issue: Do we compensate – adjust our behavior – for perceptions of safety?

In recent years, the issue of compensating for safety has been given several different labels, including risk homeostasis, danger compensation, risk-offsetting behavior, and perverse compensation. Whatever the label, the basic idea of risk compensation is quite simple and straightforward. People are presumed to change their behavior to compensate for changes in perceived risk. If a job is made safer with machine guards or the use of PPE, employees might perceive less risk and actually work more dangerously.

Perception is not reality.

This idea certainly seems intuitive. In fact, I bet every reader has experienced the phenomenon. I clearly remember the increased risks I took when wearing a standard high school football uniform. With the protective helmet and shoulder pads, I'd willingly throw my body at another player or leap high to catch a pass. I didn't perform these behaviors until perceiving security from the personal protective equipment.

I'm sure you can apply my experience to a number of competitive or recreational activities in your life. So how can the phenomenon of risk compensation be denied?

Research Findings

The notion of risk compensation made its debut among safety professionals following the theorizing and archival research of a University of Chicago economist, Dr. Sam Peltzman.[2] Peltzman systematically compared vehicle crash statistics before (1947–1956) and after (1966–1972) the regulated installation of safety engineering innovations in vehicles, including safety belts, energy-absorbing steering columns, padded instrument panels, penetration-resistant windshields, and dual braking systems.

As predicted by risk compensation theory, Peltzman found that these vehicles' manufacturing safety standards did not reduce the frequency of crash fatalities per miles driven. Perhaps the most convincing evidence of risk compensation was that the cars equipped with safety devices were involved in a disproportionately high number of crashes.

Peltzman's findings have been criticized on a number of counts, primarily statistical; but they did stimulate a number of follow-up investigations. Dr. John Adams of University College, London, U.K., for example, compared traffic fatality rates between countries with and without safety belt use laws. His annual comparisons (from 1970 to 1978) showed dramatic reductions in fatal vehicle crash rates after countries introduced seat belt use laws.[3]

Taken alone, these data would lend strong support to the safety-belt legislation. However, the drop in fatality rates was even greater in countries without safety belt use laws.

These studies compared risk behaviors across large data sets. Behavioral scientists call this a between-group design, and it can only indirectly test the occurrence of risk compensation. Since the theory predicts that individuals take more chances after perceiving an increase in safety or security, it can only be tested by comparing the same group of individuals under different conditions. Behavioral science researchers call this a within-subject design.

Most within-subject tests of risk compensation theory have been restricted to simulated laboratory investigations. This is because within-subject observations under different risk conditions are time-consuming and quite difficult to pull off in a real-world situation. One such study was conducted by Dr. Fredrick Streff and me in 1987. To conduct this research we built an oval clay go-kart track (about 100 meters in circumference) and equipped a 5-hp go-kart with an inertia reel-type combination shoulder-lap safety harness.[4]

Subjects were told to drive the go-kart around the track quickly, but at a "comfortable" speed. The 56 subjects were either buckled or unbuckled in the first of two phases of 15 driving trials. After the first phase, the safety condition was switched for half the subjects. That is, the safety belt was unbuckled for subjects previously buckled up, or the belt was used by subjects who previously did not use it. The speed and accuracy of each subject's driving trial were systematically measured. Following the first and second phases (of 15 trials each), the subjects completed a brief questionnaire that assessed their perceived risk while driving the go-kart.

The between-subject comparisons showed no risk compensation. That is, the subjects who used the safety belt for all trials did not drive faster than subjects who never used the safety belt. And the perceptions of risk were not different across these groups.

On the other hand, the within-subject differences did show the predicted changes in risk perception and behavior. That is, subjects reported feeling safer when they buckled up and subsequently drove the go-kart significantly faster than subjects who used the safety belt during both phases. The subjects who took off their safety belts reported a significant decrease in perceived safety, but this change in risk perception was not reflected in slower driving speeds (compared with drivers who never buckled up in the go-kart).

Our go-kart study was later followed up in the Netherlands using a real car on real roads. Specifically, habitual "hard-core" nonusers of safety belts buckled up at the request of the experimenter. Compared with measures taken when not using a safety belt, these buckled-up drivers drove faster, followed more closely behind vehicles in front of them, changed lanes at higher speeds, and braked later when approaching an obstacle.[5]

I'm convinced from personal experience and reading the research literature that risk compensation is a real phenomenon.

Safety Implications

So what does this mean for injury prevention?

First, the offsetting or compensating behavior doesn't negate the benefits of safety protections. Although football players increase risky behaviors when suited up, they sustain far fewer injuries than they would without the PPE.

More importantly, Professor Gerald Wilde, the leader in risk homeostasis theory and research, says safety excellence cannot be achieved through top-down rules and mandates. Under these conditions, some people only follow the rules when they are supervised and might take greater risks when they feel "free." Such behavior is predicted by risk compensation theory.

As the title of his 1994 book, *Target Risk*, indicates, Wilde advocates that safety interventions need to reduce the level of risk people are willing to tolerate. This requires a change in values. Wilde claims that improvements in safety cannot be achieved through training, engineering, or enforcement. In his words, "The extent of risk taking with respect to safety and health in a given society, therefore, ultimately depends on values that prevail in that society and not in the available technology."[6]

This means, of course, our vision should be to make safety a value, not a priority. When safety becomes a value, risks will not be tolerated, regardless of how protected and safe workers feel.

PART 3

Perceptions Can Motivate

Baseball caps, key chains, coffee mugs, umbrellas and ink pens are often used to promote personal safety and health. Do these safety trinkets work? Do they impact safety-related attitudes and behavior?

Methods of delivering safety trinkets vary widely. For some companies, a low injury record calls for delivery of safety trinkets throughout a work force. Sometimes trinkets are given to individuals after a particular safety-related behavior, such as completing a behavioral observation, removing a safety hazard, or reporting a near hit. In other situations, safety trinkets are not contingent on any safety-related outcome or behavior, but are distributed to everyone as an awareness booster.

Do Safety Trinkets Work?

Viewpoints about the impact of safety trinkets vary from one extreme to the other. Most, if not all, behavioral safety consultants advise against basing the delivery of safety rewards on injury-related outcomes. This approach can stifle the report and discussion of personal injuries, a critical process for injury prevention. Thus, most behavioral safety consultants recommend safety trinkets be behavior-based, meaning they should be contingent on behaviors that contribute to injury prevention.

Some safety consultants recommend the elimination of even behavior-based rewards, claiming that rewards for safety can detract from an individual's intrinsic motivation.[7] Some research supports this notion, but most does not.[8]

Another Rationale for Safety Trinkets

Rather than revisit issues of intrinsic vs. extrinsic consequences and outcome-based vs. behavior-based contingencies, I'd like to offer an entirely different perspective. I propose the meaning or rationale underlying a safety trinket has the greatest impact on behavior.

What do people see in a safety trinket? What does the trinket mean? Does it remind the person of a special safety-related lesson, behavior, or commitment? Is the individual proud to wear the cap or use the coffee mug with a safety slogan? Does the safety trinket connect to a memorable event in the person's life, thereby contributing to making safety personal?

Answer: The story behind a safety trinket and its meaningfulness to the individual receiving and displaying the trinket determine the behavioral and attitudinal effects. Thus, the words and emotions linked to the delivery of a safety trinket are critical to its impact.

The LiveStrong Wristband

Most of you are probably familiar with the yellow "LiveStrong" wristbands. Developed and distributed by the Lance Armstrong Foundation, the proceeds support cancer prevention research and help people live with cancer. Because of my own trials and tribulations with cancer, I purchased 100 of these trinkets last year and distributed them to my university students. Most already knew of my bout with prostate cancer.

Wearing the LiveStrong trinket reminds me of the life I took for granted before cancer, and of the need to continue with the kind of lifestyle that increases my chances of staying "cancer-free."

When my wristband broke, I was quite disappointed. Every bike store I called was out of stock. I now wear one given to me by a friend and professional colleague. He said he could no longer wear his, which I had given him earlier, because he started smoking cigarettes again after a nine-year hiatus. It was inconsistent for him to wear the yellow wristband while he continued this unhealthy behavior.

This latter part of my story reflects the greatest benefit of a safety trinket that is meaningful to those who display it. Behavior inconsistent with the rationale behind a safety trinket can cause tension, thereby activating behavior change. Of course, this tension is also alleviated when the individual chooses to stop displaying the safety trinket.

Meaningfulness makes a safety memento influential.

The Buckle-Up Wristband

My colleague who returned the yellow wristband now wears a maroon one, as do I. These maroon wristbands are embossed with the message "Buckle Up for Someone You Love – A.R.K." The initials ARK represent the name of a university student, Ashley Ryan Krueger, who was killed in an automobile crash because she was unbuckled.

University students, faculty, and staff purchased the maroon wristbands at a well-attended memorial service for Ashley. I gave the keynote address at this campus gathering and focused on giving special meaning to the buckle-up trinkets. We sold 1,000 wristbands, and several students have expressed interest in distributing these wristbands at their local high schools.

Wearing these wristbands may be a fashion statement since maroon is one of our university colors. But I'm confident the personal story and emotions linked to this safety trinket, as well as the relevant buckle-up message, activates safety belt use and perhaps even other safe-driving behaviors. Indeed, it would be inconsistent and hypocritical to wear the wristband and not buckle up.

A Bigger Vision

Recently, I discussed our Buckle-Up wristbands in a series of people-based safety presentations at the Monsanto plant in Soda Springs, Idaho. At the end of one of these talks, an audience member said my buckle-up story had special meaning for her. On October 10, 2004, she lost her grandson in a vehicle crash, and he likely would have been uninjured if he had been buckled up. The Soda Springs community maintains a memorial tree to remember Derek Smith. His grandmother and I envisioned a communitywide distribution of black (one of the colors of Derek's high school) wristbands with an embossed message: "Buckle Up – Do it for Derek."

I expect the Monsanto plant to support the production and distribution of this safety trinket. Actually, I envision a similar safety wristband for every high school and university in the country that has experienced a personal loss from a vehicle crash and wants to help prevent future tragedies. Question: What about a green wristband for safety?

In Conclusion

This article considered a quality of the safety trinket that may be more important than the timing of its delivery. Specifically, I suggest the meaning and the emotions linked to a safety trinket are most influential. In fact, the term "trinket" does not do justice to its potential impact. A more appropriate label is "safety memento," reflecting the special memory and mission linked to a safety keepsake.

The author's story made the wristband meaningful.

Bottom line: Make a safety memento personal and influential by linking it to an emotion-laden memory and a relevant injury-prevention behavior. Then safety-related attitudes and behaviors will be facilitated by what people see in a safety memento.

PART 4

Perceptions and Participation

"Accident investigation" is a common phrase in industrial safety and health. But what does it mean? It's a basic job requirement for safety pros, and they attend professional development workshops to improve their skills in this area. But, really, what's your assignment when investigating an accident? What skills do you use? What is your objective in an accident investigation?

Well, the work "accident" implies "a chance occurrence" outside your immediate control. When a child has an "accident" in his pants, we presume he was not in control. He couldn't help it.

And what about the word "investigation"? Doesn't this term imply a hunt for some single cause or person to blame for a particular incident, as in "criminal investigation"? How can we promote fact-finding over fault-finding with a term like "investigation" defining our job assignment?

To truly learn more about how to prevent injuries from an analysis of an

People see blame in a root-cause investigation.

incident, we need to approach the task with a different mindset. It's not "accident investigation" – it's "incident analysis." This simple substitution of words can have great impact on how people view the process. We can get more employee participation in the process and, in fact, reap more benefits from the entire process. Here are five reasons to change our perception – and our language – when it comes to the old "accident investigation."

1) Gain a Broader Understanding

A common myth in the safety field holds that injuries are caused by one critical factor – the root cause. "Ask enough questions," advises the safety consultant, "and you'll arrive at the critical factor behind an injury."

Do you really believe there is a single root cause of an incident, whether a near hit, damage to property, or personal injury?

Consider the three sides of "The Safety Triad" depicting environment, behavior, and person factors that affect safety performance. Environmental factors include tools, equipment, engineering design, climate, and housekeeping. Then you have the behaviors, the actions of everyone relating to an incident. Finally, there are the personal, internal feeling states of the people involved – their attitudes, perceptions, and personality characteristics.

Given the dynamic interdependency of environment, behavior, and person factors in everyday events, how can we expect to find one root cause of an

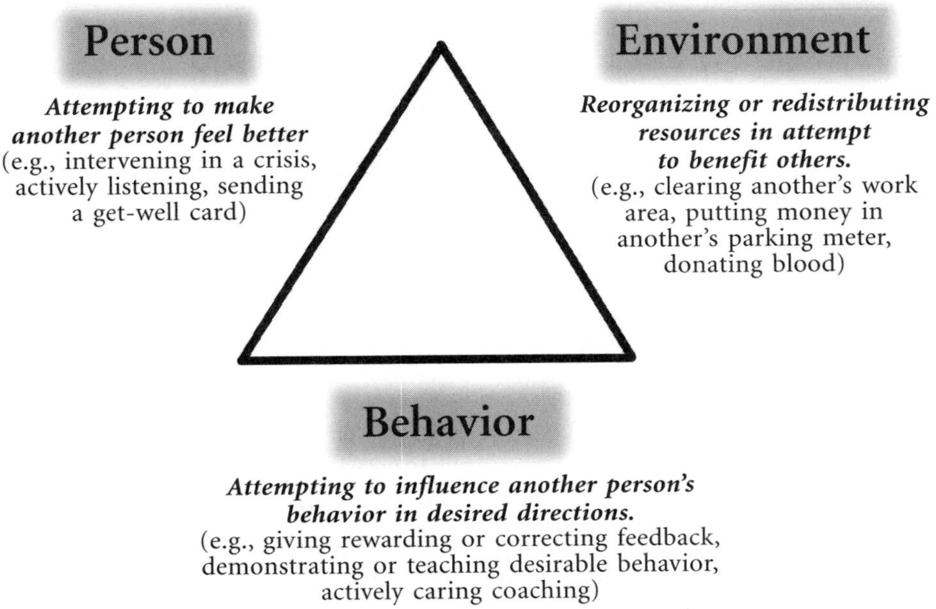

Environment, behavior, and person factors affect safety.

incident? Analysis is needed to sort through this complex web of contributing factors – not an investigation.

Take a systems approach in your analysis of environment, behavior, and person factors. Then decide which of these factors can be changed to reduce the chance of another unfortunate incident. Environment factors are usually easiest to define and improve, followed by behavior factors. Most difficult to define and change directly are the person factors, but many of these internal feelings can be affected positively by properly influencing behaviors.

2) Improve Communication

To find and correct the potential contributors to an incident, people need to talk openly about the various environment, behavior, and person factors. But this won't happen if the goal of an "investigation" is to find a single reason for the "failure." People want nothing to do with a failure.

How can we promote fact-finding over fault-finding when we use a term like "investigation"?

It's human nature. Kids will blame the other kid – "he made me do it." Adults will just keep their mouths shut. To get people to open up, we need to approach incident analysis as an opportunity for success. This is, in fact, the truth. We have an opportunity to prevent future mishaps, perhaps a much greater loss than the one precipitating the current analysis.

Let's get away from the perspective of incident-equals-failure. The focus should be on how an incident gives us the chance to learn and improve. This can lead to more reports of personal near hits and property damage. The more we report and analyze, the more opportunity we have to correct problems before a major injury to a friend or coworker occurs.

3) Increase Involvement

You can expect more participation in incident reporting and analysis if you involve workers in the actual correction phase of the process. People will contribute more if they have a say in the outcome. Of course, management needs to approve and support the corrections recommended by the workforce. But workers know more than anyone else about what it will take to make environment, behavior, and person factors more safe. Use their critical expertise and you'll motivate more ownership and involvement in the entire process.

4) Apply Systems Solutions

Here's how an accident investigation is usually wrapped up: The safety manager presents a report to management, and the recommended solution to eliminating the "root cause" is implemented in the work area where the incident occurred. An equipment guard might be replaced, more comfortable personal protective equipment ordered, or a certain employee might be "retrained" or even punished (incorrectly referred to as "discipline" in the safety literature).

People need to talk openly about various environmental, behavioral, and personal factors. But this won't happen if the goal of an "investigation" is to find a single reason for the "failure."

You'll get broader interest and involvement in an incident analysis process if corrective action plans are applied to all relevant work areas. This also promotes a systems perspective rather than the piecemeal, "band-aid" approach common to so many work cultures. Look at the bigger picture. Use the results of an incident analysis to improve relevant environment, behavior, and person factors plantwide. This sends the kind of actively caring message that not

A limited view can be deceiving.

only promotes participation but also makes that participation more constructive.

5) Promote Accountability

Both the quantity and quality of participation in an incident analysis depend on the numbers you use to evaluate success or failure. The bottom-line reactive measure – the total recordable injury rate (TRIR) – provides neither instructive guidance nor motivation to continue a particular safety process. It doesn't tell us enough about why we're succeeding or failing.

Instead, keep track of the various components of an incident analysis. Monitor the number of near hits, property damage, incidents, and injury reports. Track the number of corrective actions implemented for environment, behavior, and person factors. Now you have an accountability system that facilitates participation.

Keep the focus on successfully completing these various steps of the process. Keep score of your process achievements rather than only waiting to see a reduction in injuries. This is a more valid and instructive measure of your success than any outcome measure currently available.

> *Change Your Approach*
>
> **The old way...**
> - Focus on a single cause.
> - Correct the failure.
> - Force a solution.
> - Apply it narrowly.
> - See if injuries decline.
>
> **A better way...**
> - Look for multiple causes.
> - Focus on learning and improving.
> - Tap employees for solutions.
> - Apply solutions plantwide.
> - Track numerous activities.

PART 5

Perceiving Multiple Factors

"Root cause" is a popular term among safety professionals, especially when conducting an "accident investigation" (which I prefer calling an "incident analysis" as discussed above). For many safety pros the primary objective of an incident analysis is to find the root cause – the single most critical factor that caused the incident. They examine the setting carefully and solicit opinions from everyone who might have seen the incident. "Ask people 'why?' five times," claim some consultants, and you will get at the root cause.

I hope you see how silly it is to believe the root cause of something can be discovered by obtaining five successive answers to: "Why did this happen?" But can I convince you that there is really not one root cause to uncover – at least not with the methods typically used for an incident analysis (such as perception surveys and interpersonal conversations)?

More importantly, I want to persuade you that the term "root cause" is actually detrimental to obtaining optimal participation in an incident analysis and to defining the most effective ways to prevent recurrence of the mishap. Let's start with a discussion of cause-and-effect relationships.

What Is Cause-and-Effect?

Real-world events – both desirable and undesirable – have causes. Events, including behaviors, do not happen by themselves or for no reason. In fact, the notion that every event has a specific cause is a basic assumption of science. Researchers apply the scientific method to search for the causes of events or behaviors. But this is easier said than done. Let's consider three criteria, each of which is required to infer causation between a certain factor and an event.[9]

Covariation: This is the easiest criterion to establish. It means the presumed causal factor and the event (or behavior) vary together. In other words, the factor must be present when the event (or behavior) occurs.

This criterion for identifying a cause-and-effect relationship can be measured with a survey or by behavioral sampling. Surveys can show correlations between two or more factors, and observations of a behavior within specific surroundings can demonstrate that a behavior and an environmental factor covary – they occur together in time and space.

Time-order relationship: Demonstrating a cause-and-effect relationship, however, requires more than covariation. It is also necessary to determine which variable, factor, or event occurred first. Such a time-order relationship can rarely be obtained from surveys. And a sampling of behavioral and environmental factors does not necessarily indicate which came first. Actually, this criterion can only be satisfied when the presumed causal factor is manipulated (as an independent variable) and its impact is subsequently observed in another factor (the dependent variable.)[10]

No other explanation: Covariation and time-order relationships are necessary but not sufficient for defining a cause-and-effect relationship. One more criterion must be reached. Specifically, there can be no other viable explanation for the observed cause-and-effect relationship. Researchers manipulate an independent variable and look for predicted change in a dependent variable.

But even when researchers observe an expected change in perception, attitude, or behavior following the introduction or removal of a particular environmental factor, they do not presume a cause-and-effect relationship. Only when all other possible explanations can be eliminated is a cause-and-effect statement legitimate. For example, the researcher in the illustration should not presume the drug caused the observed change in the rat's behavior because there is an alternative explanation.

Researchers eliminate alternative explanations for a cause-and-effect relationship through experimental design. They might use a control group, for example, or observe the behaviors of the same individuals before and after introducing or removing an independent variable. A research design that eliminates other possible explanations for a cause-and-effect observation is considered "internally valid."

A discussion of various research designs and their associated internal validity is beyond the scope of this discussion. But to help you appreciate the challenge of satisfying this third criterion for causal inference, take a look at the illustration on page 241.

Does this illustration depict a cause-and-effect relationship? In fact, the humor in the

See beyond the obvious.

Be skeptical about what you see.

drawing is based on a self-evident root cause of the ringing in the cow's ear. The bell causes the ringing, right? But is there another possible explanation? Could other noises have caused the ringing problem? Is it possible the cow was born with the problem or developed it over time from other noise, independent of the bell around its neck? How can we test whether the bell is the cause?

I'm sure you guessed one answer. Take away the bell and see if the ringing goes away. Might the ringing continue after the bell is removed? Perhaps the bell has caused permanent damage to the cow's ear, and ringing continues without the bell. *Bottom line:* It is not so easy to show a cause-and-effect relationship.

Skeptical Researchers vs. Risky Safety Pros

You will rarely, if ever, hear researchers state a causal relationship between a variable they manipulated and a predicted and observed change in a certain dependent variable. They won't say, "Environmental factor A caused the observed change in behavior or attitude B." The most they would say is something like, "Factor B changed after the manipulated change in Factor A, suggesting a causal link between the two variables."

Researchers in the behavioral and social sciences are skeptical and conservative and rarely claim they found a cause-and-effect relationship. In contrast, safety professionals are quite liberal (or risky) with cause-and-effect language. They look for "root causes" of incidents and often claim they found them. How? They do this through interviews, surveys, and sometimes a few behavioral observations. These are techniques insufficient for defining causal relationships.

The author of an ISHN article in the March 2002 edition claimed his organization had accomplished research that identified nine root causes of performance excellence.[11] How did they do this? While the article did not detail methodology, it was evident the research was essentially based on perception surveys. The researchers obviously did not manipulate the presumed causal factors and observe change in organizational performance. Only the first of the three criteria needed to define causal factors could be achieved by the research purported to define "nine root causes."

Bottom line: Safety pros are too cavalier with the term "root cause." They do not and cannot use the methods needed to find a root cause. As a result, they necessarily make inaccurate or invalid interpretations when looking for cause-and-effect relationships with survey, interview, and observational techniques that can only satisfy one of the three criteria required for the identification of causal relationships.

Inhibiting involvement

If safety pros were to assume the skepticism and conservatism of the researcher, they might make more appropriate judgments about the factors potentially contributing to an incident. Plus, they might broaden the spectrum of corrective action.

Most importantly, the search for a "root cause" can seem like "fault-finding" rather than "fact-finding," leading eventually to finding one person presumed to be responsible – the "root cause." Most employees want no part of such an "investigation" or "interrogation." Instead, the objective of an incident analysis should be to define the various factors that could have contributed to an incident, whether it's a near hit, damage to property, or personal injury.

Safety leaders make inaccurate or invalid interpretations when looking for cause-and-effect relationships with survey, interview, and observational techniques.

The multiple factors that contribute to an incident can be categorized as environmental, behavioral, or personal. And a comprehensive corrective action addresses each of these domains.

You need people to help you identify the variety of possible factors contributing to an incident and explore the diverse array of corrective actions that could prevent another similar incident. Terminology like "possible" and "could" rather than "root cause" is not only more accurate, given the methodology used for an incident analysis, but it also enables a mindset or perception for the kind of frank and open dialogue needed for a comprehensive search of ways to make a workplace safer.

PART 6

Perceiving a Just World

It's not unusual to blame the victim of unfortunate circumstances – including workplace safety incidents. Psychological research has shown that victims of crimes and vehicle crashes are often perceived as causing their fate.[12]

For example, many people believe rape victims are somewhat to blame for the rape. "If she hadn't dressed and acted that way, she would not have been sexually assaulted." In other research, battered wives were viewed by some as being responsible for their abusive husbands' behavior.

Social psychologists believe this is a form of self-defense that helps us maintain our perception that life is safe, orderly, and predictable. If life were unfair and random, then innocent people like ourselves could also be victimized and injured.

In psychological terms, this attributional bias is referred to as the "just world hypothesis." It's the assumption that people get what they deserve and deserve what they get. How do we deal with the constant reminder that tragedies not only happen but are also relatively common? One way is to believe in a just world: Bad things happen to bad people, and good things happen to good people.

Position affects just-world perceptions.

Since most of us see ourselves as decent and basically good, our belief in a just, safe world means bad things won't happen to us. In the remainder of this article, we'll point out four ways this defense mechanism influences our perceptions and undercuts efforts to protect worker safety on the job.

1) Increased risk-taking

The phrase "It won't happen to me" is familiar to all of us. This perception enables us to face situations where a serious injury is possible – from the drive to and from work to numerous situations while we work. As it turns out, most days this conviction is supported. Nothing happens to us.

This belief, obviously consistent with the just-world hypothesis, increases risk-taking. We take a chance – a calculated risk – because we think we're safe and secure in a just world.

Maybe we wouldn't take as many risks if we realized our coworkers who suffered injuries also believed in a just world. They didn't expect anything bad to happen to them – only to the other guy. Now they know what it's like to be that other guy.

2) Poor incident analysis

Let's be honest: Haven't you at one time or another tried to feel better about someone getting hurt or killed by looking for things the victim could have done to prevent the incident? Do you feel more sympathy for the passengers than the driver killed in a vehicle crash?

We feel safer when we can somehow blame the victim of misfortune. Then the tragedy does not seem so tragic. We feel more secure knowing we could prevent such a misfortune from happening to us by doing what the victim didn't do.

But actual or potential behaviors of a victim are not the whole story. Any analysis of what happened can't begin and end here. But sometimes it does, and for this we can blame our belief in a just world.

3) Lack of involvement

It's not easy to get people to actively care for other people's safety. Not only must we be educated and trained to know what to do, but we also must feel comfortable intervening and believe it's the right thing to do.

We might not step in or speak up if we believe that people get what they deserve. But you can also believe it's your responsibility to help make the world just by intervening to make it safer. This includes removing environmental hazards and barriers to safe behavior as well as helping others become more mindful of their behaviors that put themselves and others at risk for injury.

4) Lack of public support

When hazards and injuries seem unfair, as when a child is molested or inflicted with a deadly disease, the public pays special attention. It's comparably easy to obtain contributions or voluntary assistance for programs that target vulnerable populations, like physically challenged individuals or learning-disabled children.

Victims of workplace injuries are not viewed as weak and defenseless. Occupational injuries are indiscriminately distributed among employees who take risks, and the "just world" perception is that they get what they deserve. This helps explain the low public and political support for agencies like OSHA.

Fatalism is a form of self-defense that helps us maintain our belief that life is safe, orderly, and predictable.

More productive lives of Americans are lost in occupational mishaps and vehicle crashes than cancer and heart attacks combined.[13] Yet the amount of government support for cancer and cardiovascular disease is many times greater than the amount allocated for research and interventions to prevent injuries and fatalities in the workplace and on the road. I believe the just-world hypothesis is partly responsible for this unjust situation.

What to Do

So what can we do about the just-world hypothesis and its impact on workplace safety? Well, we can see it differently and turn it in our favor. Through education and regular conversations, we can convince people that a just world actually depends on us. We can help make our world safer and more just by doing our part to remove environmental hazards, suggest refinements to make equipment more "user friendly," and help people improve their safety-related behavior.

A just world can be an ultimate vision made possible by our own attempts to actively care for the safety and health of ourselves and others we share our days with.

The problem with fatalism

Believing in a "just world" where people get what they deserve can:

- Lead to more risk-taking because we don't believe we deserve to get hurt.
- Stifle incident analyses because we blame the victim and leave it at that.
- Prevent us from getting involved in safety efforts because, after all, everything happens for a reason and people get what they deserve anyway.
- Reduce public funding for government agencies that target occupational safety (OSHA, MSHA, and NIOSH) compared with agencies whose work protects vulnerable populations.

PART 7

Impulsive Perceptions

Too often, "retraining" or "discipline" is selected impulsively to correct a discrepancy between what people do and what we want them to do. As detailed in Chapter 2 on "The Acting of People-Based Safety™," workers take risks for a variety of reasons. Perhaps they don't know what's expected, or they don't have the right tools or enough time. Sometimes people are rewarded for the wrong behavior or ignored or punished for performing the safe way. Useful feedback may be missing. And, as reviewed in this chapter, they may not see the risks because of perception bias.

In these cases, people know what to do, but they just aren't doing it. They are "consciously incompetent." The problem is not lack of knowledge or skill. Training is not the answer. You need to analyze and change organizational systems, workplace conditions, and interpersonal relations.

In their classic text on problem analysis, Robert Mager and Peter Pipe[14] suggest a number of ways to get the performance you want before concluding there is a need for formal training. Ask yourself these four questions:

1) Can the task be simplified?

Before developing a training program to increase on-the-job safety, make sure all possible engineering "fixes" have been implemented. Explore the many ways the environment could be changed to reduce physical effort, reach, and repetition. Entertain ways to make the job more user-friendly before deciding what behaviors are needed to prevent injury.

2) Is there a skill discrepancy?

What about those times when employees are "unconsciously incompetent" – they really don't know how to work safely? This might call for training. But Mager and Pipe claim most behavioral discrepancies are not caused by a genuine lack of skill. Usually, people can work safely if conditions and consequences are right. So, training should really be the least-used approach for corrective action.

3) What kind of training is needed?

If you determine that someone has forgotten how to perform a task, a skill maintenance program may be in order. This is the rationale behind periodic emergency training. Fortunately, emergencies don't happen very often, but since they don't, people need to go through the motions just to "stay in practice."

Skill maintenance training is also needed when a person gets plenty of practice doing the wrong thing. Here, practice only supports a bad (or risky) habit. For example, most people know how to drive a vehicle safely and once showed little at-risk driving. But safe driving often deteriorates over time.

As detailed in Chapter 3 on "The Coaching of People-Based Safety™," behavior-based feedback is critical for solving both of these skill discrepancies. Especially when desired skills have deteriorated into poor habits (as in the driving example), it's often necessary to use behavior-based coaching. The coach needs to systematically complete a critical behavior checklist (CBC) while watching for safe versus at-risk actions and then give both supportive and corrective feedback.

Critical Behavior Checklist for Driving

Driver:	Date:	Day:
Observer 1:	Origin:	Start Time:
Observer 2:	Destination:	End Time:
Weather:		
Road Conditions:		

Behavior	**Safe**	**At-Risk**	**Comments**
Safety Belt Use:			
Turn Signal Use:			
Left turn			
Right turn			
Lane change			
Intersection Stop:			
Stop sign			
Red light			
Yellow light			
No activator			
Speed Limits:			
25 mph and under			
25 mph-35 mph			
35 mph-45 mph			
45mph-55 mph			
55mph-65 mph			
Passing:			
Lane Use:			
Following Distance (2 sec):			
Totals:			

% Safe = Total Safe Observations / Total Safe + At-Risk Obs. = ____________%

A critical behavior checklist can improve driving.

Of course, there is also the training needed to introduce a new procedure or process. Here is the CBC I used to train my daughter to drive safely when she turned 15 over a decade ago. Today, I'd add a category for cell-phone use.

4) Is the person right for the job?

A skill discrepancy can be handled by changing the job or changing the person. But what if a person's interests, skills, or prior experiences are incompatible for the job?

Before investing in skill training for a particular individual, it's a good idea to assess whether the person is right for the job. If a person does not have the motivation or the physical and mental capabilities for a particular job, the cost-effective solution is to find a replacement. If you don't, you'll lower productivity and increase the risk for personal injury.

Remember, if you're not getting the performance you want from employees, the reasons often will be found in the work environment or the task itself. Don't impulsively assume the answer lies in training or discipline. Analyze the situation, the behavior, and the individuals involved to prioritize possible solutions. The recommended flow of an incident analysis lists training as a last resort and does not even include a punishment strategy.

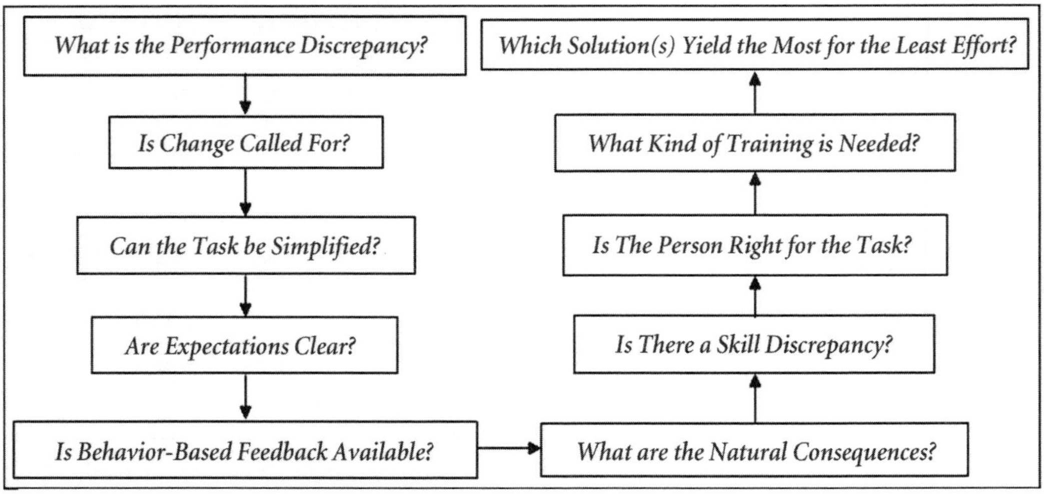

The answers to ten questions lead to injury prevention.

Don't be too fast with your fixes

Socrates said, "A prescription without diagnosis is malpractice." Ask these questions before assuming you know how to close the gap between the behavior you want and the behavior you get:

Is the job the problem?
Can engineering controls make the task more user-friendly?
Can the task be redesigned to reduce physical demands?
Can a "behavior facilitator" (color coding, instructions, and so on) be added to improve response time, reduce memory demands, or increase reliability?
Can the challenges of a complex task be shared?
Can boring, repetitive tasks be swapped?

Is it a lack of skill?
Could the person perform the task safely if his or her life depended on it?
Are the person's current skills adequate for the task?
Did the person ever know how to perform the task safely?
Has the person forgotten the safe way to perform the task?

Lack of practice or feedback?
How often is the desired skill performed?
Does the performer receive regular feedback relevant to skill maintenance?
How do performers find out how well they are doing?

Does the person have the potential?
Does the person have the physical capability to perform as desired?
Does the person have the mental capability to handle the complexities of the task?
Is the person overqualified for the job and thus prone to boredom or dissatisfaction?
Can the person learn how to do the job as desired?

PART 8

Precautionary Perceptions

In the prior chapter on "The Thinking of People-Based Safety" (i.e., Part 10), I addressed a person factor that influences our motivation and attitude toward safety: You can place yourself in one of four person-state categories by considering whether your approach to safety is seeking success or avoiding failure.

Exclusive success seekers are the most optimistic, while exclusive failure avoiders are most pessimistic. Overstrivers seek success and avoid failure; while extremely motivated, they often feel distressed and insecure. Although the failure accepters are most unmotivated and apathetic, they are typically more content than the failure avoiders and overstrivers.

States vs. Traits

I must urge caution, however, when using this four-way classification system.

First, the motivational state of an individual varies from one situation to another and from one time to the next. A certain manager could be a failure avoider for safety, a success seeker for productivity, and an overstriver for quality. And one serious injury could move a person from failure avoider to failure accepter for safety.

Let's consider a personality trait that can influence which of the four success/failure states an individual is experiencing and whether a transition to a more healthy or productive state might be expected. I'm referring to a trait rather than a state, which is an enduring personality characteristic a person brings to every situation and influences one's state and what one

Motivational states and perceptions are situational-specific.

People can get overly stressed.

pays attention to and sees.

The trait we're considering here is general anxiety, as measured 50 years ago by a highly researched survey instrument developed by Dr. Janet Taylor Spence. It's called the Taylor Manifest Anxiety Scale (TMAS).[15]

What is Anxiety?

My *American Heritage Dictionary*[16] defines anxiety as "a state of uneasiness and distress about future uncertainties." Clearly, anxiety is an unpleasant state we want to avoid. But here I'm not talking about a state, rather a trait. As a trait, anxiety is a relatively stable personality quality that determines one's motivational and emotional responsiveness to a particular circumstance. If the situation is anxiety provoking, state anxiety combines with trait anxiety to produce a most unpleasant and distressing situation.

As measured by the TMAS, high-anxious people are energetic, high-strung, self-conscious, more nervous than average, and generally work under tension. They worry over money and business matters, and have difficulty keeping their mind on one thing. Regarding the success/failure typology defined above and detailed in Part 10 of Chapter 4, high-anxiety individuals worry about being unsuccessful. They tend to be overstrivers or failure avoiders.

Passionate safety leaders cultivate a state of anxiety or concern for safety throughout a work culture.

At first, high anxiety seems to be an undesirable personality trait. But this is not necessarily so. Before bemoaning your own proneness toward high anxiety, consider the following reliable research finding.

While high-anxious people perform less competently than low-anxious people on novel tasks or jobs they could not prepare for, they often outperform those with lower anxiety on tasks for which they could prepare. Why? Because their strong desire to avoid the aversive anxiety feelings accompanying failure motivates them to do as much as possible to succeed. With proper proactive preparation, these individuals become success seekers.

People who have an ongoing internal concern about the safety of themselves and others are more likely to do whatever it takes to prevent the occurrence of personal injury.

An Illustrative Anecdote

Many readers have experienced test-taking situations they could not prepare for, like the Scholastic Achievement Test (SAT) high chool students take for entrance into college. On average, high-anxious individuals do worse than low-anxious people on these tests. Why? Because their nervousness and heightened arousal energizes a wide range of behaviors, many of which compete with execution of the correct response.

Perhaps you won't be surprised to learn that SAT scores are often not predictive of academic performance in college, as measured by grade point average. Why? Because students can prepare for tests that determine their grades, and high-anxious students are typically proactive when given opportunities to prepare for success. Their strong need to avoid the negative emotions of being unprepared motivates them to work hard to avoid failure. And if they prepare well and become confident they can make good, they can develop an achievement mindset and become success seekers.

Relevance to Safety

I hope you agree the anxiety trait defined here can be good for safety. Recall the dictionary definition of anxiety as a state of uneasiness about the future. People who have constant anxiety about the possibility of a workplace injury are going to do everything they can to put themselves in control of preventing injuries and so put their safety-focused anxiety on hold. These folks do not need an actual injury or fatality to get their attention. However, such unfortunate events are often a necessary wake-up call for the low-anxiety employees.

The term anxiety has negative connotations, so the premise that anxiety is good for safety might be difficult for some of you to accept. If so, try substituting the analogous term "concern" for "anxiety." The bottom line is that people who have an ongoing internal concern about the safety of themselves and others are more likely to do whatever it takes to prevent the occurrence of personal injury. They are more likely to see environmental hazards and remove them.

Isn't this the kind of personality trait we hope to find in our safety leaders? These are the passionate workers who are most likely to cultivate a state of anxiety or concern for safety throughout a work culture. They see potentials for personal injury, and they act constructively on their perceptions.

Approaches to safety

- Success seeker – works optimistically to achieve success
- Failure avoider – motivated by fear of failure, a sense of pessimism
- Overstriver – driven to avoid failure by working in overdrive to succeed; extremely motivated but often insecure
- Failure accepter – expects failure regardless of personal effort; most apathetic or indifferent

PART 9

How to Estimate Risk

Critics of behavioral safety claim injury prevention requires a holistic, system-level approach. Behavioral observation and feedback among line workers is not enough. Plus, management must not use behavioral safety as an excuse to shirk its responsibilities, such as developing a more user-friendly workplace and maintaining accountability systems that keep safety integral to daily work activities.

Guess what? I agree. Actually, I've never heard a behavioral-safety trainer or consultant disagree with these arguments. As detailed in Chapters 2 and 3, behavior-based safety provides a set of tools that can support any ongoing safety initiative – especially those that are holistic, system-focused, and people-based.

A Valuable Tool

The basic tools of behavioral safety can improve the actions of everyone – from the worker performing hands-on activities to the supervisor overseeing the entire effort. These tools are not limited to safety undertakings, but are pertinent to all aspects of an organization's mission statement.

This article address one of the most valuable behavioral safety tools – the critical behavior checklist (CBC). My descriptions and examples address safety, but this tool is applicable to everything people do at work. Performance of any sort cannot improve without behavior-based feedback, and feedback is often most instructive when linked to recorded observations. This tool helps people see at-risk behavior and conditions, and prevent injuries to themselves and others.

History can provide harsh lessons in severity.

Simply put, the CBC consists of a list of some of the specific behaviors required to complete a task effectively. You can also check whether each behavior is performed "competently" or "incompetently." For safety applications, this column distinguishes between "safe" and "at-risk." Definitions of "competent" vs. "incompetent" or "safe" vs. "at-risk" are developed through structured group discussions and consensus building.

Developing a practical CBC acceptable to all potential users is an invaluable process. If done right, it instills a sense of team ownership, as well as self-efficacy and personal control. These positives increase when everyone agrees to use the CBC, and are integrated into the culture whenever the CBC is used to observe coworkers and provide behavior-based feedback.

Optimal ways to observe others and give interpersonal feedback are detailed in Chapter 3 on "The Coaching of People-Based Safety." Here I addressed the challenge of selecting the behaviors for a CBC.

What's Critical?

Don't take developing your CBC lightly. When you decide what safety-related behaviors are "critical," you define aspects of a job that require the most attention and mindfulness. These are the behaviors that people will hold each other accountable to perform safely.

Sources for deciding which behaviors to include on a CBC include: injury records, near-hit reports, job-hazard analyses, standard operating procedures, rules and regulations, your site's medical staff, or anyone else who maintains injury statistics for your organization. Talk to your workforce. Employees

Observer: ____________

Person 1	**Person 2**
Date: ____________	Date: ____________
Time: ____________	Time: ____________
Department: ____________	Department: ____________
Building: ____________	Building: ____________
Floor: ______ Area: ______	Floor: ______ Area: ______

Operating Procedures	**Safe Observation**	**At-Risk Observation**
BODY POSITIONING/PROTECTING *Positioning/protecting body parts (e.g., avoiding line of fire, using PPE, equipment guards, barricades, etc.).*		
VISUAL FOCUSING *Eyes and attention devoted to ongoing task(s).*		
COMMUNICATING *Verbal or nonverbal interaction that affects safety.*		
PACING OF WORK *Rate of ongoing work (e.g., spacing breaks appropriately, rushing, etc.).*		
MOVING OBJECTS *Body mechanics while lifting, pushing/pulling.*		
COMPLYING WITH LOCKOUT/TAGOUT *Following procedures for lockout/tagout.*		
COMPLYING WITH PERMITS *Obtaining, then complying w/ permit(s).* (e.g., *confined space entry, hot work, excavation, open line, hot tap, etc.).*		

1 = observations for first person; 2 = observations for second person

% Safe Behavior: $\dfrac{\text{Total Safe Observations}}{\text{Total Safe Observations + Unsafe Observations}} \times 100 =$ ______ %

Feedback with Person 1	**Feedback with Person 2**
Date ______ Time Begin ______ Time End ______	Date ______ Time Begin ______ Time End ______

Categories of work behaviors activate specific behavioral definitions.

already know a lot about their own safe and at-risk work practices. They know which safety rules are ignored. They know when a near-hit has happened to them or to others because of at-risk behavior.

Evaluating relative risk is key to selecting critical behaviors. Which behaviors create the most risk for injury?

Estimating Risk

Risk associated with a particular behavior depends on exposure, severity, and probability. Discussing each of these dimensions facilitates the process of developing and refining your CBC.

Exposure: Every time an at-risk behavior occurs, someone is exposed to potential injury. The more often this behavior occurs and the more people performing it, the greater the exposure. For example, lifting a load greater than 40 pounds might not be very risky if done once, but multiply this risk by numerous employees making several lifts per day and you gain a different perspective.

Duration also contributes to risk exposure. The longer one carries a 40-pound load, the greater the exposure. The longer one resists using personal protective equipment (PPE), the greater the exposure. Conversely, one brief instance of donning certain PPE, from a hard hat to a vehicle safety belt, reduces risk exposure for the entire duration of usage.

Fall protection prevents high-severity injuries.

Severity: Behavioral risk also varies according to the severity of possible harm or injury. What's the worst scenario that could occur from a particular at-risk behavior? A fatality? Multiple deaths?

Sometimes history provides harsh lessons. Certain at-risk behaviors have contributed to plant explosions, vehicle crashes, asphyxiations, and to humans crushed by equipment. These are usually included on a CBC, unless their occurrence is extremely rare, making the exposure very low.

Probability: What's the probability a behavior will result in an injury? This is a subjective judgment, the most difficult risk assessment to make. Consider the act of lifting. By counting people and daily opportunities to lift per person, you can get a good estimate of exposure. It's not hard to imagine the worst possible outcome of a severe back injury. You likely know someone who has suffered a slipped or herniated disc.

Probability is the most difficult risk to assess.

But how probable is it that lifting a load greater than 40 pounds will cause a back injury of any severity? Many factors come into play – the age and physical strength of the lifter and various behavioral aspects of the lift. When lifters hold the load close and bend their knees, the probability of a back injury is greatly reduced. That's why a CBC on lifting behavior includes several specific behavioral components.

Let's look at the use of fall protection. The severity of a fall from three stories is obvious. Exposure is easy to estimate by counting the number of people working at this height and multiplying the total by the average duration per employee per day. But what about the probability of someone falling from a three-story height?

Again, numerous factors are involved, including the nature of the work and the physical and psychological state of the worker. Since these factors are impossible to appraise for an individual, it's best to assume the highest risk level for each relevant factor and use your best judgment. Assume the probability of falling is fairly high for the average worker, and put more stock in your estimates of exposure and severity.

Using ESP

Three characteristics of an at-risk behavior determine its relative risk – exposure, severity, and probability of occurrence. You can remember this as the "ESP approach" to estimating behavioral risk.

• **Exposure** fluctuates according to the frequency and duration of the at-risk behavior for all employees at a work site. It is the easiest of the three risk factors to estimate.

• **Severity** is judged by visualizing the worst possible consequence that could result from the at-risk behavior.

• **Probability** is most difficult to estimate because so many environmental and individual factors influence the likelihood of an at-risk behavior resulting in an injury. As with severity, a conservative approach is recommended. Assume bad luck, meaning all the factors that could increase the possibility of injury are in place, from unfriendly environmental conditions to an individual whose attention periodically deviates from the task.

PART 10

Scan and Focus for Risks

I drafted this section on attention and safety while flying to Erie, Pennsylvania to present an ASSE workshop. Little did I know it would underscore many of the points I wanted to make. After landing, I took a cab to my hotel. Along the way I called in for messages, but was interrupted when the cabbie started asking me about the Virginia Tech football team.

I put down my cell phone and talked Hokies football until reaching the hotel. In my room, I reached in my backpack for my cell phone to get back to those messages. Guess what? It wasn't there. I called the cab driver, and sure enough, the phone was in the back seat.

The following night I returned home and got to my car at the Roanoke, Virginia, airport about 11:30 p.m., only to find a dead battery. The headlight switch had been "accidentally" turned on. I eventually located a battery charger, but without a flashlight I couldn't find the positive and negative labels on the battery poles. What I thought was the black cover to the negative pole was not. Guess what? I fried my battery, blew a main fuse. At 2:00 a.m., I was being towed 40 miles to Blacksburg, Virginia.

Daily Diversions

Yes, these glitches illustrate the critical role of attention in accomplishing everyday routines – and how easily our attention can be diverted and lead to at-risk behavior and negative consequences. Plus, it's not enough simply knowing how important attention is to safely accomplishing activities.

Awareness of "inattentional blindness" – a term coined by psychologists who have studied people's inability to detect unexpected objects in their field of vision when their attention is focused elsewhere[17] – is just the start. What can we do about this potential cause of an injury?

Obviously, changing our attentional focus can remove the "blinders." But this is easier said than done. When we're busy, it's annoying to divert attention elsewhere. But this is a recommended intervention. When focusing on details, step back intermittently and take a wider view of the situation. Scan for possible risks and safety-related consequences. Competent workers know where to focus their attention and what to tune out. They also know when to take a wide-angle view of their environment. We call this "scanning."

Plan to Scan

Some tasks require more scanning than focusing. Take driving, for example. Sustained focus on one aspect of driving is quite risky, say when you're punching in numbers on your cell phone. Competent drivers shift their attention: from the road and oncoming traffic to vehicles beside and behind them; and they occasionally check the speedometer. They continually scan the visual fields observed through their windshield, side windows, and rear-view mirror.

Biased perceptions can cause dangerous inattention.

Lack of periodic scanning or excessive focusing contributes to a number of workplace injuries. Many slips, trips, and falls are caused by narrowly focused attention without sufficient environmental scanning. Many harmful contacts between body parts and machinery occur because of insufficient environmental scanning for moving objects. Some injuries occur because people lose track of where their arms or legs are in relation to an environmental hazard. We're busy, we're rushed, we've got things to do after work, and then our foot gets run over by the wheel of a forklift.

It's often critical to vary attention from scanning to focusing. Developing a critical behavior checklist (CBC) should include discussing when and how often to scan versus focus visual attention while performing a particular task. A CBC is a good coaching tool to increase the kinds of ongoing attention strategies we need in the workplace.

PART 11

Ease Sensory Overload

Eliminate signs, slogans, exhortations, and objectives from the workplace, W. Edwards Deming told us.[18] Did he mean we ought to stop giving people directions to follow, goals to shoot for? If he did, he was denying the basic activator-behavior-consequence framework for behavior-based safety, as I discussed in Chapters 2 and 3. Substantial research has verified that behavior is influenced markedly by activators (like signs preceding behavior) and by consequences (pleasant or unpleasant events following behavior.)[19]

I don't think Dr. Deming was disregarding this research with his point about eliminating signs, slogans, and exhortations. Rather, he was criticizing the standard top-down development and display of performance activators. As currently used for safety, they might only raise expectations without giving relevant and meaningful direction. If that's the case, they might as well be eliminated.

Let's consider six guidelines for increasing the impact of activator techniques. After considering them, be prepared to change, or perhaps drop, how you currently use signs, slogans, goals and exhortations.

Get Specific

Signs that refer to a specific behavior can be beneficial. Don't expect signs or slogans that urge employees to "Think Safe," "Eliminate Accidents," and "Achieve Zero Injuries" to do much good. More effective are messages that alert employees – "Hard-Hat Zone," "Designated Smoking Area," and "Ear Protection Required" – or instruct, such as "Lift With Legs," "Walk Within the Yellow Lines," and "Buckle Up for Safety." Note, too, that these signs are not overly complex.

Avoid Complacency

It is perfectly natural for sign messages to lose their impact over time. It's human nature to habituate, or no longer respond, to everyday activators in our environment that are not supported by some consequence. This is the case with many safety activators. A sign requesting the use of personal protective equipment might eventually be ignored, for example, if consequences (positive feedback or penalties) are not in place to support the message.

Vary the Message

Over the years I've noticed a variety of techniques for changing the

Some signs are misleading.

message on safety signs, such as removable slats to place different messages and computer-generated signs with an infinite variety of safety messages. Some plants even have video screens in break areas, lunch rooms, visitor lounges, and hallways that display many kinds of safety messages, conveniently controlled by user-friendly computer software. The same people expected to follow these specific messages should have as much input as possible in defining their content.

Involve the Workers

We're talking about the power of ownership here. When public trash receptacles include the logos of nearby businesses, the merchants whose logos are displayed typically take care of the receptacle, and keep the surrounding area clean. Consider the success of "Adopt-a-Highway" programs that have groups keep a certain roadway clear of litter and perhaps beautified with plants, shrubs, or flowers. The same sense of commitment is possible in the workplace.

Carefully Consider Placement

A safety message placed in the work area where the behavior it specifies is to occur has greater impact than putting the same message in a memo, newsletter, or safety talk. It's like "point-of-purchase advertising" – placing ads at locations where the target products can be purchased.[20] Similarly, road signs that gave drivers feedback on the percentage of vehicles exceeding posted speed limits have been found through research to be more effective at reducing speeding than public service announcements on radio and television.[21]

Specify Consequences

Activators are most potent when they refer to internal (self-imposed) or external consequences – in terms of incentives and disincentives.

One last point: We really don't need more messages telling us what to do in our lives. We're already bombarded at work and at home by information. We should plan our messages so they receive the attention and ultimate action they deserve.

Safety signs without behavioral directions are overload.

PART 12

Take Off the Blinders

The rock-and-roll band I joined last year accepted my choice for a new name – "Magic Moments." At the time, I thought the name particularly appropriate because most of our music is classic southeast beach, typified by the Drifters' 1959 classic – "This Magic Moment."

But now I have another, perhaps more important, reason to appreciate our band's name. By paying attention to the magic moments of our lives, we realize the simple and irreplaceable joy of our everyday existence. And in the process, we reduce the probability of personal injury.

After all, the past is gone (learn from it), the future may or may not be (set goals and anticipate), but the current moment is always a gift – a "present" to enjoy. So live in and be mindful of the present and your chances of enjoying a safe and pleasurable day on or off the job increase.

So what's your story? How often do you shortcut the moment (and shortcut safety) and not only miss present pleasures, but perhaps put yourself at-risk for personal injury? Sometimes circumstances and other people set us up for thinking about what lies ahead rather than experiencing the pleasure of the process. I'm reminded of this every time I observe the hustle and bustle at an airport terminal. We've got to fight the urge to dive in and join the rat race, take a deep breath, reflect on the pleasure principle (and the safe way of getting work done), and experience (safely) where we are and what we are doing. Too often this is easier said than done.

See the pleasures of the moment.

Relevance to Safety

I hope you can see how "living in the moment" connects with occupational safety and health. I suspect you already do. When we are mindful of and attend to our ongoing behavior in every respect, we are unlikely to experience

It's risky to focus on the future rather than the present.

personal injury. Living in the moment means we are using all relevant senses to recognize what we are doing and where we are doing it. Our antennae are fully extended. We fully encounter the present – at home, on the road, at work – and make a mishap unlikely.

The connection between personal safety and living in the moment is painfully obvious to me. I say "painfully" because the many injuries I've sustained over the years have been caused in part by me being inattentive to the present. Yes, I am definitely "injury prone." From childhood through adulthood, I've had my share of serious injuries – many more than average. Why?

I'm convinced my continual, future-oriented mindset is a primary cause of my injuries. Just the other day, for instance, I tripped over my own feet while walking on campus and nearly fell flat on my face.

"You were not watching where you were going," said a friend walking next to me. I had to admit she was right. I was not attending to the present; I was contemplating my destination and upcoming activities. I was thinking of my next step, rather than focusing on the ongoing behavior – my current step.

I defended my close call (or near fall) by telling my friend a story I heard about Albert Einstein when he was teaching physics at Princeton University. After stopping and talking to a university colleague, Professor Einstein asked his friend which direction he had come from before stopping to talk. After his colleague pointed and said, "From over there," Dr. Einstein replied, "Good, that means I've eaten lunch."

Of course it's a joke to link my problem with the genius of Albert Einstein.

But both stories do reflect neglect of the present and, as a result, potential for personal injury. Moreover, the actor in each story missed out on some pleasures of the moment.

"Plan ahead." "Prepare for tomorrow." "Create a vision of your future." Slogans like these are common in our culture. They reflect a proactive and achievement-oriented mindset, and are basic guidelines for highly successful people. The benefit of these slogans cannot be denied. But I'll argue for another perspective: "Live in the moment." Today is all we've got. Yesterday is history, and tomorrow never comes. Let's make today a safe and pleasurable one.

Cherish the Present

In his 2003 book, *The Present*, Spencer Johnson (author of *Who Moved My Cheese?*) advises us to learn from the past and plan for the future, but live in the present.[22] Similarly, Paul Pearsall's popular audiotape program, *The Pleasure Principle*,[23] teaches the joy of living *in* the moment (not *for* the moment). The key point is that pleasure comes from experiencing the present – the situation we are in right now. Simply put, this means focusing on where we are and what we are doing, and thinking now.

To truly cherish the present, we need to use all of our relevant senses. When eating, for example, we should use more than our taste buds to savor the distinctive features of a meal. We live more in the moment when we sense the texture of the food, its aroma and the visual display. And of course the context of the eating environment should be treasured, perhaps with a focus on picturesque scenery and playful chatter with one or more companions. With undivided attention to the many pleasures of a simple dinner, you can get caught up in the moment and maybe even consume fewer calories – a healthy side effect for some people.

Have you ever seen people shovel popcorn? With kernels flying everywhere and mouths stuffed like Vermont Teddy Bears, the focus seems to be on the outcome of getting filled up, instead of enjoying each tasty piece of popcorn. Actually, it's not farfetched to consider such rapid eating to be at-risk behavior. Have you ever choked on a piece of popcorn or another food particle because of eating too fast?

Be sensuous about simple everyday pleasures, Dr. Pearsall advises us. "Take time to feel the warmth of your bed, linger in your morning shower,

An outcome focus detracts from pleasures of the process.

savor the taste of your breakfast orange juice, reflect a few minutes on the setting sun, listen for the evening birds' songs, and hold someone close at the end of your day," he says.

Consider that depressed individuals typically dwell on past disappointments. "If only I had done that differently, or made another choice," they ruminate to themselves. In contrast, many anxiety-ridden people live in pessimistic anticipation of the future. "What if I can't pull this off?" "What if my support system crumbles?" "What if Murphy's Law prevails, as usual, and I fail miserably? My future will be ruined."

Depressed and overly anxious people are obsessed with the past or the future, respectively. They miss the pleasures of the moment that could help them relax and rejuvenate. Melancholy over the past and insecurities about the future can actually be cast aside by the rapture of the present, if only our hectic lives would permit that to happen.

Bottom line: Whatever your situation, wherever you find yourself, be there. You can never be there again, not under the exact same circumstances. Later it will be only a memory; now it's enjoyment to experience.

Notes

1. Mayo, D. G., & Hollander, R. D. (1991) (Eds.). *Deceptable evidence: Science and values in risk management.* New York: Oxford University Press.
2. Peltzman, S. (1975). The effects of automobile safety regulation. *Journal of Political Economics, 83,* 677-725.
3. Adams, J. (1995). *Risk.* London: UCL Press.
4. Streff, F. M., & Geller, E. S. (1988). An experimental test of risk compensation: Between-subject versus within-subject analysis. *Accident Analysis and Prevention, 26,* 277-287.
5. Janssen, W. (1994). Seat-belt wearing and driving behavior: An instrumented-vehicle study. *Accident Analysis and Prevention, 26,* 249-261.
6. Wilde, G. J. S. (1994). *Target risk* (p. 228). Toronto, Ontario, Canada: PDE Publications.
7. Krause, T. (1995). Transitioning away from safety "incentives," *Perspectives in Behavioral Management*, First Quarter, 1-4; Krause, T. R., & Hudson, S. J. (1998). A close look at safety incentives, *Occupational Health & Safety*, *67*(1), 28-36.
8. Cameron, J., & Pierce, W. D. (1994). Reinforcement, reward, and intrinsic motivation: A meta-analysis. *Review of Educational Research, 64*(3), 363-423; Carr, C., Mawhinney, T., Dickinson, A., & Pearlstein, R. (1995). Punished by rewards? A behavioral perspective, *Performance Improvement Quarterly, 8*(2), 125-140; Eisenberger, R., & Cameron, J. (1996). Detrimental effects of reward: Reality or myth, *American Psychologist, 54*(11), 1153-1166.
9. More details regarding the root-cause myth are given in Geller, E. S. (2004). Assessing SH&E Research: Key principles and practical strategies improve understanding. *Professional Safety, 49*(9), 22-29.
10. Goodwin, C. J. (1998). *Research in psychology* (Second Edition). New York: John Wiley & Sons, Inc.
11. Krause, T. R. (2002). Predicting safety success: Examine these nine factors. *Industrial Safety & Hygiene News, 36*(3), 52-53.

12. Lerner, M. S. (1980). The belief in a just world: A fundamental delusion. New York: Plenium Press.
13. *Injury in America: A continuing public health problem.* Washington, DC: National Academy Press; Sleet, D. A. (1987). Motor vehicle trauma and safety-belt use in the context of public health priorities. *The Journal of Trauma, 27,* 695-702.
14. Mager, R. F., & Pipe, P. (1997). *Analyzing performance problems or you really oughta wanna* (Third Edition), Atlanta, GA: Center for Effective Performance.
15. Taylor, J. A. (1953). A personality scale of manifest anxiety. *Journal of Abnormal and Social Psychology, 48,* 285-290.
16. *American Heritage Dictionary* (1991), Second Edition, New York: Houghton Mifflin Company.
17. Mack, A., & Rock, I. (1998). *Inattentional blindness.* Cambridge, MA: MIT Press.
18. Deming, W. E. (1991, May). *Quality productivity and competitive position.* Four-day workshop presented in Cincinnati, Ohio, by Quality Enhancement Seminars, Inc.
19. Geller, E. S., Winett, R. A., & Everett, P. B. (1982). *Preserving the environment: New strategies for behavior change.* New York: Pergamon Press; Kazdin, A. E., & Wilson, G. T. (1978). *Evaluation of behavior therapy: Issues, evidence, and research strategies.* Cambridge, MA: Ballinger; Peterson, D. (1989). *Safe behavior reinforcement.* New York: Aloray, Inc.
20. Tillman, R., & Kirkpatrick, C. A. (1972). *Promotion: Persuasive communication in marketing.* Homewood, IL: Richard D. Irwin, Inc.
21. Van Houten, R., & Nau, P. A. (1983). Feedback interventions and driving speed: A parametric and comparative analysis. *Journal of Applied Behavior Analysis, 16,* 253-281.
22. Johnson, S. (2003). *The present.* New York: Doubleday.
23. Pearsall, P. (1999). *The pleasure principle: Discovering a new way to health* (audiotape series), Niles, IL: Nightingale Conant.

CHAPTER SIX

Gaining and Sustaining *Engagement* in People-Based Safety™

Introduction

OK, Dr. Geller, now what? I understand the interdependency of ACTS – the Acting, Coaching, Thinking and Seeing components of People-Based Safety. I see how the principles and skills work together to build a Total Safety Culture. What do I do to keep it going?

"We need more leadership in safety," writes Dr. Geller (*Part 1*). That's your cue. Much of this final chapter in *People-Based Safety™: The Source* can be taken as a primer on how to be a safety leader. Leaders help build self-directed responsibility for safety – one of the key objectives of People-Based Safety.

In fact, one of the benefits of implementing the skills and principles of People-Based Safety is that you'll strengthen your own leadership abilities in the process.

"When it comes to safety, people need your leadership," writes Dr. Geller. "More importantly, they need the right kind of leadership." He's referring to empathic leadership (*Part 2*) – observing, listening, questioning, and putting yourself in the other person's steel-toed boots before diagnosing a safety-related issue and offering advice for improvement.

Before you can go very far taking the lead for safety, you need to assess levels of trust in your workplace (*Part 3*) and increase trust (*Part 4*) when necessary. Simply put, it's impossible to build and sustain a Total Safety Culture in the absence of trust.

There are numerous other leadership roles you will assume along the way. At some point you'll be called on to:

• Sell people on change (*Part 5*). Empathy helps you anticipate and deal quickly with the concerns people have about change.

• Nurture your safety heroes (*Part 6*). It's not always easy to find and recruit safety talent, but these dedicated people form an essential support network.

• Change "me first" mindsets (*Part 7*). Be prepared: Learning to work effectively as a team takes patience.

• Create a sense of excitement about safety (*Part 8*). Ralph Waldo Emerson said it: "Nothing great was ever achieved without enthusiasm."

• Build a palpable sense of momentum for safety (*Part 9*). Look for success stories to recognize and celebrate. Develop feelings of achievement and an optimistic atmosphere.

• Fuel the participation factor (*Part 10*). Remember, use principles founded on accepted psychological theory and empirical research rather than common sense.

• Build a bedrock belief in safety (*Part 11*). Focus on factors that enhance actively caring: self-esteem ("I am valuable"), belonging ("I belong to a team"), self-efficacy ("I can do it"), personal control ("I am in control"), and optimism ("I expect the best").

Daunting assignments, yes. Can you do it on your own? No. You'll rely on that foundation of trust. Your "safety heroes" will serve on committees, run meetings, and lead teams. Remember the real meaning of TEAM – Together Everyone Achieves More. Performance measures will help track your successes and sustain momentum and motivation. The atmosphere of your organization – optimistic and supportive – is an essential ingredient.

Dave Johnson, Editor
Industrial Safety & Hygiene News

PART 1

Safety Needs Your Leadership

While "management" is a popular term in the challenge to reach an injury-free workplace, I think leadership is more important. And we need more "leadership" in safety.

Leaders help build self-directed responsibility for safety. Let's consider six specific differences between safety management and safety leadership. This is not meant to belittle management or even to suggest we need less management. We do, though, need more leadership in safety – and this is not the same as management.

But managers can be leaders, too!

1) What's your focus?

Managers are typically held accountable for numbers, and they use numbers to motivate others. In safety the outcome numbers are based on the relatively rare occurrence of an injury. These numbers are reactive, reflect failure, and are not diagnostic for prevention.

Safety leaders hold people accountable for accomplishing activities that can prevent injuries. When people see improvement in the process numbers, they are reinforced for their efforts and develop a sense of personal responsibility for continued contributions and continual improvement.

2) Do you educate or train?

In industry, "training" is a more common term than "education." With a training mindset, managers can come across as demanding a certain activity because "I said so" rather than because "it's the best way to do it."

Leaders educate – offering rationale and examples rather than policy and directives. This enables individuals or work teams to select procedures that best fit their situation. And in the process of refining a set of procedures, people assume ownership and follow through from a self-directed or responsible perspective.[1]

3) Do you speak first, or listen?

Under pressure to get a job done, managers often speak first and then listen to concerns or complaints. This is a reasonable strategy for efficient action. After all, managers must make things happen according to an established plan, and this requires specific directives and compliance. After describing an action plan and accountability system, managers answer a lot of questions from workers who want to make sure they will do the right thing.

Leaders ask questions.

Leaders take time to learn another person's perspective before offering direction, advice, or support. Active listening is key to diagnosing a situation. This is not the most efficient approach to getting a job done. It requires patience and a communication approach that asks many questions before giving advice. But this is how individuals or work teams can customize a plan or process for achieving a particular outcome.

4) How do you motivate?

Managers direct by edit for efficiency. While they might get compliance, they might also stifle self-directed motivation. Behaviors performed to comply with a prescribed standard, policy, or mandate are accomplished to satisfy someone else – and they are likely to cease when they cannot be monitored. This happens, for example, when personal protective equipment is used at work but not at home for similar or even riskier behaviors.

Leaders give a reasonable rationale for a desired outcome and then offer opportunities for others to customize methods for achieving that outcome. They facilitate a special kind of motivation. This motivation comes from inside people – it is not directed by others. It's internal or self-directed motivation. People participate because they want to, not because they have to.

5) Do you leave room for choice?

Most work behavior starts because someone asked for it. The important issue is whether behavior remains other-directed or advances to self-directed. This depends to some extent on how you ask.

Managers favor mandates, reflected in regulatory compliance issues and

Managers...

- Go by the numbers.
- Emphasize training.
- Speak first, then listen.
- Strive for compliance.
- Lean on mandates.
- Live by measurements

the common slogan, "Safety is a condition of employment." Mandated behavior is likely to require constant "management."

Leaders use expectations rather than mandates to instill self-directed motivation. What's the difference? Expectations imply choice. There is room for individual and group decisions regarding procedures and methods. When people realize what's expected of them but perceive some personal control in how to reach specific goals, they are more likely to own the process and move from depending on the directions of others to directing themselves.

6) Must it be measured?

Managers focus on the numbers, and in safety that means injury records and compensation costs. When I discuss People-Based Safety principles and procedures with managers, I inevitably get the question, "What's the return on investment?" Managers want to know how much the process will cost and how long will it take for the numbers to improve. This analytical approach is obviously inspired by the popular management principle, "You can only manage what you can measure."

Leaders...

- Focus on activities.
- Emphasize education.
- Listen first, then speak.
- Offer opportunities.
- Emphasize expectations.
- Don't measure everything

Leaders certainly appreciate the need to hold people accountable with numbers, but they also understand you can't measure everything. There are some things you do and ask others to do because it's the right thing to do. Leaders believe, for example, it's important to increase self-esteem, self-efficacy, personal control, optimism, and a sense of belonging throughout a work culture.

The Bottom Line

The leadership characteristics described here can help build self-directed responsibility for safety. It's usually more desirable for people to be self-directed than other-directed, especially when trying to promote safety and health. When people are self-directed to perform safely they don't need an external accountability system. Plus, they are prone to actively care for the safety and health of others.

The bottom line: Safety management is necessary at times to motivate people to do the right things for injury prevention. But it is not sufficient to achieve a Total Safety Culture. Safety managers need to know when to become safety leaders and build responsibility rather than hold people accountable.

PART 2

Empathic Leadership

When it comes to safety, people need your leadership. More importantly, they need the right kind of leadership. After all, you can insult people with too much supervision, or confuse them with too little. To effectively take the lead in safety, you need to know what style of leadership is required. This means practicing empathic observing, listening, and questioning.

In this article, I discuss the value of empathic leadership. As discussed in Chapter 3 on "The Coaching of People-Based Safety," we are empathic when we put ourselves in the other person's shoes before diagnosing a behavior-related problem and offering advice for improvement.

Let's consider four different ways you can lead others. At any point in time you can coach, instruct, support, or delegate, depending on your empathic diagnosis of the situation.

To understand the difference between these approaches, recall the basic ABC paradigm of behavior-based safety detailed in Chapter 2 on "The Acting of People-Based Safety." "A" stands for activator or the various conditions or events that precede behavior ("B") and direct it. "C" refers to the consequences that follow behavior and influence whether it will occur again. Consequences motivate behavior.

Coaching

Coaches give direction and provide feedback. They present a plan, perhaps specific behaviors needed for a certain task, and then follow-up with support and empathic correction to pinpoint what worked and what did not. Periodic activators (direction) keep people on the right track, while intermittent consequences (feedback) provide motivation to keep people going.

Without empathy, leaders can't relate.

Delegating

Sometimes it's best to give an assignment in general terms (without specific directions) and to limit interpersonal behavior-focused feedback. This is true when team members are already motivated to do their best and will give each other direction, support, and feedback when needed. These individuals should be self-accountable (or responsible), and expected to use self-management techniques (activators and consequences) to keep themselves motivated and on the right track.

Instructing

Some people are already highly motivated to perform well, but don't know exactly what to do. This is often the case with new hires. In this case, you need to focus on giving behavior-focused instruction.

Supporting

What about the experienced worker who does the same tasks day after day? This individual doesn't need your direction, but could benefit if you periodically give sincere thanks for a job well done. Broadening a job assignment, varying the task components, or assigning leadership responsibilities are other means of providing support.[2]

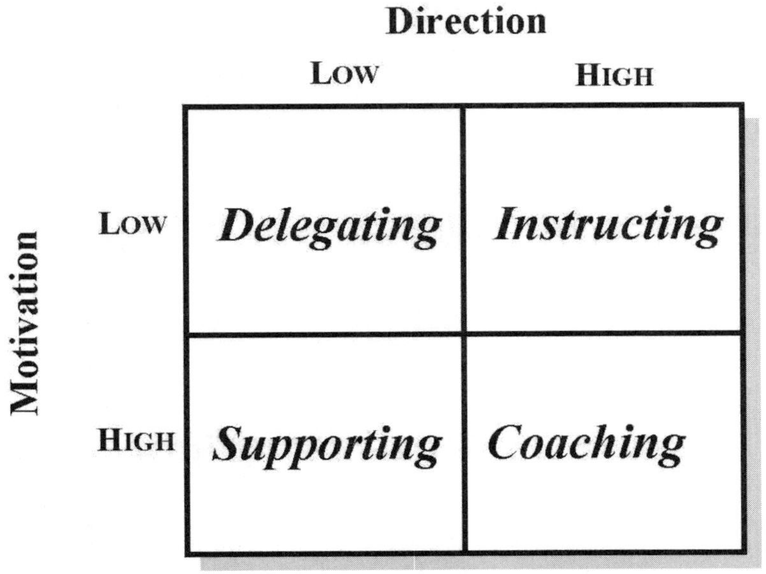

Leadership style is determined by amount of direction and motivation needed.

Competence and Commitment

So how do you know which leadership style to use? This is where empathy comes into play. Your assessment of situations and people – through observing, listening, and questioning – will determine what approach to use. Look for two critical characteristics: competence and commitment.

Coaching is needed when a person's competence and commitment regarding safety are relatively low. You can improve competence through specific direction and feedback, and increase commitment by sincerely giving appreciation and support. Anything that increases a person's perception of importance or self-worth on the job can enhance commitment. What makes that happen? It's not always obvious, but if you listen, observe, and ask questions you'll find out.

Delegating is relevant when people know what to do (competence) and are motivated to do it (commitment). Delegating leaders provide clear expectations and show sincere appreciation for worthwhile work. They enable self-direction and self-motivation.

Empathic leaders usually know when an individual or work team advances to this level because they have observed successive progress. But it's often useful to ask people whether they are ready for this style of leadership. If they say "no," then ask what they need to reach this stage. Do they need more

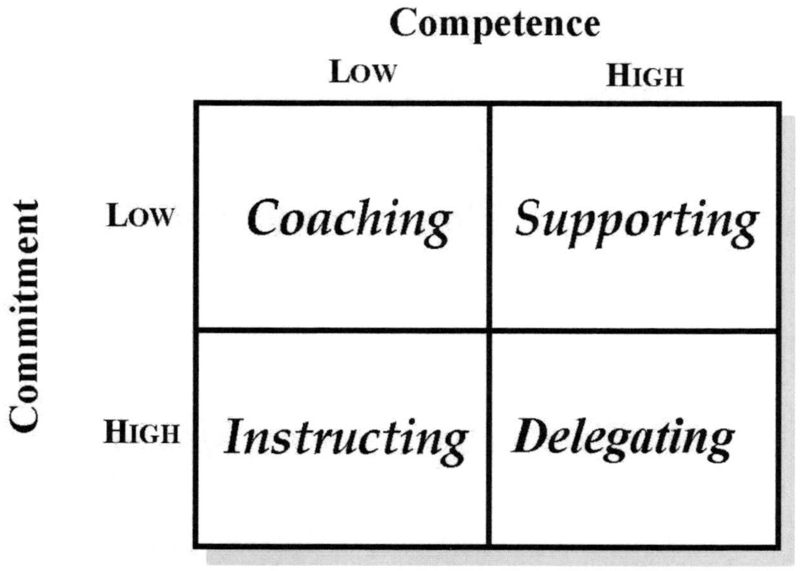

Leadership style is determined by the recipient's level of competence and commitment.

competence through direction? More commitment through some kind of support the organization could make available?

Instructive leadership is called for when people are internally motivated to perform well, but don't know how to maximize their efforts. In this case, empathic leaders focus on giving specific behavior-based directions.

Supportive leadership is needed when people know what to do for safety, but don't always follow through. This problem can't be solved with direction or training. People need supportive leadership when their motivation or commitment is low. This is particularly evident when workers perform irregularly or inconsistently. Their good days indicate they know what to do, but their bad days suggest a motivational problem. Support must be given, but how? This can only be answered through empathic listening, observing, and questioning.

Causes of low commitment vary dramatically, from interpersonal conflict on the job to emotional upheaval at home. Such causes can only be discovered through empathic listening. At times, diagnosing and treating a motivational problem requires special assistance. The best you can do here is recognize a need for professional help and offer advice and support.

Don't Keep It A Secret

You might want to consider the benefits of telling people what leadership style you plan to use, asking permission for a particular approach, or asking an individual or team what style they would prefer. This is particularly useful when moving from one approach to another. If you feel it's time to move from giving instructions to delegating, announce your change and explain the reasons.

Empathic leadership works best when everyone involved understands the four approaches and the two critical factors that determine the need for one style over others. Then people can request a certain leadership style from their flexible and empathic leaders.

Flex Leaders

Leadership styles change depending on circumstances. Whether you coach, instruct, support, or delegate depends on your periodic assessments of what's needed. Since people and organizations are dynamic and always changing, so will your leadership styles.

New employees need instruction at first, for example. As he or she becomes familiar with the routine, your support will be more important than instruction. If you later decide to expand the work assignment with no increase in compensation, you'll probably need to be a coach, providing both direction and support, at least at first. Eventually, a delegating approach might be most appropriate. The employee is now self-directed and self-motivated. Remember to give genuine words of appreciation when your expectations are met.

PART 3

Assess Levels of Trust

"No way," workers sometimes tell me when I introduce the observation and feedback process of behavioral coaching. They don't like the idea of a coworker watching them and tallying safe and at-risk behaviors for a feedback session. Managers and safety directors sometimes will agree with the basics of the process, but then say, "Our plant is not ready for such a process."

Why the Resistance?

It all comes down to one word – trust. A behavior-based observation and feedback process won't succeed without a high degree of trust. First you must believe the process is valid, a good tool for improving safety. Then you need confidence your coworkers will know how to observe and give feedback correctly. Beyond ability, you must trust the person observing and recording your behaviors doesn't have a hidden agenda. This is called trusting the intentions of an observer, and it's critical. So, too, is trusting the intentions of your company's managers who are responsible for bringing the process into your workplace.

A little freedom goes a long way.

How do you know if your organization is ready to trust the behavior-based coaching process? Will coworkers trust each other as coaches? Does enough confidence exist between management and the workforce? I'd like to give you a better understanding of the feelings that go into trust. You'll also come away with a tool for measuring trust in your organization.

Defining Trust

"Confidence in the integrity, ability, character, and truth of a person or thing" is the first definition of "trust" given in the 1991 *American Heritage Dictionary*.[3] This definition refers to behavior (as in "ability") as well as internal or person-based dimensions (as in "integrity" and "character"). These are the characteristics my colleagues and I measure to assess trust between people in a work culture, using a survey based on research by John Cook and Toby Wall.[4] The survey distinguishes between intentions and ability. In other words, you can be confident a person means well, but you might doubt his or her ability to complete the intended task. In this case, you trust the individual's intentions but you're not so sure things will work out as planned. You lack confidence in the person's ability to make good on his or her promise.

This is a common perception of workplace safety efforts. Well-intentioned managers or safety leaders can talk about missions, goals, or policies employees view as idealistic or unrealistic. And when punishments or rewards are not carried out consistently and fairly, employees don't trust the abilities of those running the program. The reverse also happens. Employees might have faith in the ability of others, but mistrust their intentions. When a policy change is sprung on workers without warning or rationale, they might suspect management's intentions. They might believe managers have the intellect and skills to make things happen, but will they do the right thing? "Do they really have our welfare in mind?" suspicious minds ask.

For instance, what if management sets up a safety incentive program that offers everyone a prize if no one gets hurt for six months? Employees feel pressure not to report an injury. If they do, everyone loses their reward. So what's management's true agenda? Is it to keep the numbers down, or to keep employees from being hurt?

The same issues of trust play out every day between coworkers. You might have confidence in a coworker's ability to perform a job safely and competently, but you might not want to confide in that person. "My partner might use the information against me to get the promotion before me," could be your thought. Similarly, you might trust the intentions of a coworker ("He would never take advantage of me") but lack confidence in his ability ("I'm sure he'll try his best, but he just doesn't have enough experience").

Measuring Trust

As you can see, there are four dimensions to trust: faith in the intentions and in the ability of either coworkers or managers. These four dimensions were used by Cook and Wall in 1980 to develop a questionnaire asking for responses to 12 statements in order to assess "interpersonal trust at work."

The instructions for this survey tool and the actual items are on page 284. The researchers originally gave this survey to employees by reading them each item and asking them to indicate on a seven-point scale their degree of agreement with a particular statement. My colleagues and I include these 12

	Management	Coworkers
Intention	Questions 1, 7, 12	Questions 3, 5, 8
Ability	Questions 2, 4, 6	Questions 9, 10, 11

Four dimensions define interpersonal trust at work.

statements on a questionnaire along with many others to draw conclusions about a work culture. We ask respondents to give their opinions on a five-point scale.

Except for statements #2 and #12, the higher scale value equates with greater interpersonal trust. Statements #2 and #12 are negatively phrased, and need to be reverse scored. By totaling the scores for all 12 statements (with #2 and #12 reverse scored) you have an estimate of an individual's perception of interpersonal trust in his or her work culture. You can obtain an overall trust index by calculating the mean survey score from many respondents.

The numbers in the cells of the 2X2 matrix indicate the questions that refer to the particular kind of trust. You can examine the totals per cell to compare levels of different kinds of trust in your workplace.

There is nothing special or magical about the wording of these statements. Feel free to reword statements if different language fits better with your culture. And you can add or substitute new statements. One more point: This scale was developed to measure interpersonal trust from the viewpoint of an hourly worker. With only slight adjustments, the scale can also estimate interpersonal trust from a manager's perspective.

Once you arrive at an estimate of the level of trust in your workplace, the question becomes: How can we increase it? After all, safety improvement depends on a sense of interdependence among coworkers and managers. Everyone must look out for the safety of everyone else. This means trusting each other's intentions and abilities to do the right thing. How to increase trust is our next topic.

ASSESSING INTERPERSONAL TRUST

The statements below express opinions that people might hold about the confidence and trust that can be placed in others at work, both fellow workers and management. Circle the scale numbers next to each statement to indicate how much you agree with it.

Statement	Highly Disagree	Disagree	Not Sure	Agree	Highly Agree
1. Management in my company is sincere in its attempts to meet the workers' point of view.	1	2	3	4	5
2. Our company has a poor future unless it can attract better managers.	1	2	3	4	5
3. If I got into difficulties at work I know my coworkers would try and help me out.	1	2	3	4	5
4. Management can be trusted to make sensible decisions for the company's future.	1	2	3	4	5
5. I can trust the people I work with to lend me a hand if I need it.	1	2	3	4	5
6. Management at work seems to do an effective job.	1	2	3	4	5
7. I feel quite confident that the company will always treat me fairly.	1	2	3	4	5
8. Most of my coworkers can be relied upon to do as they say they will.	1	2	3	4	5
9. I have full confidence in the skills of my coworkers.	1	2	3	4	5
10. Most of my fellow workers can do their work well even when supervisors are not around.	1	2	3	4	5
11. I can rely on other workers not to make my job more difficult by careless work.	1	2	3	4	5
12. Our management would be quite prepared to gain advantage by deceiving the workers.	1	2	3	4	5

These questions assess interpersonal trust.

PART 4

Increase Levels of Trust

How can we increase levels of trust at work to improve safety? This is a critical question, specifically when it comes to getting the most out of a behavior-based observation and feedback process, as detailed in Chapter 3 on "The Coaching of People-Based Safety." For workers to accept feedback, they need to trust an observer's capability (accuracy) and intentions (caring, not punishing).

Finding little real-world research on building interpersonal trust, I called together a group of my research students and colleagues and asked them to brainstorm and reach a consensus on how to build trust. After almost two hours, we arrived at an interesting and seemingly useful list of proposals. We also learned something first-hand about developing feelings of trust. This brainstorming process brought us together as a group that relied on each other for ideas and feedback.

I urge you to conduct a consensus-building exercise similar to the one we used. Your ideas will likely be similar to ours – but the recommendations will be owned by your group. And people are more likely to follow recommendations they had a hand in developing.

Blind trust can be hazardous.

We reached a consensus that the following words – all beginning with the letter "C" – capture the essence of trust building. Use them to kick off your own discussion of trust.

Communication

What people say and how they say it influences our trust in both their capability and their intentions. I'm sure you've heard many times that how something is said, including intonation, pace, facial expressions, hand gestures, and overall posture, has greater impact than what was actually said.

There is probably no better way to earn someone's trust in your intentions than by listening attentively to what that person has to say – call it active listening. When you listen to others first before communicating your own perspective, you increase the chance they will reciprocate and listen to you, and you also learn how to present your message to get the best possible understanding, appreciation, and agreement.

Caring

When you take the time to listen to another perspective, you send a most important message that you care. And when people believe you care about them, they will care about what you tell them. They trust you will look out for them when applying your knowledge, skills, or abilities. They trust your intentions because they believe you care.

Asking questions also communicates caring and builds trust. Not typically generic questions like, "How are you doing?" but deeper, more probing questions. Questions targeting a specific aspect of a person's job send the signal you care about him or her. You're showing genuine interest in what people are doing and how they feel. It's especially powerful when your words reflect actively caring about health and safety.

Too much candor can hurt.

Candor

We trust people who are frank and open with us. They get right to the point, whether asking for a favor or giving us behavior-based feedback. Of course, candor does not give you permission to be tactless and inconsiderate. And when candid individuals don't know an answer to our question, they don't ignore us or hem and haw. They tell us outright when they don't know something, and they tell us they'll get back to us later. Then our trust in both their intentions and abilities increases when they get back to us soon with an answer.

Candor also requires a lack of prejudice. Candid people are not judgmental. We all tend not to trust people who show a tendency to evaluate or judge others on the basis of some stereotype or preconceived notion. How fair are these people going to be? Even when their prejudice is not directed toward you, are you going to trust their abilities and intentions?

Consistency

We usually trust the intentions of people who confess openly their inability to answer our question. But we expect them to follow through when they say they'll get back to us. What happens when they don't – when their actions are not consistent with their words?

Whether the promise regards a positive reward or negative threat of punishment, trust decreases when the consequence is not delivered.

Commitment

People who are dependable and reliable are not only consistent, they demonstrate commitment. When you follow through on a promise or pledge to do something, you tell others they can count on you. You can be trusted to "walk the walk and talk the talk." Making a commitment and honoring it builds trust in both intention and ability.

Consensus

When a group of people reach consensus about something, group members are signaling trust in the opinions or recommendations of others. If a decision is reached that leaves out a minority view, there might be active or passive resistance on the part of those who have "lost" in the process. Without everyone's buy-in, commitment, and involvement, we can't trust the process to come off as expected.

So how can group consensus be developed? It requires candid, consistent, and caring communication among all members of a discussion or decision-making group. In her book, *Teamwork from Start to Finish*,[5] Fran Rees lists six basic steps to reach a consensus decision:

- Set a decision goal. What is the aim or purpose of the consensus-building exercise?
- Spell out the criteria needed to make the group decision acceptable. What qualities or characteristics of the decision are needed to satisfy the goal? One criteria might be to stay within budget constraints.
- Gather information. What information is useful for making the decision?

With consensus-building, everyone wins.

Where is this information and who can provide it?

• Brainstorm possible options. Does everyone understand each option and its ramifications? Has everyone had a chance to voice a personal opinion?

• Evaluate the options against the group's criteria. Which solutions meet the "must have" criteria? Which options meet the "nice but not necessary" criteria? Can certain options be combined to meet both criteria?

• Make the final decision as a team. Which option or combination of options best meets all of the "necessary" criteria and most of the "desirable" criteria? Who has reservations and why? How can individual skepticism be resolved? Can everyone support the most popular option? What can be altered in the most popular action plan to attract unanimous support and ownership? I'm sure you see there's no quick fix to reaching consensus.

Character

A person of "character" is considered honest, ethical, and principled. All of the characteristics discussed here to describe a trusting culture are practiced by a person of character. I'd like to add a few additional qualities:

First, individuals with character admit vulnerability. They realize they aren't perfect and need behavioral feedback from others, for example:

Having the courage to admit your weaknesses means you're willing to apologize when you've made a mistake and to ask for forgiveness. You should also indicate what you will do better next time, or you should ask for specific advice on how to improve.[6]

The surest way to reduce interpersonal trust is to tell one person about the weakness of another. In this situation it's natural to think, "If he talks that way about her, I wonder what he says about me behind my back." People with character, as defined here, always talk about other people as if they can hear you.

Back-stabbing leads to more back-stabbing, and eventually to a work culture of independent people doing their own thing, fearful of making an error, and unreceptive to any kind of performance-based feedback. Key aspects of people-based safety-team building, interpersonal observation, and coaching are extremely difficult or impossible to implement in such a culture. Start to build interpersonal trust by making a personal commitment and implementing a team policy of no back-stabbing.

The seven words reviewed here are easy to remember and although their meanings overlap to some extent, each offers distinct directives for trust-building behavior. The process of building trust in an organization is ongoing. Consider it a continuous journey, one that is essential if you want to reap the many benefits of People-Based Safety.

People with character own up to their weaknesses.

PART 5

Selling People on Change

Let's talk about six basic concerns of people when a new process or procedure is introduced in the workplace. If you anticipate and deal quickly with the critical issues people have about change, it's possible to launch a new initiative with more participants and fewer resisters.

1) Why is the change needed?

This is perhaps the most obvious issue to address, but it's often overlooked. Answer the question: Why is the new approach better than the old way? This is a matter of education – explaining the rationale, theory, or principles behind the change.

Remember, there's a difference between "education" and "training," as I mentioned earlier in this chapter (Part 1). Training programs that only teach step-by-step procedures can be perceived as a top-down "flavor of the month." Educating people about the principles or rationale behind a new safety policy, program or process enables understanding and critical thinking. It also allows you to customize procedures for particular work situations.

When you're too good for your own good.

2) What's in it for me?

Everyone tunes into radio station WIIFM – What's In It For Me? So it's important to clarify the costs and benefits of any new program or process. Don't let your people speculate on how a particular change will affect them. Be honest about the extra effort or adjustment involved in making the change work, and emphasize the positive consequences that can be expected. If you can't define positive gains and/or negative consequences avoided due to the new process, you'll have a difficult time motivating participation.

3) What will I have to do?

People want to know what they will need to do differently. Do they have the knowledge, skills, and resources to accomplish their role in your change effort? It's important to convince potential participants that the new responsibilities are within their capabilities. If they don't currently have the ability to perform these tasks competently, assure them they will be taught relevant procedures.

4) Who else will be involved?

This question targets issues of collaboration and teamwork, and personal versus interpersonal control. Does the success of the new process depend on input from others inside and outside the work culture? From people we don't know, or people we have little influence over?

Spell out the degree of coordination and cooperation needed for success. If interdependent support is needed, suggest ways to make it happen. Remember, if success hinges on cooperation from people on different work teams, individual participants will perceive they have little personal control over the outcome, and will be more uncertain of success.

5) How will my participation be evaluated?

People are naturally concerned about accountability. Everyone wants to know how their performance will be judged. Employees want to participate competently in worthwhile endeavors, but their feelings of competence are influenced by the methods used to observe and rank performance.

Be prepared to answer these questions: "Will the external measure of competence be objective?" "How much of my effectiveness score will be determined by factors outside my personal control?" "If we feel an evaluation is unfair, can we suggest another approach?"

6) Can we suggest improvements?

If you convince your audience change is called for and their participation is needed, you better anticipate suggestions for customizing and refining the new process.

In fact, you might skip giving specific step-by-step procedural instructions completely. Instead, give your vision for breakthrough improvement and a general structure or set of guidelines for accomplishing the desired change. Leave plenty of room for individuals and work teams to derive specific procedures. Tailoring a process to one's own work area spurs creativity and ownership – and also provides the most suitable procedures for a particular situation.

It's important to encourage continuous refinement of a new safety process. When people gain competence at performing a task they believe is worthwhile, they will develop new and better ways to succeed. Make it clear from the start this is expected. The start of something different is only the first phase of continuous improvement. Indeed, change is a constant. And the more people you have participating, the better each change will be. As Frank Bird put it "Good better best; may we never rest until good is better, and better best."[7]

Some will resist change.

It's a process

There are five levels of participation in a change process:

Level 1 – Leaders or innovators who are totally involved;

Level 2 – Those who want to participate but need a little direction and support;

Level 3 – Those (usually the majority) who are neutral or nervous about change and need prodding and encouragement from others;

Level 4 – Passive resisters who are critical and untrusting of something new imposed on them, and use apathy and cynicism as excuses to remain uninvolved; and,

Level 5 – Active resisters who view change as a threat or a loss of personal control, and might exert measures to stifle the participation of others.

Active resisters stick out and attract attention. Nonparticipants use them to rationalize their own commitment to stay in their comfort zones. Managers aim their attention on these individuals, sometimes using punitive measures. But this only builds resentment of the system among all resisters, and makes it less likely they'll join your change process.

Instead, focus your attention on participants rather than nonparticipants. If possible, active and passive resisters should be ignored.

Watch for those who display immediate interest and commitment in your initiative. These individuals are innovators who have dramatic positive influence on the rest of the workforce. Encourage those totally involved in the process (Level 1) to help people who believe in the change but are not yet totally immersed (Level 2). Then these two groups can work with the majority (Level 3) who need direction, support, and examples to follow.

Be aware of the need to develop feelings of competence among potential participants. Many might like your new plan but are unsure of their ability to handle the change. Give these folks all the education and skills training they need.

What about the resisters? Leave them alone. Don't give them opportunities (through punishment, for example) to dig in and become more committed to their contrary opinions. Give them opportunities to receive training and participate in the new process when they decide it's worth their effort. That will happen soon after the majority of the workforce recognizes the change is beneficial and gets involved in continuous improvement.

When the change becomes the norm, the passive resisters (Level 4) will feel the peer pressure and fall in line. Some active resisters (Level 5) may never participate, but at least they will become passive and harmless to the status quo.

PART 6

Nurture Your Heroes

Some people have a "talent," you might say, for contributing to your safety processes. How do you find and support that talent in order to sustain your safety efforts? It's not easy, especially given some popular management myths I believe can be detrimental.

The title of a 1999 Simon & Schuster book by Buckingham and Coffman sums up what needs to be done: *First, Break All the Rules.*[8] The conclusions of these authors are quite consistent with other books on leadership, and with the leadership gurus I've heard at day-long workshops, including Tom Peters, Stephen Covey, and Ken Blanchard.

Still, you probably won't agree all ten of these common beliefs are truly myths. But I hope you'll at least begin to think about how they can limit your ability to nurture safety heroes.

Myth: People can perform any job if they persist and try hard enough.

Reality: It sounds good, but few of us can become the professional athlete, entertainer, or movie star we'd like to be. Environmental, physical, and psychological factors limit our potential and narrow the range of things we can do with our lives. By the time we reach employment age, there is a finite range of jobs we can perform effectively.

This shouldn't lead to despair. We should attempt to become the best we can within our limitations. We can learn new tasks and expand our possibilities, but there is a limit. It's very important to recognize and understand our limitations, as well as to realize our special interests and skills.

Myth: Brainpower, experience, and desire make the difference.

Reality: Talent is the key to success, not brainpower, motivation, or desire. These factors contribute to an individual's interests and abilities. But talent is the ultimate observable factor determining whether a particular task is done well.[9]

Behavioral observations are an example of a tool that helps you assess a person's special interests and skills, which together define talent. Then you need to match those talents with tasks or functions.

Myth: Varied experiences make an employee more valuable.

Reality: Experience is valuable only if it supports one's talent for performing a particular job. In most work situations, individuals continue to improve when they focus on a particular task and receive objective, behavior-based feedback.

How to be a safety talent scout:

Pay attention

It's not easy to find safety talent. Perhaps you're looking for someone to be on a committee, run meetings, or lead a team. Survey instruments are often unreliable. Interviews are brief and not representative. It's critical to carefully observe ongoing behavior and actively listen to ongoing conversations. Then you might be able to discover employees' competencies that will help your safety program in different areas.

Play up strengths

Help people find out what safety assignments they like to do and are good at doing. Then provide training, experiences, and feedback to hone their skills.

Offer support

When you find the right individual for a particular safety job, look for ways to keep that person committed and positive. Don't be too quick to promote them to another role. Make them feel like a hero for their contributions, and give your heroes more personal control, status, and other forms of recognition. When people feel good about what they do for safety, they're more likely to continue doing it.

Myth: Help workers become more "well-rounded."

Reality: Help people find out what job assignments (or safety assignments) they like to do and are good at doing. Then offer the training, experiences, and feedback to hone their skills in these areas so they become a more valuable employee (and safety contributor).

Myth: Identify workers' weaknesses and fix them.

Reality: Few managers or supervisors have the talent and time to "fix" an employee's weaknesses. They can provide objective feedback, of course, to support desired (safe) behavior and correct undesired (at-risk) behavior. But in a broader sense, it's far more cost effective to identify people's strengths and give them the kind of jobs that benefit from their talents and enable them to flourish.

Myth: Spend more time with your least productive workers.

Reality: Attempting to fix people's weaknesses takes time, and the more weaknesses people have, the more time it will take. In many, if not most, workplaces today, resources and managerial support are limited. It's far more cost-effective to concentrate on keeping talented personnel working at optimal levels than helping those less talented improve their effectiveness. Your talented and productive employees contribute more to your success, and they need supportive feedback and recognition.

Myth: Don't play favorites.
Reality: You should play favorites. You need to spend more time with your more talented employees.

Myth: Reward excellence through promotions.
Reality: After finding the best talent for a job and enabling that talent to flourish and improve, you need to keep that talent on the job – not see it leave for another position.

For this to happen, though, recognition and promotion need to occur within the same job assignment. It must be possible for an employee to be promoted to a higher status level by doing the same job, rather than leaving for another. How much of a paradigm shift would this be for your company? Can your culture develop heroes at every role?

Unique experience influences unique interpretation, and vice versa.

Myth: There's one best way to perform every job.
Reality: This stifles creativity and the ability to keep talents (safety and otherwise) thriving on the same job. Sustaining talent on a job requires workers to feel like heroes. They need to believe they are contributing individually and creatively. This is unlikely if they feel they're only following someone else's protocol.

Allow and expect your employees to find better ways to perform a job safely. That's how you achieve continuous improvement.

Myth: Follow the Golden Rule – Treat others as you want to be treated.

Reality: Should you really treat people the way you want to be treated? What kind of job recognition do you want – public or private? What do you respond to more – an emphasis on competition or cooperation? What incentive works for you – cash, dinner for two, tickets to a football game? Or are you insulted by incentive offers?

I hope I've made my point. We are all unique, and have different needs, desires, and interests. It's simply not wise nor valid to assume everyone else wants to be treated as you do.

It's safe to make some generalizations: Few people like criticism and most people enjoy genuine praise. But exactly how to give praise, feedback, directions, or advice depends on the individual. Don't assume what others like or dislike. Listen with empathy and observe carefully to find out how to treat others.

PART 7

Change "Me-First" Mindsets

Despite all the talk about teamwork, it's not always easy to get teams working the way you want them to. Teamwork just doesn't come naturally to some of us. After all, look at how we've been raised. "Be independent," we're told. We compete with other individuals to get ahead, whether at work or at play. Remember, "Nice guys finish last." A win-lose, me-first mindset is promoted by everything from the grades we get in school to salary promotions at work.

The power of paradigms

Learning to work effectively as a team takes patience. Teamwork calls for different approaches to work than most of us are used to. Sometimes policies or procedures get in the way, and we can modify them to remove a teamwork barrier. But often we need to change our perspective or expectations regarding teamwork, and then adjust our behavior accordingly.

We're talking about changing paradigms here. As discussed in the first chapter, paradigms are powerful personal perceptions, or biases, if you will. Whatever your attitude toward a particular experience, or your expectation of how things will work out, that's your paradigm.

Paradigms influence how we view a situation, and what we take from it. As a result, we often experience what we expect to happen, and learn what we expect to learn. It's like a self-fulfilling prophesy. We act a certain way to be consistent with our paradigm, and so increase the likelihood what we believe will actually occur.

Consider the following five paradigm shifts needed for high-performance teamwork. We can literally act ourselves into

A me-first paradigm stifles teamwork.

becoming a better team player – if we follow these interconnected paradigm shifts.

1) From individual to team performance

Traditional work holds people accountable for their own behavior. Effective teamwork, though, requires mutual accountability. It's not, "What you do is what you get," but rather, "How you collaborate with others is what the group gets." Effective collaboration nets performance results greater than what individuals can do by themselves. This is a synergistic outcome.

2) From individual jobs to team tasks

This synergy occurs when each team member contributes individual talent and effort to improve team performance. Team members receive task assignments from each other, and carry out their responsibilities to support the rest of the team. This is much different than traditional work, which has us completing individual job assignments to please a supervisor.

Teamwork requires a shift from working exclusively to achieve personal goals to working to achieve shared team goals. This takes a belief in the power of teamwork, a commitment toward the team's mission, and trust that every team member will do his or her part to meet team objectives.

3) From competitive rewards to rewards for cooperation

It takes a special mindset to revel in the accomplishments of a team effort. When team members value their mutual purpose and believe teammates will cooperate to achieve shared goals, they put forth their best efforts. And when they see cooperation pay off, they develop a unique appreciation for teamwork.

Trust, cooperation, and interdependency reap synergistic rewards.

Team members feel personally recognized when their team is rewarded. Then they cooperate more to fulfill their team's next objectives. But experiencing the rewards of cooperation is benefited by the next paradigm shift.

4) From self-dependence to team dependence

We come into this world dependent on others to take care of us. As children we depended on our family for all of our basic life needs. As adolescents, however, we looked for opportunities to be on our own. It seems, in fact, a primary mission of most teenagers is to resist dependency and assert independence.

This reliance on self rather than others is promoted and reinforced throughout our culture, from high school and college classrooms to corporate board rooms. But high-performance teamwork requires a dependency perspective. This might seem like regression, but it's really progression.

It's actually more appropriate to consider this a paradigm shift to interdependence rather than dependence. That's because the dependency between team members is reciprocal. While you depend on team members to complete their task assignments, others depend on you to do your part.

We're moving from independence to interdependency here. The more you trust the ability and intentions of the other individuals on your team, the more you will depend on your teammates for their contributions – and the more you will feel obligated to complete your own task assignments.

5) From one-to-one communication to group interaction

Trust and interdependency are developed and supported through interpersonal communication. Some of this certainly happens through one-to-one interaction. But the synergistic power of teamwork is more readily realized through effective team meetings. For example, I can assess the individual talents and motives of my students and research associates during one-to-one conversation, but I learn much more about our team's potential to meet a challenge during group meetings.

Through group interaction, individuals see how their diverse talents can combine to produce synergistic results. This leads to greater feelings of self-esteem and self-effectiveness, and it increases personal commitment to meet team objectives. It also cultivates group cohesion and feelings of belonging, which in turn motivate high-performance teamwork.

Effective group discussions build trust in the abilities and intentions of team members. Trust leads to cooperation. This strengthens a paradigm of interdependency, and increases personal motivation to work harder for the team. As a result, team members appreciate the real meaning of TEAM – Together Everyone Achieves More.[10]

PART 8

Create Excitement for Safety

While attending a seminar by Dr. Kenneth Blanchard, coauthor of the classic best seller, *The One-Minute Manager,* I discovered that he had written a 1998 book with Sheldon Bowles that I think applies to our discussions on safety. *Gung Ho! Turn On the People in Any Organization* reveals three basic "secrets" for getting more enthusiastic employee involvement.[11]

I want to teach you these three secrets as they relate to increasing involvement in safety-related efforts. This information won't be new to you, but the creative way Blanchard and Bowles state the obvious is invaluable. Learning these three secrets can improve your ability to teach basic philosophies you already know but perhaps don't use enough.

Secret 1: The Spirit of the Squirrel

Watch squirrels scurrying about collecting and storing food. They work at high energy because they're motivated, and they're motivated because their work is critical. If they don't store enough food for the winter, they will starve. So the Spirit of the Squirrel is "worthwhile work."

Convince employees their work is worthwhile, and they'll be more motivated on the job. How? Help people see the bigger picture beyond their daily work routine, Blanchard advises. A bricklayer, for example, could describe his job as "laying brick" or as "building a community recreation center to bring people together for healthy recreation and exercise." Both descriptions are accurate, but you know which one sounds more worthwhile and stimulating. Whatever employees are doing, they're making a difference. Help them understand their contribution.

Worthwhile work is the spirit of the squirrel.

Safety leaders naturally have the Spirit of the

Squirrel. Safety work is obviously worthwhile. You care for everyone's primary asset – their safety and health. The challenge is to convince people that routine safety-related activities, from wearing uncomfortable protective equipment to conducting periodic environmental and behavioral audits, are really worthwhile.

As I've said more than once already, personal testimony is more effective than company statistics to get this point across. When employees can visualize injuries prevented by their involvement, they can see how their safety work is worthwhile. Like the squirrels' work, their safety-related actions help colleagues and friends make it through the winter and beyond.

Secret 2: The Way of the Beaver

A squirrel's behavior is fluent, filled with purposeful energy, but it can be rather chaotic and noncooperative. Two squirrels might fight over a single acorn, and acorns buried by one squirrel for the winter will be another's treasure if they are found. Squirrels work hard – but they do so independently.

Beavers work interdependently. They have the Spirit of the Squirrel, but as the more intelligent rodent, they cooperate to get the job done. Blanchard emphasizes there is no "boss beaver." You can't watch beavers work and determine who is in charge.

The Way of the Beaver is being self-directed to achieve goals that benefit everyone. This secret exemplifies empowerment as I discussed in Chapter 4 on "The Thinking of People-Based Safety." People who feel empowered believe they can make a difference and are more likely to actively care for the safety and health of others. Remember, research has linked three mental states to perceptions of empowerment: self-efficacy ("I can do it"), response-efficacy ("It will work"), and outcome-expectancy ("It is worth it").[12]

Empowered interdependency is the way of the beaver.

The Way of the Beaver reflects these three states. Beavers know their job (self-efficacy) and know their

Cheerleading is the gift of the goose.

behavior – storing twigs and sticks, gnawing down trees, dragging or floating lumber, and so on – will build the dam. Do they believe the results are worth their effort? It surely seems they are motivated by expected consequences; just look at how eagerly each beaver works.

Secret 3: The Gift of the Goose

Geese epitomize interdependency. Just look at them in flight. They form a "V" with a leader up front and each following goose flying in the draft created by the one immediately in front. The lead goose eventually tires of the head wind and moves back in the "V", replaced by another goose. This is true interdependence.

There's something else about geese in flight – that honking sound. Which geese are honking? It's all of them. Each one frequently honks, as though they are cheering each other on.

That's the Gift of the Goose. Geese provide each other with constant verbal support, recognizing how each member of the flying team allows the group to make headway. Their "cheering" encourages continued cooperation.

Recognizing and encouraging behaviors that make a difference reflects the remarkable power of positive recognition and rewards. This is a key principle of People-Based Safety. When work cultures display as much teamwork and cheerleading for safety-related action as reflected in a flock of geese, exemplary levels of safety performance are attained.

Don't forget, though, you need something to cheer about. Start by developing a behavior-based coaching process in your workplace that involves people working interdependently to reduce at-risk behaviors and environmental hazards. Then injuries will be prevented. Now that's something to honk about.

To get people involved...

- Convince workers routine safety activities are really worthwhile.
- Use personal testimony to show how safety actions can make a difference.
- Educate and train workers so they're confident they can handle safety tasks.
- Make sure they have personal control over achieving safety goals.
- Encourage expectations of achieving good results.
- Recognize individual and group safety contributions and achievements.
- Praise individuals when they go beyond the call for safety.
- Hold team celebrations for group safety achievements.

PART 9

Building Momentum for Safety

In 2004 the football team at my university, known as the "Virginia Tech Hokies" won the ACC Championship, the first year they joined the Atlantic Coast Conference. At the start of the 2004 Season, the Hokies were ranked seventh in the ACC. From careful comparisons of the talent on the ACC football teams, coaches and sports writers did not give our team much of a chance. But they didn't account for leadership, team chemistry, and the focus here – momentum. Here, I discuss how we can harness momentum to improve our safety processes.

Coaches are very aware of the power of momentum. For example, research published in the *Journal of Applied Behavior Analysis* in 1991 systematically analyzed 14 college basketball games during the 1989 NCAA tournament and found that basketball coaches called time-out from play when being outscored by their opponents an average of 2.63 to 1.0.[13] Calling time-out usually stopped the other team's momentum – the rate of successful plays during the three minutes immediately after a time-out was nearly equal for both teams.

Let's consider factors relevant to increasing momentum We can return to the sports analogy for intuitive answers to the question, "How can we build and maintain momentum?" I think you'll agree from personal experience that three factors are critical to momentum-building: achievement of the team, atmosphere of the culture, and attitude of the leaders. The three ingredients start with the letter "A," so they're easy to remember. And they are clearly overlapping and interrelated.

Achievement

It's obvious that success builds success. Good performance is more likely after a run of successful behaviors than failures. In sports, a succession of winning plays or points creates momentum.

Sports psychologists talk about momentum as a gain in psychological power – including confidence, self-efficacy, and personal control – that changes perceptions and attitudes, and enhances both mental and physical performance. It all starts with noticing a run of individual or team achievements. How can we apply this to safety management?

We've got to keep score. We need a system to track the small wins in safety that can build momentum. At sporting events, fans constantly check the scoreboard to measure their team's performance. I'm convinced this is a prime reason we like to watch or participate in sporting events. We get objective and fair feedback regarding ongoing performance.

"Knowing the score" creates excitement if our team is performing well, or urgency if performance must improve. This kind of observable and equitable appraisal is a performance measure that can be used as feedback to improve subsequent performance and increase the probability of more success and continued momentum.

To successfully manage safety, we must find an ongoing objective and impartial measure of performance that allows us to regularly evaluate our progress. When employees see continuous improvement in their safety "score," they recognize momentum and stay motivated to participate in the achievement-oriented process.

This is why in People-Based Safety we emphasize the need to:

- Develop up-stream process measures (such as number of audits completed or percentage of safe behaviors);
- Set process-oriented goals that are specific, motivational, achievable, relevant, trackable, and shared;
- Discuss safety performance in terms of achievement – what people have done for safety, and what additional achievement potential is within their domain of control;
- Recognize individuals appropriately for their accomplishments; and,
- Celebrate group or team accomplishments on a regular basis.

A winning score builds momentum.

Atmosphere

In sports, it's called the "home-field advantage." It means having fans available to help create or sustain momentum. By packing the stands and cheering loudly, fans create an atmosphere that can motivate the home team to try harder. A run of successful plays can lead to a score, and then momentum to achieve more. This stimulates the home crowd to cheer more, and momentum is supported.

I hope the relevance to safety is clear. Continuous participation in a safety-improvement effort is influenced by the atmosphere surrounding the process. Is the work culture optimistic about the safety effort, or is the process viewed as another "flavor of the month"? Do the workers trust management to give adequate support to a long-term intervention, or is this just another "quick fix" reaction that will soon be replaced by another "priority"?

Before helping a work team implement a People-Based Safety process, my partners at Safety Performance Solutions insist everyone in the work culture learn the principles underlying the process. Everyone in the culture needs to learn the rationale behind the safety process, even those who will not be involved in actual implementation. This helps to provide the right kind of atmosphere or cultural context to support momentum.

When the vision of a work team is shared optimistically with the entire workforce, people are likely to buy in and do what it takes to support the mission. When this happens, interpersonal trust and morale builds, along with a winning spirit. People don't fear failure but expect to succeed, and this atmosphere fuels more achievement from the process team.

Attitude

The coach of an athletic team can make or break momentum. Coaches initiate and support momentum by helping team members and the team as a whole recognize their accomplishments. This starts with a clear statement of a vision and attainable goals. Then the leader enthusiastically holds individuals and the team accountable for achieving these goals.

The wrong attitude saps momentum.

A positive coach can even help members of a losing team feel better about themselves, and give momentum a chance. The key is to find pockets of excellence to acknowledge, thus building self-confidence and self-efficacy. Then specific corrective feedback will be heard and accepted as key to being more successful and building more momentum.

It does little good for safety leaders to reprimand individuals or teams for a poor safety record, unless they also provide a method people can use to do better. And the leader must explain and support the improvement method with confidence, commitment, and enthusiasm.

For momentum to build and continue, support means more than providing necessary resources. It means looking for success stories to recognize and celebrate. This helps to develop feelings of achievement among those directly involved (the team) and an optimistic atmosphere from others (the work culture). These are the ingredients for safety momentum. Keep these in place and your momentum will be sustained. Then you can truly expect the best from your efforts to implement People-Based Safety.

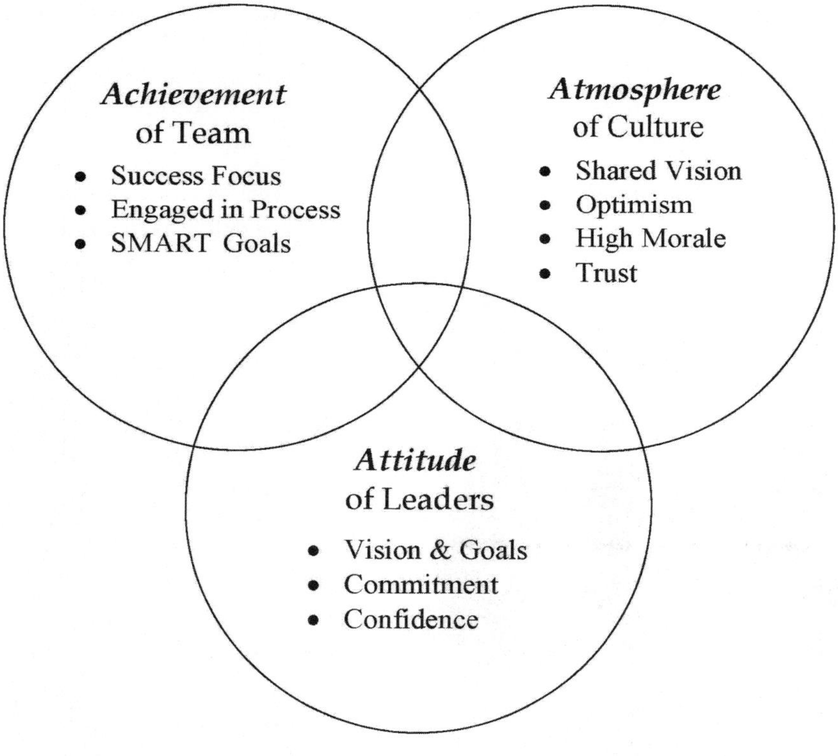

Three "A" factors build and maintain momentum.

PART 10

Fuel Participation

Let's review specific ways to get more people involved in efforts to prevent injuries on the job. The twenty principles presented here are founded on accepted psychological theory and empirical research rather than common sense. Much of this list serves as a review of critical principles presented earlier in this book. Let's start with the most basic strategy of all, and probably the most important – our language.

1) Watch your language

Words shape our feelings, expectancies, attitudes, and behaviors.[14] Safety professionals commonly use words like "accident," "compliance," "regulation," "investigation," "occupant restraint," and "loss control."

Such language certainly limits voluntary participation. Who wants to get involved in an "accident investigation" that seemingly attempts to find out who didn't "comply" with some safety "regulation" and therefore contributed to a "loss"? And who feels good about putting on an "occupant restraint" in order to comply with a corporate "mandate"?

Language affects thinking, seeing, and acting.

2) Shift safety from a priority to a value

Calling safety the "Number One Priority" puts management in an awkward position. Employees know safety is not number one – profit is. If the company does not make money, there are no jobs, and there's no need for occupational safety. So stop putting safety in a position to compete with profit-making. Instead, give safety a separate and special category – value. Our vision should be to make safety a value linked to every activity or priority in a work culture.

3) *Take advantage of the competence motive*

Stop talking about safety as if it's altruistic or self-sacrificing. This gives people an excuse for compromising safe operating procedures. "I just didn't have time to follow all of the precautions this time."

People want to be judged competent.[15] If safety is a value – inherent to every job – disregarding any relevant safety process means the job is done incorrectly. The operator is incompetent. And remember, competence can only be improved through feedback.

4) *Provide behavior-focused feedback*

Practice does not make perfect. Only with appropriate feedback can we improve. In the workplace, competence-improving feedback that is objective, impersonal, and specific can be delivered in three basic ways: 1) through one-on-one coaching; 2) through periodic performance appraisals; and 3) through group data graphs that display a work team's level of specific performance. Whatever the method for providing directional and/or motivational feedback, the context must be positive.

5) *Make feedback positive*

People more often link feedback with "reprimand" than "praise." So don't

Group feedback improves group performance.

expect people to naturally accept and look forward to receiving behavioral feedback. The nature of your conversation or group discussion surrounding a feedback session will determine whether such a process will be appreciated, supported, and sustained. Your first feedback session needs to be predominantly positive and completely constructive.

6) Help people feel important

Negative feedback can degrade one's sense of importance, and that's disastrous for voluntary participation. That's why it's so important to emphasize a person's positive contributions to worthwhile work. When people believe their work is genuinely appreciated, they want to improve. When they become competent at a valuable job, their sense of personal importance increases. Then, in the spirit of increasing their competence at a valuable work process, people will accept and apply relevant corrective feedback.

7) Look ahead, not back

When we have opportunities to coach or offer advice to individuals or groups, we need to move the communication from past to future and then to the present. Conversations about past experiences are pleasant and functional. They define mutual interests, attitudes, or experiences and enable recognition for prior accomplishments, helping people feel important. But if you want productive change from a conversation, don't allow talk to get stuck in the past.

Move your communication from the past to a consideration of future possibilities or ideal improvement. Then, after pondering aloud what could be, bring the talk back to the present. Discuss things that can be put into effect now to bring the ideal future a step closer.

8) Set SMART goals

A conversation about progress can lead to beneficial change if SMART goals are set. The letters of SMART represent the essential components of an effective goal – Specific, Motivational, Achievable, Relevant, and Trackable. Literally thousands of studies have demonstrated the power of SMART goals to improve performance at individual, group, organizational, and community levels.[16] We set a poor example when we refer to goals that are not SMART. In safety this happens whenever we say, "Zero injuries is our goal." This is not SMART; it misuses and abuses goal setting.

9) Distinguish goals from purpose

Please talk about zero injuries as a purpose or vision. "An injury-free work culture" is the ultimate result of gaining and sustaining maximum employee involvement in safety-related activities. So your purpose is to reach and maintain zero injuries. Participation is needed for various process activities that contribute to injury prevention and the attainment of a vision of "injury-free." Process activities can be defined in terms of a certain number of specific actions that need to occur in a given period of time in order to be "successful."

10) Use process measures

Keep score on the various proactive things individuals and groups do for safety. Monitor the numbers of near hits, property damage incidents, and injuries reported. Track the number of corrective actions implemented and evaluated, the number of environmental and behavioral audits conducted, the number of environmental hazards eliminated, the number of safety suggestions and safety work orders submitted, and so on. Graph and post the percentage of individuals who participate in various safety-related activities, as well as the percentage of safe work environments and behaviors observed during systematic audits. This will give you an accountability system that can facilitate participation.

11) Elevate self-efficacy

Self-efficacy reflects a "can do" attitude. It refers to a person's perception that he or she can organize and execute the procedures necessary to reach a certain goal. This is the "achievable" component of SMART goals – the "A" in the acronym. To assess whether self-efficacy is sufficient, ask the question, "Do you believe you can do this?" If the answer is "no," then ask, "What would it take to convince you that you can attain the goal?"

12) Enhance response-efficacy

Response-efficacy refers to one's belief that a certain technique or strategy will actually produce the desired outcome. It's not enough to know what to do and have the confidence to do it. You must believe the effort will pay off. This is the "relevant" feature of SMART goals – the "R". You've got to believe that reaching the goal (conducting a certain number of behavioral audits, etc.) will be instrumental in reducing injuries.

13) Sell outcome-expectancy

Outcome-expectancy means you believe the effect of participating, of completing a safety activity or reaching a certain goal, will produce worthwhile consequences. This is the "motivational" component of SMART goals – the "M".

And this is where you can often run into resistance. You can build that "can do" attitude and sell the soundness of your strategy to reduce injuries, but some still might not participate. Why? Perhaps the consequence – reducing injuries beyond an already low rate – doesn't seem important enough to justify the extra time and inconvenience.

So what do you do? Often safety professionals use group statistics like total recordable injury rate (TRIR) or workers' compensation costs to motivate more participation. But these numbers are too abstract, too remote. The consequence workers can relate to is an individual one – a personal report of an injured employee they know.

14) Encourage testimonies

Listeners can relate to an individual's story and put themselves in the same situation. A personal account of an injury that could have been prevented by a certain safety procedure is a powerful motivator. So is an anecdote about someone who avoided an injury by using a particular technique or procedure.

Your challenge is to get individuals to open up and speak frankly about their close calls and actual injuries. They need to own up to things they could have done to prevent an incident.

15) Build ownership and trust

You're not going to get this with a "command and control" mindset that puts OSHA regulations at the center of a safety process. People will open up when they feel part of the process, and trust those in charge of that process. The next two strategies help build ownership and trust to fuel the participation factor.

16) Put principles before procedures

When people are educated about the principles and rationale behind a process, they can customize specific procedures for their own work areas. Then the relevance of the training process is obvious, and participation is enhanced. Remember, people are more likely to accept and follow procedures they helped to develop. Safe operating procedures become "the best way to do it" rather than "a policy we must obey."

17) Customize your process

Don't build your safety efforts around off-the-shelf programs. People want to be trained on their implementation procedures.

When you're guiding the customizing of a safety process, don't give mandates or directions. Instead, display a mix of both confidence and uncertainty. Effective leaders are confident a set of procedures will be developed – but don't know the best way to do it. This gives employees room to be mindful, innovative, and self-motivated, which increases ownership and trust, and in turn leads to more involvement.

18) Cultivate self-persuasion and self-accountability

Choice, ownership, and trust contribute to self-accountability – a necessity for maintaining an injury-free workplace. When people work alone, they need to hold themselves accountable to follow safe operating procedures. This often requires a significant amount of self-persuasion or self-discipline.

Severe threats and large incentives are often not the best motivators. Research has shown that the more external justification a person feels for a certain activity, the less internal justification or self-accountability the individual develops.[17] The principles discussed here for fueling the participation factor are especially powerful because they help to develop self-persuasion and self-accountability.

19) Use the hypocrisy effect

Instead of threats and large incentives, try this technique: First, obtain a public commitment that participants will perform a designated safe behavior(s). Then ask for a list of personal at-risk actions that are inconsistent with this safe behavior. You're stirring up tension between words (the commitment) and deeds (prior behavior), which in turn increases self-persuasion and self-accountability to live up to the initial commitment.

By getting participants to experience hypocrisy (or feelings of inconsistency), they are more likely to perform the safe behavior when working

Don't buy a program, customize a process.

alone in order to reduce that tension. The need to be consistent in word and deed can have broad impact, as reflected in the final guideline I'll give you here for fueling participation.

20) Promote systems thinking

When you choose to change a behavior, you adjust your attitudes and beliefs to be consistent with your actions. This change in attitude can influence more behavior change – a spiraling, reciprocal interdependency between outward actions and inward feelings. This is how small changes in behavior and attitude can eventually lead to personal commitment and total involvement.

Systems thinking and the scholarship of continuous improvement gurus such as Stephen Covey[18] and Edwards Deming[19] are consistent with this concept, and can be used to increase the quantity and improve the quality of people's involvement in all aspects of occupational safety. Such thinking helps people realize their importance in solving problems without fear of being blamed as a "root cause." It advances understanding of factors outside and inside people that influence participation, and provide direction for self-persuasion and self-accountability.

PART 11

Build a Belief in Safety

Let's add ten more strategies to our list of ways to cultivate the kinds of behaviors, beliefs, feelings, and attitudes that fuel more participation in safety-related activities.[20] These ten additional recommendations also review key techniques discussed in more detail earlier in this book.

1) Focus on facts, not faults

Safety's traditional root cause investigation stifles the open conversation needed to analyze incidents and near hits. It focuses on what went wrong, and people don't want to talk about failure, especially if they suspect the finger of blame could point at them. Just as important, there really is no single root cause of an incident. Environmental, behavioral, and attitudinal factors contribute to almost every injury or near hit.

2) Diagnose carefully

I'm sure you've heard these recommendations following an investigation: "The employee will be retrained" and "The employee will be disciplined." These should be "last resort" interventions. Instead, ask these ten questions:

- What is the discrepancy between observed and ideal performance?
- Is change called for?
- Can the task be simplified?
- Are expectations clear?
- Is performance feedback available?
- What are the natural or intrinsic consequences?
- Is there a skill discrepancy?
- Is the person right for the job?
- What kind of training is needed?
- Which corrective action is most cost-effective?

You need to take the time to find the facts and interpret them carefully before planning a safety intervention.

3) Deliver quality recognition

I'm sure you've heard the expression that too much recognition can give a person a "big head." Well, guess what? A big head is good. The more recognition people receive, the better they feel about themselves. And the better people feel about themselves, the more they will actively care for the safety of others.

People can't get too much behavior-based recognition.

And remember, quality one-to-one recognition needs to be given privately, not publicly. Many people feel embarrassed when receiving special attention in a group context.

4) Take it all in

Reactions to recognition help determine future participation. Here are five guidelines for receiving recognition:

- Avoid denials and disclaimers.
- Actively listen with sincere appreciation.
- Relive the recognition later.
- Reward the recognition process.
- Ask for recognition when it's deserved.

5) Celebrate success

Speaking of recognition, follow these guidelines for conducting quality safety celebrations:

- Don't promote cheating by announcing an injury-reduction criterion needed for a celebration.
- Focus on the journey – the processes that contributed to reaching the injury-reduction milestone.
- Management should listen more than speak, and line workers should talk more about their participation than listen to managers' pleasure with the bottom line.

• Relive the participation by discussing the activities that led to success.

• Show how difficult it was to reach the milestone by pointing out hardships endured.

• Use tangible rewards that support the memory of an occasion by displaying a relevant safety theme or slogan.

6) Punish as a last resort

Punishment is detrimental to long-term participation, and it can turn individuals and an entire work culture against those doing the punishing.

If you must send people home for punishment, let them have their pay and in return ask them to prepare a comprehensive plan for specific improvement, including ways to secure management and peer support. And after a supervisor approves an individual's plan for corrective action, both should offer mutual commitment and support by signing a written summary of the improvement plan.

Five person factors influence people's willingness to actively care.

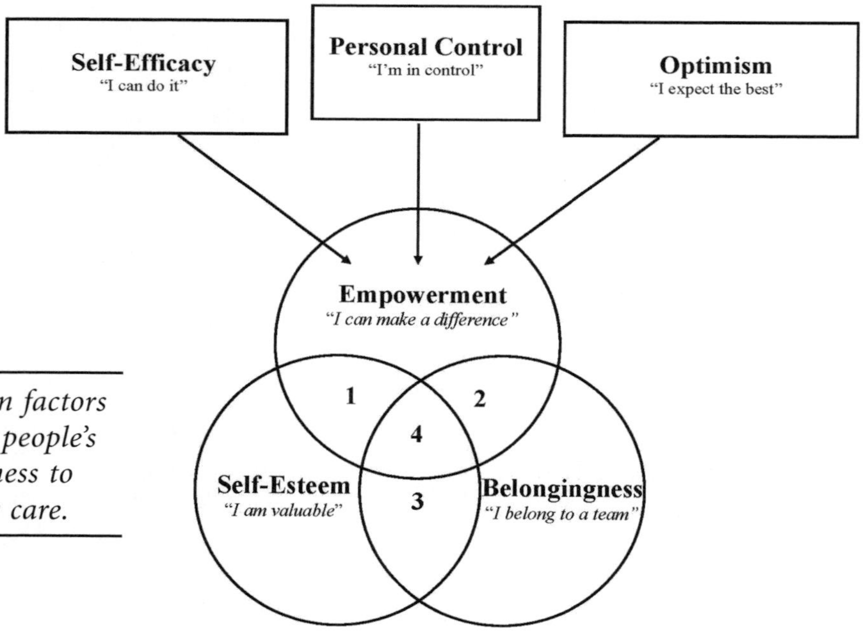

1. I can make a valuable difference.
2. We can make valuable differences.
3. I'm a valuable team member.
4. We can make valuable differences.

7) Enhance "actively caring"

Five factors influence people's willingness to help others: self-esteem ("I am valuable"), belonging ("I belong to a team"), self-efficacy ("I can do it"), personal control ("I am in control"), and optimism ("I expect the best").[21]

Ask participants to specify recent situations and/or activities that decreased and increased these particular traits in them. Then brainstorm practical ways to cultivate these "person states" in the future.

8) Promote interdependence

When people understand interdependency, they realize their safety-related behaviors influence the safety of others. They participate in a safety process because they don't want anyone to get hurt, and they realize their good example contributes interdependently to the vision of an injury-free workplace.

9) Look beyond the numbers

Leaders certainly appreciate the need to hold people accountable with numbers, but they also understand you can't measure everything. They don't attempt to measure their success at increasing the actively caring person states I just mentioned. They do things on a regular basis to inspire these feeling states in others, but don't worry about measuring their direct impact.

10) Build and maintain momentum

Three factors – achievement of your participants, atmosphere of your culture, and attitude of your coaches and team leaders – influence momentum.

Achievement: You've got to keep score. You need a system to track small wins in safety that can build momentum:

- Develop up-stream process measures such as number of audits completed or percentage of safe behaviors occurring.
- Set process-oriented goals that are SMART – specific, motivational, achievable, relevant, and trackable.
- Discuss safety performance in terms of accomplishment – what people have done for safety, and what additional achievement potential is within their domain of control.
- Recognize individuals appropriately for their accomplishments.
- Celebrate group or team accomplishments on a regular basis.

Atmosphere: Before helping to launch a new safety-improvement process, my partners at Safety Performance Solutions insist everyone in the work culture learn the principles underlying the process. Everyone in the culture needs to learn the rationale behind the safety process – even those who will not be involved in actual implementation. This helps to provide the right kind of atmosphere or cultural context to support the process.

Attitude: Start with a clear statement of a vision and attainable goals. Then enthusiastically hold individuals and the team accountable for achieving these goals. Offer recognition when goals are reached.

A positive coach can even help members of a losing team feel better about themselves, and give momentum a chance. The key is to find pockets of excellence to acknowledge, which builds self-confidence and self-efficacy. Then specific corrective feedback will be accepted as key to being more successful, and to building more momentum.

PART 12

Strategies for Sustaining Safety

I want to continue addressing ways to get more people involved in safety activities. Here I review seven principles gleaned from social science research. We're talking about basic social dynamics that reflect – and influence – the culture of an organization. They can inhibit or facilitate participation in safety. You can use these social influence principles to analyze the dynamics that hinder optimal involvement in safety, and decide which can be changed to fuel more participation.[22]

1) We try to be consistent.

Commitments are most influential when they are public, active, and perceived as voluntary or not coerced. When we make a choice or take a stand, we face personal and social pressures to stick to our commitment. So it's better to have employees make a public rather than a private commitment to perform a certain safe behavior.

And it's better to have them sign their name to a card rather than merely raise their hands. People live up to what they write down. Inconsistencies between promises and behaviors lead to unflattering labels such as "flighty," "scatterbrained," or "two-faced."

Of course, it's very important for those pledging to do something for safety to believe they made the commitment voluntarily.

2) We want to return a favor.

Basically, if you're nice to people, they will feel obligated to return the favor. What does this mean for safety management? Look for opportunities to go out of your way for another person's safety. When we actively care for someone else's safety, we set the tone for what is called "reciprocity." We increase the likelihood that person will actively care for the safety of someone else.

3) We help those we like.

Who will you go out of your way to help or care for – someone you like or dislike? It's obvious, right? So we need to build positive relationships in our workplaces. How? Here are three strategies:

• Emphasize similarities: "Birds of a feather flock together." Through initial informal conversation and astute observation, you can find common bonds between you and others you'd like to influence. Maybe you enjoy the same hobbies or recreational activities, or have matching educational backgrounds or employment histories, or have similar opinions about current events, corporate issues, and even politics.

• Give praise: Genuine one-to-one praise, recognition, and rewarding feedback builds relationships. The person you reward likes you more; and because their behavior deserves recognition, your appreciation for that person increases.

• Promote cooperation: Cooperation works better than contests and competition in forging positive relationships. You want to build a sense of interdependency toward achieving a common goal. We're more likely to work with, and help, those we depend on.

Similarity breeds familiarity and liking.

4) We follow the crowd.

We see examples of conformity every day, from the types of clothes people wear to their styles of communication to the products we buy. Don't overlook the power of conformity in influencing participation. And the pressure to conform is greater when the consensus (say a commitment to safety) comes out of a large group, and when group members are seen as relatively experienced.

Experienced employees should feel especially responsible to demonstrate safe work practices to new employees. People look for guidance in unfamiliar situations. So supervisors should give new hires opportunities to work with experienced employees who are most enthusiastic about safety-related activities.

5) We respect authority.

Experienced employees have credible authority. That makes them influential. But there's a flip side to the power of authority. Following orders gives us an excuse to escape taking personal responsibility for what we are doing. If someone with authority tells us to take a risk, we're often willing to comply because if something goes wrong, it won't be our fault. We can blame the person who told us to do it. Be aware of the power of authority, and encourage people to resist the temptation to follow orders blindly and mindlessly.

6) We want what is hard to get.

The value of something – front-row seats at a game, stamps, baseball cards, antique furniture – increases with the perception of scarcity. People will collect, go out of their way to purchase, and get caught up in bids and bargains for items considered scarce.

So what can the scarcity principle teach us about getting more people involved in a safety process?

• Emphasize unique features: First, we ought to emphasize the unique features of a safety process. How is a particular approach to injury prevention better than the rest? How is it leading edge? When people believe they have a rare opportunity to test a new – even "experimental" – approach to safety, their motivation is powered by the scarcity principle.

• Play up the fear of losing: Social psychologists have shown that people are especially motivated to avoid a loss. Think about it. When it's evident you need to act immediately in order to avoid losing something, you are aroused to mindful action.

We dress to conform.

So how do we demonstrate the potential losses that can come from unsafe acts and environments? Personal testimonies from workers injured on the job, or who just missed being injured, are powerful reminders of what's at stake. Scare tactics, handled correctly, can also be effective.

7) We want what is novel.

We are drawn to what is new or different as well as

what is scarce or rare. The novelty principle is reflected in our desire for excitement and surprise in our relationships with others. This appeal of newness and unpredictability facilitates the beginning of a relationship, while the lack of novelty in a familiar routine can be the key factor in the breakup of a relationship.

The novelty principle activates unusual styles.

The implication for safety? The uniqueness of a new approach to injury prevention promotes initial involvement; but over time, the same safety routine can seem dull and uninspiring, leading to a drop in the quantity or quality of participation.

It's important to find ways to vary aspects of a particular safety process. Actually, it's essential for continuous improvement. A mechanism for continually refining and upgrading your procedures should be established at the start. This usually requires the ongoing involvement of a safety steering committee that solicits and reviews employee suggestions for program refinement, decides which refinement(s) to implement first, and then monitors the impact of certain changes to an injury-prevention process.

Your safety steering committee not only supports the vision of "never-ending improvement," but also maintains a degree of novelty in the safety-related activities of an organization.

Notes

1. Geller, E. S. (1998). *Beyond safety accountability: How to increase personal responsibility.* Neenah, WI: J. J. Keller & Associates, Inc.
2. Ken Blanchard calls this "situational leadership" as introduced in Blanchard, K. P., Zigami, P., & Zigarini, D. (1985). *Leadership and the one-minute manager.* New York: William Morrow and Company, Inc.
3. *American Heritage Dictionary* (1991), (Second Edition), New York: Houghton Mifflin Company.

4. Cook, J., & Wall, T. (1980). New work attitude measures of trust, organizational commitment and personal need non-fulfillment. *Journal of Occupational Psychology, 53,* 39-52.
5. Rees, F. (1997). *Teamwork from start to finish.* San Francisco: Jossey-Boss, Inc.
6. In the book, *Good to great* (2001, New York: Harper Collins Publishers, Inc.) Jim Collins attributes this quality to the great leaders.
7. Bird, Jr., F. E., & Davies, R. J. (1996). *Safety and the bottom line.* Loganville, GA: Febco.
8. Buckingham, M., & Coffman, C. (1999). *First, break all the rules: What the world's greatest managers do differently.* New York: Simon & Schuster, Inc.
9. This was also the conclusion of Jim Collins and his research team as described in Collins, J. (2001). *Good to great,* New York: Harper Collins Publishers, Inc.
10. Geller, E. S. (2001). *Building successful safety teams.* Rockville, MD: Government Institutes.
11. Blanchard, K. (1999, November). *Building gung ho teams: How to turn people power into profits.* Workshop presented at the Hotel Roanoke, Roanoke, VA.
12. Bandura, A. (1997). *Self-efficacy: The exercise of control.* New York: W. H. Freeman and Company; Geller, E. S. (2002). *The participation factor: How to increase involvement in occupational safety.* Des Plaines, IL: American Society of Safety Engineers.
13. Geller, E. S. (1999, March). Building momentum for safety. *Industrial Safety & Hygiene News,* 33(3), pp.16,18.; Mace, F. C., Lalli, J. S., Shea, M. C., & Nevin, J. A. (1992) Behavioral momentum in college basketball. *Journal of Applied Behavior Analysis,* 25, 657-667.
14. Hayakawa, S. I. (1978). *Language in thought and action,* (Fourth Edition). New York: Harcourt Brace Jovanovich, Publishers.
15. Kaplan, S. (2000). Human nature and environmentally responsible behavior. *Journal of Social Issues, 56,* 411-508; White, R. W. (1959). Motivation reconsidered: The concept of competence. *Psychological Review, 66,* 297-333.
16. Locke, E. A., & Latham, G. P. (1990). *A theory of goal setting and task performance.* Englewood Cliffs, NJ: Prentice Hall; Locke, E. A., Shaw, K. N., Saari, L. M., & Latham, G. P. (1981). Goal setting and task performance: 1969-1980. *Psychological Bulletin, 90,* 125-152.
17. Aronson, E. (1999). The power of self-persuasion. *American Psychologist, 54,* 875-884; Bem, D. J. (1972). Self-perception theory. In L. Berkowitz (Ed.). *Advance in experimental social psychology,* Vol. 6 (pp.1-60). New York: Academic Press.
18. Covey, S. R. (1989). *The seven habits of highly effective people.* New York: Simon and Schuster, Inc.
19. Deming, W. E. (1986). *Out of the crisis,* Cambridge, MA: Center for Advanced Engineering Study, Massachusetts Institute of Technology; Deming, W. E. (1993). *The new economics for industry, government, education.* Cambridge, MA: Center for Advanced Engineering Study, Massachusetts Institute of Technology.
20. Geller, E. S. (2002). *The participation factor: How to increase involvement in occupational safety.* Des Plaines, IL: American Society of Safety Engineers.
21. See reviews of the actively caring model in Geller, E. S. (2001). Actively caring for occupational safety: Extending the performance management paradigm. In C. M. Johnson, W. K. Redman, & T. C. Mawhinny (Eds.). *Handbook of organizational performance: Behavior analysis and management* (pp.303-326). New York: The Haworth Press; and Geller (2003). People-Based Safety: The psychology of actively caring. *Professional Safety, 48*(12), 33-43.
22. Geller, E. S. (2002). Social influence principles: Fueling participation in occupational safety. *Professional Safety, 47*(10), 25-31.

About the Author

E. Scott Geller, Ph.D. is a Senior Partner of Safety Performance Solutions, Inc. – a leading-edge organization specializing in behavior-based safety training and consulting. Dr. Geller and his partners at Safety Performance Solutions (SPS) have helped companies across the country and around the world address the human dynamics of occupational safety through flexible research-founded principles and industry-proven tools. In addition, for more than three decades, Professor E. Scott Geller has taught and conducted research as a faculty member in the Department of Psychology at Virginia Polytechnic Institute and State University, better known as Virginia Tech. In this capacity, he has authored more than 350 research articles and over 75 books or chapters addressing the development and evaluation of behavior-change interventions to improve quality of life.

His recent books in occupational health and safety include: *The Psychology of Safety*; *Working Safe*; *Understanding Behavior-Based Safety*; *Building Successful Safety Teams*; *Beyond Safety Accountability: How to Increase Personal Responsibility*; *The Psychology of Safety Handbook*; *Keys to Behavior-Based Safety from Safety Performance Solutions*; *The Participation Factor* and the primer: *What Can Behavior-Based Safety Do For Me?* His latest book, titled *People-Based Safety™: The Source,* was published in June 2005 by Coastal Training Technologies Corporation.

Dr. Geller is a Fellow of the American Psychological Association, the American Psychological Society, and the World Academy of Productivity and Quality Sciences. He is past Editor of the *Journal of Applied Behavior Analysis* (1989-1992), current Associate Editor of *Environment and Behavior* (since 1982), and current Consulting Editor for *Behavior and Social Issues*, the *Behavior Analyst Digest*, and the *Journal of Organizational Behavior Management*.

Scott Geller's caring, dedication, talent, and energy have helped him earn a teaching award in 1982 from the American Psychological Association and every university teaching award offered at Virginia Tech. In 1983 he received the Virginia Tech Alumni Teaching Award and was elected to the Virginia Tech Academy of Teaching Excellence; in 1990 he was honored with the all-university Sporn Award for distinguished teaching of freshman-level courses; and in 1999 he was awarded the prestigious W.E. Wine Award for Teaching Excellence.

Dr. Geller has written more than 100 articles for *Industrial Safety & Hygiene*

News, a trade magazine disseminated to more than 75,000 companies. He has collaborated with Tel-A-Train Inc. and J. J. Keller and Associates in the development of various training series, which include videotapes, workbooks, and facilitators' guides. For these innovative and creative works, beginning with a 1995 nationally renowned seminar series – Actively Caring for Safety – the Society for the Advancement of Behavior Analysis honored Dr. Geller with an award for Effective Presentation of Behavior Analysis in the Mass Media.

Dr. Geller and his colleagues at SPS have worked with numerous organizations, both public and private, to tailor training and implementation efforts related to the psychology of safety. Past customers include both small and large organizations representing manufacturing, chemical processing, transportation, and service industries, including Advanced Elastomer Systems; Allied Signal; American Standard; ARCO Chemical; ARCO Pipeline; AT&T; Bayer; Bechtel; BF Goodrich; BHP; Bristol-Myers Squibb; Cargill; Coca-Cola; Champion International; Chevron; Corning; ExxonMobil Chemical; Eli Lilly; Estee Lauder; Florida Power & Light; Ford; General Dynamics; General Motors; Georgia-Pacific; Hercules; Hewlett-Packard; Hoechst Celanese; Honeywell; Imperial Oil; Infineum; JEA; Johnson & Johnson; Koch Refining; L.L. Bean; Leprino Foods; Lockheed; Lucent Technologies; Monsanto; National Park Service; NORPAC; Pacificorp; Pennsylvania Power and Light; Pfizer Pharmaceuticals; Pike Electric; Pool Well Services; Power Bar; Rayonier; Rohm & Haas; Searle; Sentry; Solutia; Square D; Textron; 3M; Toyota; TrusJoist MacMillan; Union Pacific Railroad; Wal-Mart; Westinghouse; Westvaco; Weyerhaeuser; and Wisconsin Electric.

Dr. Geller has been the Principal Investigator for more than 75 research grants that involved the application of behavioral science for the benefit of corporations, institutions, government agencies, or communities in general. Both government agencies and corporations have funded his research including: the National Science Foundation; the National Institute for Occupational Safety and Health; the U.S. Department of Health, Education, and Welfare; the U.S. Department of Energy; the U.S. Department of Transportation; the National Highway Traffic Safety Administration; the National Institute on Alcohol Abuse and Alcoholism; the Centers for Disease Control and Prevention; General Motors Research Laboratories; the Alcoholic Beverage Medical Research Foundation; and the Virginia Departments of Energy, Transportation, Litter Control, Agriculture and Commerce, and Welfare and Institutions. In 2001, Virginia Tech awarded Dr. Geller the University Alumni Award for Excellence in Research. In 2002, the University honored Scott Geller with the Alumni Outreach Award for his exemplary real-world applications of behavioral science, and in 2003 Dr. Geller received the University Alumni Award for Graduate Student Advising. In 2005, E. Scott Geller was awarded the statewide Virginia Outstanding Faculty Award by the State Council of Higher Education.

Index